Contents

Introduction

Mathematics is widely regarded as the language of physics. Fluency and accuracy in mathematics is therefore a requirement for success in pre-university physics courses and will enable students to progress to higher level studies in physics and engineering.

This book is written as a course companion for post-16 students in pre-university physics courses in England and Wales. These courses are:

- the A-Level Physics examinations of AQA, Edexcel, OCR and WJEC
- the International Baccalaureate
- the Cambridge International Examinations Pre-U
- the Oxford University Physics Aptitude Test.

The mathematical requirements of all the courses are very similar – indeed the A levels have a common nationally prescribed mathematical content – so there is no need to distinguish between them when working through the text. In this text, 'A-Level Physics' refers to all these courses.

Physics students develop their mathematical skills over the two years of their A-Level courses. Many study A-Level Mathematics alongside Physics; many do not. All students need to negotiate the high step change in mathematical demands from their pre-A-Level courses. Mathematical concepts are often needed by physics students before their introduction in maths courses, where taken. Students benefit from working through maths problems that relate to physics. Non-maths students will benefit from working through the chapters under guidance from their physics teachers – maths students can concentrate on working through the exercises – both the **Quickfire** questions and the **Test Yourself** sets of questions in each chapter. It should be noted that the questions in the Test Yourself exercises are of graded difficulty – many of those towards the end of the exercises, especially in the later chapters, are included to stretch the more able student.

The mathematics that students need to tackle examination papers is a subset of that required in A-Level Physics courses. Many of the equations that students use are derived from basic relationships. The mathematical techniques applied in their derivation, from the straightforward application of simultaneous equations to the solution of differential equations, are often not tested in pre-university physics examinations. This book aims to cover the mathematics behind the results presented at A-Level Physics. Some derivations are given in Chapters 1–11; Chapter 12 is devoted to deriving a set of mathematical and physics relationships for which the derivations are often omitted in physics text books. By covering this material the authors aim to demonstrate to students the uses of mathematics to the physics they are familiar with and to prepare the ground for the mathematical demands of physics and engineering courses in higher education.

Maths: Physics Content Map

The grid gives an idea of the chapters in the book which provide support for the different topics of A level Physics. This will depend on the details of the Physics specification you are following.

Topic	Chapter/Section														
AS	1	2	3.1 –3.3	3.4*	4.1 –4.2	4.3 –4.4	5	6	7.1 –7.4	7.5	7.6	8.1 –8.3	8.4 –8.5	9.1 –9.4	9.5
Quantities	✓	✓			✓										
Force & equilibrium	✓	✓			✓		✓		✓						
Force & motion	✓	✓	✓		✓		✓	✓	✓						
Energy	✓	✓	✓		✓			✓							
dc electrical circuits	✓	✓			✓			✓							
Waves	✓	✓		✓	✓			✓							
Refraction/optics	✓	✓					✓	✓							
Wave/particle duality	✓	✓			✓										
AS Practical	✓	✓	✓	✓	✓		✓	✓	✓						
A2															
Vibrations/shm	✓	✓	✓	✓	✓	✓	✓	✓	✓				✓		
Circular motion	✓	✓			✓		✓	✓	✓						
Force and momentum	✓	✓	✓		✓		✓		✓	✓	✓				
Electric fields	✓	✓			✓		✓	✓	✓			✓	✓	✓	
Gravitational fields	✓	✓			✓		✓	✓	✓			✓	✓	✓	
Radioactivity	✓	✓	✓		✓	✓									
Thermal physics	✓	✓			✓			✓							
Capacitance	✓	✓	✓		✓	✓									
Magnetic fields	✓	✓	✓		✓		✓	✓	✓			✓			✓
e-m induction	✓	✓			✓		✓	✓	✓			✓			✓
r/a; nuclear energy	✓	✓	✓		✓	✓		✓							
ac theory	✓	✓	✓	✓	✓	✓	✓	✓	✓				✓		
Medical physics	✓	✓	✓		✓	✓		✓							
Materials	✓	✓	✓		✓	✓	✓	✓							
A2 Practical	✓	✓	✓	✓	✓	✓	✓	✓	✓			✓	✓		

* Section 3.4 covers the binomial series and the binomial approximation. It will not be examined in physics papers but it is necessary for an understanding of the AS topic of the Young slits as well as e^x, logs, trigonometry, simple harmonic motion and calculus.

Chapters 10, 11 and 12 contain material which is unlikely to be examined directly in A level Physics papers. They provide the mathematical underpinning for much of A level Physics; familiarity with the content of these chapters will be of great benefit to people intending to study physics, engineering or mathematics at university level.

How to use this book

Mathematics for A-Level Physics is not arranged as a learning sequence. Indeed, given the interconnected nature of mathematics, it would be impossible to do this. For example, the addition of vectors requires basic trigonometry; more advanced trig relies on graphs, vectors and calculus.

That being said, the early chapters on units, algebra, indices, geometry and graphs, revisit pre-A-Level Maths concepts and develop them to allow students to make the difficult transition to A-Level Physics, with its increased mathematical formalism. These will be of particular use to AS candidates.

The text in each chapter is subdivided numerically, e.g. in Chapter 5:

5   Geometry and Trigonometry

    5.5 Right-angled triangles

        5.5.1   Trig ratios

        5.5.2   Reciprocal trig ratios

        5.5.3   Calculators and trig ratios

In addition to the main text, each chapter contains the following:

- **Quickfire** questions, which enable students to test their developing understanding; it should be noted that some of these questions are not very quick to answer! Answers are provided at the end of the book.

quickpire 8.1

Use the values in Table 5.1 on page 54 and Figure 8.1 to determine:

(a) $\sin\left(\frac{\pi}{3}\right)$,

(b) $\sin\frac{13\pi}{6}$ [Hint: $\frac{13\pi}{6} = 2\pi + \frac{\pi}{6}$],

(c) $\sin\frac{15\pi}{4}$ [Hint: $\frac{15\pi}{4} = 4\pi - \frac{\pi}{4}$]

- **Examples** – worked problems which clarify the text.

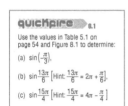

Example G: Evaluate $\frac{3}{7} + \frac{2}{10}$

$\frac{3}{7}$ is the same as $\frac{3 \times 10}{7 \times 10} = \frac{30}{70}$. Also $+\frac{2}{10}$ is the same as $\frac{2 \times 7}{10 \times 7} = \frac{14}{70}$.

So

$$\frac{3}{7} + \frac{2}{10} = \frac{30}{70} + \frac{14}{70} = \frac{30 + 14}{70} = \frac{44}{70}$$

Of course, if it's a straight numerical example, it is probably easier to use the calculator, like this

$\frac{3}{7} + \frac{2}{10} = 0.4286 + 0.2 = 0.6286$, which you can check is equal to $\frac{44}{70}$.

- **Data Exercises** (in some chapters); students are encouraged to use a spreadsheet to investigate some of the mathematical techniques, especially those associated with graphs. In most cases, answers are not provided to these exercises but the link to the text is clear.

Data Exercise 4.1

Use your calculator or a spreadsheet to plot a graph of y against p for the function $y = (1 + p)^{\frac{1}{2}}$ for $-\frac{1}{2} \le p \le 1$, in other words, for p between $-\frac{1}{2}$ and $+1$. Suggested initial values of p are: $-\frac{1}{2}, -\frac{1}{4}, \frac{1}{4}, \frac{1}{2}$ and 1. Don't try $p = 0$; well you can try!

- **Pointers** – which give additional information.

Pointer

Other dimensionless quantities are e, the base of natural logarithms and the golden ratio.

- **Test Yourself** exercises – graded questions which test students' understanding; answers are provided on the Illuminate Publishing website.

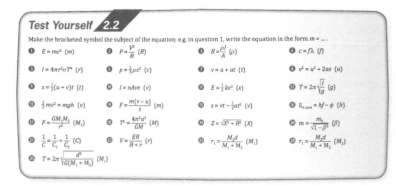

Test Yourself 2.2

Make the bracketed symbol the subject of the equation; e.g. in question 1, write the equation in the form $m = \dots$.

1. $E = mc^2$ (m)
2. $P = \frac{V^2}{R}$ (R)
3. $R = \frac{\rho l}{A}$ (ρ)
4. $c = f\lambda$ (f)
5. $I = 4\pi r^2 \sigma T^4$ (r)
6. $p = \frac{1}{3}\rho c^2$ (c)
7. $v = u + at$ (t)
8. $v^2 = u^2 + 2as$ (u)
9. $s = \frac{1}{2}(u + v)t$ (t)
10. $I = nAve$ (v)
11. $E = \frac{1}{2}kx^2$ (x)
12. $T = 2\pi\sqrt{\frac{l}{g}}$ (g)
13. $\frac{1}{2}mv^2 = mgh$ (v)
14. $F = \frac{m(v-u)}{t}$ (m)
15. $s = vt - \frac{1}{2}at^2$ (v)
16. $E_{k,max} = hf - \phi$ (h)
17. $F = \frac{GM_1M_2}{r^2}$ (M_2)
18. $T^2 = \frac{4\pi^2 a^3}{GM}$ (M)
19. $Z = \sqrt{X^2 + R^2}$ (X)
20. $m = \frac{m_0}{\sqrt{1-\beta^2}}$ (β)
21. $\frac{1}{C} = \frac{1}{C_1} + \frac{1}{C_2}$ (C)
22. $V = \frac{ER}{R+r}$ (r)
23. $r_1 = \frac{M_2 d}{M_1 + M_2}$ (M_1)
24. $r_1 = \frac{M_2 d}{M_1 + M_2}$ (M_2)
25. $T = 2\pi\sqrt{\frac{d^3}{G(M_1 + M_2)}}$ (M_1)

Chapter 12, Miscellaneous Proofs and Derivations, is the exception to this structure. Its aim is to give mathematical justification to the various techniques and mathematical formulae used in A-Level Physics.

Answers to all Test yourself questions are available as a download from the Illuminate Publishing website.

Chapter 1

Quantities, Units and Dimensions

1.1 Introduction

Physics deals with measurable quantities such as speed, pressure, power and luminous intensity. These are expressed as the product of a basic unit and a number. For example, a power of 100 W indicates that the power is 100×1 W. In order to express all the quantities we encounter, we need a basic set of units with defined values. The definition of the units can change with developments in the technology of measurement. The metre has been defined variously over the centuries as:

- the length of a pendulum with a half-period of 1 s [proposed in 1668 but never adopted]
- one 10 millionth of the distance from the equator to the north pole along the meridian through Paris [1791]
- the length of a prototype metal bar [1793, revised in 1889]
- 1 650 763.73 wavelengths of a Kr-86 emission line in a vacuum [the orange–red line] [1960]
- the distance travelled by light in a vacuum in $\frac{1}{299\,792\,458}$ s [1983]

Interestingly, the current definition echoes the 1668 one in defining the metre in terms of the second.

1.2 The dimensions of physical quantities

The quantities in A-level physics can be expressed in terms of a set of *base dimensions*. The set that the scientific community has decided upon is:

length (L), mass (M), time (T), electrical current (I), temperature (Θ)

The symbols in the brackets are the standard symbols. The dimensions of other quantities can be expressed in terms of these,

e.g. speed $= \dfrac{\text{distance}}{\text{time}}$, so the dimensions of speed $= \dfrac{\text{L}}{\text{T}} = \text{L T}^{-1}$

It is rather tiresome to write 'the dimensions of' so we use square brackets and write:

[speed] $= \text{L T}^{-1}$.

Similarly: [acceleration] $= \text{L T}^{-2}$ and [force] = [mass] × [acceleration] $= \text{M L T}^{-2}$.

To work out the dimensions of a quantity we need to know the equation which relates it to the base dimensions.

Example A:

What are the dimensions of pressure?

Equation first: pressure $= \dfrac{\text{force}}{\text{area}}$, ∴ [pressure] $= \dfrac{[\text{force}]}{[\text{area}]} = \dfrac{\text{M L T}^{-2}}{\text{L}^2} = \text{M L}^{-1}\,\text{T}^{-2}$.

We'll see in Section 1.4 how useful this can be.

Pointer

If you are not familiar with negative indices, e.g. L^{-1} or T^{-2}, see Chapter 4 on indices and logs.

quickfire 1.1

Use the equation
Work = force × distance,
to find the dimensions of work.

Pointer

Energy = the ability to do work, so the dimensions of the two are the same.

quickfire 1.2

Find the dimensions of power.

quickfire 1.3

Find the dimensions of electrical charge.
[Hint: charge = current × time]

1.3 Le Système International d'Unités (SI)

You should have covered most of this section in your pre-A-level course. It is presented here for completeness and for quick reference.

1.3.1 Base units

The scientific community uses a system based upon the following quantities with their units. The units of the base quantities are:

Quantity	Symbols	SI unit	Abbreviation
length	$l, x, s \dots$	metre	m
time	t	second	s
mass	m, M	kilogram	kg
electric current	I	ampere / amp*	A
temperature	T, θ	kelvin	K
quantity of matter	n	mole	mol

* Ampere is usually shortened to amp, especially in speech.

A seventh base quantity is luminous intensity [symbol, I; unit, candela; abbreviation, cd] but this is not currently used in A-level physics.

Notice that, in printed material, symbols of quantities are written in *italic* characters but that units are written in Roman (upright) characters. In handwriting, no distinction is made.

Pointer

The symbol T is usually reserved for kelvin temperatures; θ is usually used for celsius temperatures.

1.3.2 SI multipliers

The following multipliers are used with SI units:

Pointer

Celsius temperatures are defined by:
$\theta/°C = T/K - 273.15$.

Multiplier	Factor	Symbol
yotta	10^{24}	Y
zetta	10^{21}	Z
exa	10^{18}	E
peta	10^{15}	P
tera	10^{12}	T
giga	10^{9}	G
mega	10^{6}	M
kilo	10^{3}	k
hecto*	10^{2}	h
deca*	10^{1}	da

Multiplier	Factor	Symbol
deci*	10^{-1}	d
centi*	10^{-2}	c
milli	10^{-3}	m
micro	10^{-6}	μ[1]
nano	10^{-9}	n
pico	10^{-12}	p
femto	10^{-15}	f
atto	10^{-18}	a
zepto	10^{-21}	z
yokto	10^{-24}	y

* hecto is only used in hectare [1 are = 10 m × 10 m = 100 m^2], deca is not generally used, deci is used by chemists in dm^3, centi is used only in cm.

The basic unit of mass, the kilogram, includes a multiplier. Perhaps for this reason multipliers greater than 1 are not generally used for mass. A mass of 2×10^6 kg **could** be written as 2 Gg but this is rarely seen. The tonne, 1000 kg, can be used instead as the unit for large masses. So 2×10^6 kg can be written as 2×10^3 tonne or 2 kilotonne. On the other hand 2×10^{-6} kg would be written as 2 mg [2 milligram].

1.3.3 Using your calculator

Take care when entering a quantity with a multiplier into your calculator. Use the EXP key followed by the appropriate number and use the $^+/_-$ button if necessary. Do **not** enter 10 or use the 10^x button.

---

[1] The Greek letter, μ [pronounced mew in classical Greek but mi in modern Greek]. Confusingly, '250μ' on a Greek road sign means 250 m!

Example B:

Enter 2.5 MN into your calculator.

[Ignore the N]. Keystrokes: 2 . 5 EXP 6 [because M = mega = 10^6]

Example C:

Enter 7.2 mA into your calculator.

[Ignore the A]. Keystrokes 7 . 2 EXP ⁺/₋ 3

[On the author's calculator, you could use the ⁺/₋ button *after* 3]

1.3.4 Compound units

Most quantities have **compound units**, comprising two or more of the base units. These are derived in the same way as the dimensions of non-base quantities,

e.g. density = $\dfrac{\text{mass}}{\text{volume}}$, so the unit of density = $\dfrac{\text{kg}}{\text{m}^3}$ = kg m⁻³

Notice that a small gap is left between the kg and m in kg m⁻³. This becomes important when multipliers are used.

Many compound units have their own names, usually that of a scientist who is associated with the quantity. Examples:

Quantity	Unit	Symbol
pressure	pascal	Pa
electric charge	coulomb	C
force	newton	N
self-inductance	henry	H
activity	becquerel	Bq
electrical resistance	ohm	Ω

Example D:

Write the unit C in terms of the base SI units.

Equation: Charge = current × time. ∴ Unit of charge = unit of current × unit of time = A s

How to write units

The following rules apply:

1 Always leave a small gap between the number and the unit.

2 In compound units leave a small gap between the different parts, e.g. kg m⁻³.

3 There is no gap between a multiplier and the unit it multiplies.

4 Generally multipliers greater than 1 have a capital letter, but note that k [for kilo] is small.

5 Abbreviations of units that are named after people start with a capital letter, e.g. N, Pa. However, when writing name units in full a lower case [small] letter is used, e.g. 1 newton, unless the unit comes at the beginning of a sentence, e.g. 1.013×10^5 pascal but 'Pascal' is the unit of pressure.

Pointer

SI multipliers greater than k are rarely used for distance: 150 000 000 000 m could be written as 1.5×10^{11} m, 150 million km, 1.5×10^8 km, 150×10^6 km but never 150 Gm.

Pointer

It helps always to write dimensions and base units in the same order, e.g. M, L, T, I, Θ and kg, m, s, A, K.

quickfire 1.4

To check you are entering multiplier data correctly on you calculator work out the following:

(a) 3 mA × 1.5 kΩ

(b) 25 km s⁻¹ × 2 ms.

quickfire 1.5

Write the following using the most appropriate SI multiplier:

(a) 5000 N

(b) 0.0015 A

(c) 2×10^{11} Pa

(d) 1.6×10^{-19} C.

quickfire 1.6

Write the following in abbreviated form:

(a) 10 milligram

(b) 3.5 meganewton

(c) 15 kilamp [= kilo-ampere]

(d) 9.6 microcoulomb

6   Units are only used in the singular, 10 cm **not** 10 cms. This also applies when writing the unit out in full, e.g. 10 newton **not** 10 newtons [but this is frequently ignored in speech].

These rules look daunting but they are not difficult to apply. Some are more significant than others. For example, look at 2, 3 and 6, then consider the following: ms^{-1} and $m\,s^{-1}$. The first one means 'per millisecond' and the second means 'metre per second'.

quickfire 1.7

Write these quantities using numbers between 1 and 999:
(a) 0.4 MPa
(b) 1500 kN
(c) 0.015 mA
(d) 4000 MPa

quickfire 1.8

Write these in engineering notation:
(a) 200 kN
(b) 0.076 A
(c) 75 000 V
(d) 0.9 µg

1.3.5 Style – multipliers and powers of 10

It is usual practice, when using SI multipliers, to use numbers between 1 and 999, e.g. 50 µA, 870 kV. This is because most multipliers involve factors of 1000. There is, however, nothing incorrect about writing 50 µA as 0.05 mA. It is a matter of ease of communication. For example, in an experiment in which most currents are in the milliamp range but there are a couple which are lower, it might be sensible to express them all in mA – in fact it might be misleading to use different units for some.

Similarly, a stress of 4×10^9 Pa could be written as 4×10^3 MPa or 4000 MPa if that were sensible for comparison purposes.

In **Engineering Notation**, SI multipliers are not used but the powers of 10 are restricted to multiples of 3. So 15 000 amp would be written as 15×10^3 A. Again the number multiplying 10^x should lie between 1 and 999.

To stress, once again, these are matters of style only. The authors cannot guarantee that an examination candidate would escape penalty for writing 5 kg as 5×10^9 µg but, although it might be considered perverse, there is nothing actually incorrect about doing so.

1.4 Areas and volumes

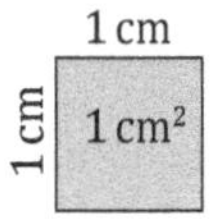

Calculations involving areas and volumes often cause difficulties for A-level students when SI multipliers are used. The unit of area is m^2 [metre squared]. It is important to understand what is meant by cm^2.

$1\,cm^2$ ['1 centimetre squared'] is the area of a square of side 1 cm, **not** a hundredth of $1\,m^2$.

So $1\,cm^2 = 1\,cm \times 1\,cm = 1 \times 10^{-2}\,m \times 1 \times 10^{-2}\,m = 1 \times 10^{-4}\,m^2$.

And $1\,km^2 = 1\,km \times 1\,km = 1 \times 10^3\,m \times 1 \times 10^3\,m = 1 \times 10^6\,m^2$.

1 cm

1 cm   1 cm²

Figure 1.1

quickfire 1.9

Convert the following:
(a) $27\,cm^2$ to m^2
(b) $0.057\,m^2$ to mm^2
(c) $9\,mm^3$ to m^3
(d) $25\,km^2$ to m^2.

Example E:

Express $8.5\,mm^2$ in m^2.

$1\,mm^2 = 1 \times 10^{-3}\,m \times 1 \times 10^{-3}\,m = 1 \times 10^{-6}\,m$.

So $8.5\,mm^2 = 8.5 \times 10^{-6}\,m^2$.

Similarly, $1\,cm^3$ ['1 centimetre cubed'] is the volume of a cube of side 1 cm.

Hence $1\,cm^3 = 1 \times 10^{-2}\,m \times 1 \times 10^{-2}\,m \times 1 \times 10^{-2}\,m = 1 \times 10^{-6}\,m^3$.

Example F:

A sample of rock with a volume of 40 cm³ has a mass of 0.112 kg. Calculate its density in base SI units.

Volume = 40 cm³ = 40×10^{-6} m³.

$$density = \frac{mass}{volume} = \frac{0.112 \text{ kg}}{40 \times 10^{-6} \text{ m}^3} = 2800 \text{ kg m}^{-3}.$$

quickfire 1.10

Calculate the cross-sectional area of a wire with a **diameter** of 0.32 mm and express your answer in m².

In many calculations in practical work you measure diameters and lengths in mm or cm and have to calculate areas in m² (or volumes in m³). The easiest way to avoid mistakes is to convert to m before calculating an area or volume. E.g. to calculate the volume of a 1 mm radius steel sphere, express this as 1.0×10^{-3} m and then perform the calculation $V = \frac{4}{3}\pi(1.0 \times 10^{-3})^3$. In this way, the calculator takes care of the conversion from mm³ to m³.

Pointer

Using the data in Example F, the density can be written as 2.8 g cm⁻³. So 1 g cm⁻³ = 1000 kg m⁻³.

1.5 Doing calculations with units

1.5.1 Multiplying and dividing

If two quantities are multiplied, so are their units. If one quantity is divided by another, so are their units. We can treat the unit as part of the calculation. To give a couple of familiar examples:

1   $speed = \dfrac{distance}{time}$, so if a car travels 500 m in 25 s its speed is $\dfrac{500 \text{ m}}{25 \text{ s}} = 20$ m/s i.e. 20 m s⁻¹.

2   $density = \dfrac{mass}{volume}$, so if an object has a mass of 90 g and a volume of 18 cm³

   $density = \dfrac{90 \text{ g}}{18 \text{ cm}^3} = 5 \text{ g cm}^{-3}$. Or in base units: $density = \dfrac{0.090 \text{ kg}}{18 \times 10^{-6} \text{ m}^3} = 5000 \text{ kg m}^{-3}$.

Example G:

The resistance, R, of a wire is given by $R = \dfrac{\rho l}{A}$, where ρ is the resistivity, l the length and A the cross-sectional area. If $\rho = 4.7 \times 10^{-7}$ Ω m, $l = 5$ m and $A = 0.25$ mm², find R.

Converting the mm² to m²: $R = \dfrac{4.7 \times 10^{-7} \text{ Ω m} \times 5 \text{ m}}{0.25 \times 10^{-6} \text{ m}^2} = 9.4 \dfrac{\text{Ω m}^2}{\text{m}^2} = 9.4$ Ω. [The m² cancels].

If a quantity is **raised to a power**, e.g. squared or cubed, so is the unit. We have already used this idea for areas and volumes. What is the unit of v^2, where v is a speed?
Answer : $(\text{m s}^{-1})^2 = \text{m}^2 \text{ s}^{-2}$.

The square root of a quantity has the square root of its unit.

1.5.2 Adding and subtracting

'What do we get if we add 5 apples to 3 oranges?' We can only express the answer as a single number if we redesignate the produce as 'items of fruit' in which case the answer is, '8 items of fruit'.

In a similar way, we can only add and subtract quantities if they are of the same kind. We can add two velocities or subtract one mass from another but we cannot add a mass to a velocity. More generally, we can only add or subtract two quantities if they have the same dimensions.

Can we add 5 m and 3 m? Of course. 5 m + 3 m = 8 m. Notice that the units do not add!

Can we do 5.00 m + 2 cm? These are both distances, so the sum makes sense, but we can only get a single number if the distances are expressed in the same units.

∴ 5.00 m + 2 cm = 5.00 m + 0.02 m = 5.02 m [or ... = 500 cm + 2 cm = 502 cm]

1.5.3 Dimensionless quantities

A consequence of the dividing rule is that some quantities have no units. They are referred to as *dimensionless quantities*. An example is π. It is defined as the ratio of the circumference of a circle to the diameter. A 10 cm diameter circle has a circumference of 31.4159 cm [to 6 sf].

So $$\pi = \frac{31.4159}{10.0000 \text{ cm}} = 3.14159 \text{ [to 6 sf]}$$

Expressing these distances in inches [using the conversion 1″ = 2.54 cm]

$$\pi = \frac{12.3685″}{3.93701″}, \text{ which gives the same answer}$$

[all right, there's a rounding error → 3.14160 [6 sf]]

What this means is that π has the same value, whatever the system of units. It has no unit of its own and is a pure number, like 6.

The rules for combining dimensionless quantities with other quantities are the same as in Sections 1.5.1 and 1.5.2. The following examples make it clear:

- 3 + 4 m s^{-1} ✗ This doesn't make sense.
- 3 × 4 m s^{-1} = 12 m s^{-1} ✓ The unit of m s^{-1} is unaltered.
- $\frac{4 \text{ m s}^{-1}}{3}$ = 1.33 m s^{-1} [3 s.f.] ✓ the unit of m s^{-1} is unaltered

1.6 Expressing units in base units

We saw in Section 1.2 how to find the dimensions of physical quantities, i.e. how a measurement of a quantity is related to measurements of the base quantities of mass, length, time, current, etc. Similarly, we can express the unit of a quantity in terms of the base units, kg, m, s, A, etc.

Using the same example as in 1.2, we shall express the newton, the unit of force, in terms of the base units:

Starting from the equation: $F = ma$, and using square brackets to denote 'the unit of ....' [See footnote[2]]

$[m]$ = kg; $[a]$ = m s^{-2}.

$[F] = [m] \times [a]$, so N = kg m s^{-2}.

Compare this to the dimensions of force: [force] = M L T^{-2}. You'll see they correspond; each SI dimension has its corresponding base unit.

Example H:

The drag force, F, on a sphere of radius a moving at velocity v through a fluid is given by $F = 6\pi\eta av$, where η is the viscosity of the liquid. This is called Stokes' Law.

(a) Express the unit of η in the base SI units.

Equation first: $\eta = \frac{F}{6\pi av}$. 6 and π are both dimensionless,

$$\therefore [\eta] = \frac{[F]}{[a][v]} = \frac{\text{kg m s}^{-2}}{\text{m} \times \text{m s}^{-1}} = \text{kg m}^{-1}\text{ s}^{-1}$$

---

[2] The use of [...] to denote 'the dimensions of...' is standard. Its second use as 'the unit of ...' is not as widespread but it has the advantage of brevity and examiners will recognise it.

Pointer

Other dimensionless quantities are e, the base of natural logarithms and the golden ratio.

quickfire 1.11

Calculate:

(a) $\frac{30 \text{ m}}{12 \text{ s}}$,

(b) 15 N × 7 s,

(c) 2.5 m s^{-2} × 8 s,

(d) 0.573 kg – 25 g,

(e) $\sqrt{100 \text{ m} \times 1.44 \text{ m s}^{-2}}$

Pointer

When deriving the unit of a quantity or expressing its unit in the SI base units, always start with a defining equation.

quickfire 1.12

Express the joule, the unit of work, in base SI units

[Hint: Work = force × distance]

quickfire 1.13

Use your answer to QF 1.12 to express the watt in base SI units.

[Hint: Watt is the unit of power]

(b) A textbook gives the unit of η as N s m^{-2}. Show that this is equivalent to the answer to (a).

From Section 1.6, N = kg m s^{-2}. $\therefore$ N s m^{-2} = kg m s^{-2} × s × m^{-2} = kg m^{-1} s^{-1}. QED

quickfire 1.14

Express the coulomb, the unit of charge, in base SI units.
[Hint: charge = current × time].

Example I:

(a) Suggest a suitable unit for the Planck constant, h.

(b) Express the unit of h in terms of the base SI units.

(a) Start from the equation: $E = hf$, so $h = \dfrac{E}{f}$.

$[h] = \dfrac{[E]}{[f]} = \dfrac{J}{Hz}$. But Hz = s^{-1}, so $[h]$ = J s.

NB. There are other possible units, e.g. W s^2, but J s is the obvious one.

(b) $[h]$ = J s = (kg m^2 s^{-2}) × s = kg m^2 s^{-1}.

Note that the dimensions of the Planck constant are M L^2 T^{-1}.

Grade boost

Learn the following base unit equivalents:
N = kg m s^{-2}
J = kg m^2 s^{-2}
W = kg m^2 s^{-3}

Grade boost

Learn the dimensionality of:
[Force] = M L T^{-1}
[Work] or [Energy] = M L^2 T^{-2}
[Power] = M L^2 T^{-3}

1.7 Investigating relationships using units or dimensions

1.7.1 Checking an equation

We have seen that we can only add or subtract quantities if they have the same dimensions [units] and that if we multiply or divide quantities, the dimensions [units] are combined in the same way. In addition to these statements it is clear that for two quantities to be equal, they must have the same dimensions: a velocity cannot be equal to an electric current because they have different units.

We can apply these ideas to investigating equations. Consider the following: a student has misremembered one of the kinematic equations as $s = u + \frac{1}{2}at^2$, with the usual symbols.

Let us look at the dimensions of the different terms, starting on the right-hand side:

$[u]$ = L T^{-1} $\qquad$ $\left[\frac{1}{2}at^2\right]$ = L T^{-2} × T^2 = L

Conclusion: The right-hand side of the equation cannot be correct: u cannot be added to $\frac{1}{2}at^2$.

The correct equation is $s = ut + \frac{1}{2}at^2$. Now the dimensions of the right-hand side are:

$[ut]$ = L T^{-1} × T = L $\qquad$ $\left[\frac{1}{2}at^2\right]$ = L T^{-2} × T^2 = L

These terms have the same dimensions and so can be added together to give something with dimension L. This is the same as the left-hand side and the equation is said to be *homogeneous*.

We can perform the same analysis using units rather than dimensions – see Example J.

Example J:

Use units to show that the equation $s = ut + \frac{1}{2}at^2$ is homogeneous.

Take the terms on the right-hand side:

$[ut]$ = m s^{-1} × s = m $\qquad$ $\left[\frac{1}{2}at^2\right]$ = m s^{-2} × s^2 = m

The unit of both terms is m [metre] so these can be added to give an answer in m. The unit of the left-hand side, s, is also m, so the equation is homogeneous.

quickfire ▶ 1.15

Show that the equation $v^2 = u^2 + 2as$ is homogeneous. Use either units or dimensions.

Note that showing an equation to be homogeneous doesn't necessarily make it correct. For example, the equation $v = u + \frac{1}{2}at$ is homogeneous [check this] but incorrect. We can, however, weed out equations which couldn't possibly be correct. When checking an equation, should we use units or dimensions? In an exam, read the question – most exam boards allow either approach.

1.7.2 Suggesting relationships

Sometimes we may suspect that a certain quantity is related to other quantities but we do not know the form of the relationship. We can use the fact that any equation which relates the quantities must be homogenous. This is most easily introduced by way of an example. For the work that follows, you will need to be familiar with indices, x^2, y^k, etc. If necessary, postpone this section until you have worked through Section 4.2.

Consider a simple pendulum. It is suspected that the period, T, of the pendulum is related to the length, l, the acceleration due to gravity, g, and the mass, m, of the pendulum bob.

Suppose the relationship is of the form $T = kl^a g^b m^c$, where k is a dimensionless constant.❸

In terms of dimensions: $[T] = $ T; $[l] = $ L; $[g] = $ L T^{-2} and $[m] = $ M

If the relationship is of the proposed form, $\qquad$ T = L^a (L T^{-2})^b M^c $\qquad$ (1)

∴ using the rules for combining indices $\qquad$ T = M^c L^{a+b} T^{-2b}

Notice that M and L do not appear on the left-hand side. We'll put them in as M^0 and L^0:

∴ $\qquad$ M^0 L^0 T^1 = M^c L^{a+b} T^{-2b}

If the two sides of this equation are to be identical, the same powers of M, L and T must be present.

quickfire ▶ 1.16

Write equation (1) from section1.7.2 in terms of the base units, s, m and kg rather than dimensions.

So we can write: $\qquad$ Equating powers of M $\qquad$ $0 = c$ $\qquad$ (2)

$\qquad$ Equating powers of L $\qquad$ $0 = a + b$ $\qquad$ (3)

$\qquad$ Equating powers of T $\qquad$ $1 = -2b$ $\qquad$ (4)

From equation (2) we see that $c = 0$, so T does not depend upon the mass, m, of the pendulum. You may already have known this!

Equation (4) tells us that $b = -\frac{1}{2}$ and substituting this value in equation (3) gives $a = \frac{1}{2}$.

So the only homogeneous relationship between these quantities is:

$$T = kl^{\frac{1}{2}}g^{-\frac{1}{2}} = k\sqrt{\frac{l}{g}}.$$

If you are familiar with the simple pendulum already, you will know that the equation is $T = 2\pi\sqrt{\frac{l}{g}}$. The full derivation of this requires calculus.

Example K:

The period, T, of a mass, m suspended from a spring with a spring constant, k, is thought to be given by an equation of the form:

$$T = ck^x m^y g^z$$

where g is the acceleration due to gravity and c is a dimensionless constant.

The constant k is defined by the equation $F = k\Delta l$, where F is the tension in the spring and Δl is its increase in length.

(a) Find the unit of k in terms of the base SI units.

(b) Use unit analysis to find values of x, y and z.

(a) $k = \frac{F}{\Delta l}$, so $[k] = \frac{N}{m} = \frac{kg\,m\,s^{-2}}{m} = kg\,s^{-2}$

❸ Note that not all constants are dimensionless, e.g. c the speed of light, ε_0 the permittivity of free space.

(b) Because c is dimensionless, $[T] = [k]^x[m]^y[g]^z$, $\therefore$ s $= (\text{kg s}^{-2})^x \text{ kg}^y (\text{m s}^{-2})^z$.

$\therefore$ s $= \text{kg}^{x+y} \text{ m}^z \text{ s}^{-2(x+z)}$

Equating powers of kg, m and s: kg $\quad 0 = x + y$ $\hspace{5cm}$ (1)

$\qquad\qquad\qquad\qquad\qquad$ m $\quad 0 = z$ $\hspace{5.5cm}$ (2)

$\qquad\qquad\qquad\qquad\qquad$ s $\quad 1 = -2x - 2z$ $\hspace{4.3cm}$ (3)

Equation (2) tells us that $z = 0$. Putting $z = 0$ into equation (3) gives $x = -\frac{1}{2}$. Substituting this into equation (1) gives $y = \frac{1}{2}$.

So the relationship is $T = c\sqrt{\dfrac{m}{k}}$.

Test Yourself 1.1

1 Potential difference, V, may be defined by the equation $P = VI$, where P is the power transferred when a current I passes. Express the volt in terms of the base SI units.

2 The force, F, between two objects of mass m_1 and m_2 separated by a distance d is given by $F = \dfrac{Gm_1m_2}{d^2}$, where G is the Universal gravitational constant. Express the unit of G in terms of the base SI units.

3 The force, F, between two charges, Q_1 and Q_2, separated by r, is given by $F = \dfrac{1}{4\pi\varepsilon_0}\dfrac{Q_1Q_2}{r^2}$, where ε_0 is the *permittivity of free space*.

    (a) Show that a suitable unit for ε_0 is $\text{C}^2 \text{ N}^{-1} \text{ m}^{-2}$.

    (b) Express the unit of ε_0 in terms of the base SI units.

4 The energy, E, of a photon of frequency, f is given by $E = hf$, where h is the Planck constant.

    (a) Give a suitable unit for h.

    (b) Express h in terms of the base SI units.

5 The force between two wires of length l, each carrying a current I, separated by a distance r is given by $F = \dfrac{\mu_0 I^2 l}{2\pi r}$, where μ_0 is the *permeability of free space*. The unit of μ_0 is henry per metre [H m^{-1}]. Express the henry in terms of the base SI units.

6 The charge, Q, stored on a capacitor with a pd of V is given by $Q = CV$, where C is the *capacitance* of the capacitor. The unit of capacitance is the farad, F.

Express the farad in terms of the base SI units.

7 A pd of 5.0 kV is applied across a high resistance component which passes a current of 2 mA. What is the resistance of the component?

8 James Clerk Maxwell showed that $c^2 = \dfrac{1}{\varepsilon_0\mu_0}$ where c is the speed of electromagnetic radiation. Use the answers to questions 3 and 5 to show that this equation is homogeneous.

9 The power, P, radiated by a black body of surface area A and temperature, T is given by: $P = \sigma A T^4$.

    (a) Give a suitable unit for σ.

    (b) Express dimensions of σ in terms of M, L, T and Θ.

10 The wavelength, λ_{max}, of the maximum emitted power of a black body of temperature T is given by $\lambda_{max} = WT^{-1}$, where W is the Wien constant. Find the dimensions of W.

11 Use the equation $P = I^2R$ to express the ohm (Ω) in terms of the base SI units.

12 The specific heat capacity, c, of a substance is defined by $Q = mc\Delta\theta$, where Q is the heat input into a substance, m is the mass and $\Delta\theta$ is the temperature rise.

    (a) Give a suitable unit for c.

    (b) Express the unit of c in the base SI units, kg, m, s and K.

⑬ The momentum p of a non-relativistic particle is given by $p = mv$ where m is the mass and v the velocity. The unit of momentum is either N s or kg m s^{-1}. Show that these are equivalent.

⑭ The work done, W, by an expanding gas is given by $W = p\Delta V$, where p is the pressure and ΔV the increase in volume. Show that the equation is homogeneous.

⑮ The relationship between energy, E, and momentum, p, is $E = p^2c^2 + m^2c^4$ for a relativistic particle. Show that the equation is homogeneous.

⑯ The current, I, in a wire is given by $I = nAev$ where n is the number of electrons per unit volume, A is the cross-sectional area of the wire, e is the charge on an electron and v is the drift velocity of the electrons. Show that the equation is homogeneous.

⑰ A current of 5 mA is in a wire of diameter 0.27 mm, which has 8.5×10^{28} conduction electrons per m^3. Calculate the drift velocity of the electrons and express you answer in μm s^{-1}. The electronic charge is 0.16 aC. Use the equation in question 16.

⑱ The maximum kinetic energy $E_{k\,max}$ of photoelectrons from a metal surface is given by $E_{k\,max} = hf - \phi$, where f is the frequency of the em radiation, h is the Planck constant and ϕ is the work function of the metal. Giving your reasoning, state the unit of ϕ.

⑲ The pressure p of a gas is given by $p = \frac{1}{3}\rho c^2_{rms}$, where ρ is the density of the gas and c_{rms} is the rms speed of the gas molecules. Show that this equation is homogeneous.

⑳ The *de Broglie* relationship between the momentum, p, and the wavelength, λ, of a photon is $p = \frac{h}{\lambda}$, where h is the Planck constant [see Qs 4 & 13]. Show that this equation is homogeneous.

㉑ The speed, c, of sound waves in a gas is gas is given by $c = \sqrt{\frac{\gamma p}{\rho}}$, where γ is a dimensionless constant, p is the pressure and ρ the density. Show that the equation is homogeneous.

㉒ The gravitational potential energy of two objects of mass M_1 and M_2 separated by a distance r is given by $E_p = -\frac{GM_1M_2}{r}$. Show that this equation is homogeneous. [Hint: Use the answer to Q2]

㉓ If the pressure on a sample of a substance increases by Δp the volume will decrease by ΔV. The *bulk modulus*, K, of a substance is defined by $K = V\frac{\Delta p}{\Delta V}$. The speed, v, of seismic waves [P-waves] through the material of the mantle is given by $v = cK^a\rho^b$, where c is a dimensionless constant. Use dimensional analysis, or units, to find a and b.

[Hint: First find the dimensions or a suitable unit for K].

㉔ The period of T of a satellite orbiting a planet of mass M at a distance r is thought to be given by an expression: $T = kG^aM^br^c$, where k is a dimensionless constant and G is the universal constant of gravitation. By using dimensions or units, find values for a, b and c. [G is defined in Q2].

㉕ The speed, c, of transverse waves on a wire is thought to be related to the tension T in the wire, its mass, m, and length l by an equation of the form $c = kT^xm^yl^z$. Use dimensional analysis, or units, to find values for x, y and z.

Chapter 2

Basic Algebra

Most calculations in A-level Physics rely on algebra. This is the way in which we manipulate numbers, whether we know their value [in which case, it is called *arithmetic*] or they are unknown. In A-level Physics, you will meet only *Real Numbers*. These are the numbers of everyday life, such as 75, 5.3, 0, -1.6×10^{-19}, $\frac{8}{3}$ and π. We will start with a summary of the rules for the manipulation of such numbers and then go on to look at a range of applications of algebra.

2.2 The rules of algebra

If you were happy with the algebra in GCSE Mathematics, you probably won't need this section. It is worth reading it through to check, however, because it underpins everything that comes later in this chapter.

1   **Addition**. This is indicated by the + sign.

Examples: $5.0 + 7.5$, $x + y$, $-6.3 + \pi$, $a + (-10)$.

2   **Multiplication**. This is indicated by the × sign. When dealing with unknown numbers indicated by letters, e.g. a and b, multiplication can be indicated by ab; similarly $3a$ is $3 \times a$.

Examples: 5×6, $153.7 \times (-2)$, $3a$, $2\pi r$.

3   **Subtraction**. This is indicated by the − sign.

Examples: $3 - 5$, $a - \pi$.

Subtraction is the *inverse operation* to addition. In other words, if we add a number and then subtract the same number, we get the original number: $a + b - b = a$. This is an important concept in equation manipulation.

4   **Division**. The sign on the calculator for this is ÷, but in algebra the fraction sign is used to indicate division:

a divided by b is indicated by $\frac{a}{b}$.

Division is the inverse operation to multiplication, i.e. $\frac{3 \times 5}{5} = 3$ and $\frac{ab}{a} = b$.

5   **Distributive law**. Multiplication and division are *distributive* over addition and subtraction. This means: $a(b + c) = ab + ac$ and $\frac{x + y}{z} = \frac{x}{z} + \frac{y}{z}$. This is useful in algebra.

6   **Powers / Indices** (see Chapter 4)

$a \times a$ is abbreviated as a^2 – this is referred to as 'a squared' or 'a to the power of 2'.

$a \times a \times \ldots \times a$ [n-times] $= a^n$ ['a to the n']. About indices:

- $a^1 = a$
- $a^0 = 1$ for any value of a [apart from 0]
- multiplication $a^m \times a^n = a^{m+n}$
- division $\frac{a^m}{a^n} = a^{m-n}$

See Chapter 4 for more details on indices.

Pointer

Addition and multiplication are *commutative*: $3 + a = a + 3$ and $25x = x25$ [but we normally write $25x$].

Pointer

The × sign is optional when multiplying a bracket, e.g. $15(2 - 7)$ is unambiguously $15 \times (2 - 7)$.

Pointer

Subtracting a number is the same as *adding minus the number*: e.g. $b - 25 = b + (-25)$.

Pointer

Division by a number, x, is the same thing as multiplication by $\frac{1}{x}$

e.g. $\frac{10}{8} = 10 \times \frac{1}{8}$.

Pointer

$-(a - b) = (b - a)$.

Pointer

$\frac{1}{\left(\frac{a}{b}\right)} = \frac{b}{a}$.

quiCKFire 2.1

Work out 150 (5.3 + 2.8) in two ways:

- Use the distributive law.
- Add the number in the bracket and then multiply by 150.

You should get the same answer.

quiCKFire 2.2

Evaluate $\dfrac{1}{\left(\frac{3}{5}\right)}$

quiCKFire 2.3

Evaluate $3 \times \dfrac{1}{4}$

quiCKFire 2.4

Evaluate $\dfrac{4^5}{4^3}$

2.3 The evaluation of algebraic expressions

Whatever the physics problem, you are almost certain to have to evaluate an arithmetic expression. Look at this expression: $5 \times (3^2 + 6) - 2 \times 7$.

Where does one start? Mathematicians have developed a standard way of interpreting such expressions. It is summarised in the mnemonic BODMAS – Brackets, Orders[1], Division, Multiplication, Addition, and Subtraction. What it means is: Start with expressions in brackets, sort out powers / roots, do any division or multiplication, finally add or subtract.

Pointer

In $2 \times \sqrt{(12^2 + 52)}$, the bracket is unnecessary: the top of the square root sign does the same job: In $\sqrt{12^2 + 52}$, you must evaluate $12^2 + 52$ first and then take the square root.

Pointer

The brackets are not needed in these expressions: $\dfrac{(3+4)}{5}$ and $\dfrac{3}{(4+5)}$.

quiCKFire 2.5

Evaluate:

(a) $3 \times 4 + 5$

(b) $3 \times (4 + 5)$

quiCKFire 2.6

Express as simple fractions:

(a) $\dfrac{(3+4)}{5}$

(b) $\dfrac{3}{(4+5)}$

Example A: $5 \times (3^2 + 6) - 2 \times 7$

$5 \times (3^2 + 6) - 2 \times 7 \quad = 5 \times (9 + 6) - 2 \times 7$	Sort out the bracket first – within the bracket $3^2 = 9$.
$= 5 \times 15 - 2 \times 7$	That's the bracket finished with
$= 75 - 14$	Multiply before subtracting
$= 61$	

Example B: $17 \times 3 - 2 \times \sqrt{(12^2 + 52)} + 42$

$17 \times 3 - 2 \times \sqrt{(12^2 + 52)} + 42 = 17 \times 3 - 2 \times \sqrt{196} + 42$

That's sorted out the bracket; remember to do the squaring before the addition.

$= 17 \times 3 - 2 \times 14 + 42$	Square root
$= 51 - 28 + 42$	Multiplication
$= 65$	Add and subtract

Example C: $\dfrac{15 + 6}{3} = \dfrac{21}{3} = 7$. The division line acts as brackets for the 15 + 6.

Example D: $\dfrac{12}{4 + 3} = \dfrac{12}{7} = 1.71$ (to 3 s.f.) The division line acts as brackets for the 4 + 3.

Example E: $\dfrac{1}{5} + \dfrac{23}{8} = 0.2 + 2.875 = 3.075$ Divisions first then add.

[1] *Orders* means powers / indices

Test Yourself 2.1

This is a set of questions of graded difficulty. Suggestion: Do the odd number questions first and check your answers. If several of your answers are incorrect, ask your teacher for help and then do the even questions.

Evaluate the following expressions

1 $2 + 3 \times 7$

2 $25 - 2 \times 18$

3 $30 \times 3.2 - 40 \times 2$

4 $17 \times 5 - 22 \times 1.5$

5 $153 \times (17 - 15)$

6 $1050 \times (2 + 18)$

7 $(17 - 2) \times 40$

8 $(-5 + 8) \times 14$

⑨ $2 \times 10 + 5 \times 10^2$

⑩ $3.2 \times 20 + 0.5 \times 20^2$

⑪ $\left(\dfrac{10 + 20}{2}\right) \times 5$

⑫ $\left(\dfrac{10 - 6}{2}\right) \times 20$

⑬ $\dfrac{25 - 40}{5}$

⑭ $\dfrac{37 + 18}{11}$

⑮ $\dfrac{10 \times 5}{10 + 5}$

⑯ $\dfrac{12 \times 12}{12 + 12}$

⑰ $0.5 + \dfrac{3}{4} - 1.05$

⑱ $1.7 + \dfrac{8}{10} - 3.0$

⑲ $\sqrt{10^2 + 2 \times 0.22 \times 100}$

⑳ $\sqrt{48 - 2 \times 1.5 \times 4}$

㉑ $\dfrac{-5 + \sqrt{5^2 + 4 \times 2 \times 18}}{2 \times 2}$

㉒ $\dfrac{-8 - \sqrt{8^2 + 4 \times 4 \times 1.5}}{2 \times 4}$

㉓ $\sqrt{2 \times 9.81 \times 100}$

㉔ $\dfrac{1.5 \times 6}{6 + 1.2}$

㉕ $\dfrac{12 \times 50}{50 + 25}$

2.4 Manipulating equations

2.4.1 General rules

Physics A-level specifications require students to be able to handle lots of equations. How many? Estimates vary, but typically about 120. Here are a few [you may not have met all of them yet!]:

$$s = ut + \tfrac{1}{2}at^2 \qquad P = \frac{V^2}{R} \qquad T = 2\pi\sqrt{\frac{l}{g}} \qquad g = \frac{GM_1M_2}{r^2} \qquad E^2 = p^2c^2 + m^2c^4$$

This section is about changing the appearance of an equation whilst keeping its validity. We need to do this:

- to change the subject of an equation, e.g. to write u = <an expression> instead of $s = ut + \tfrac{1}{2}at^2$ so we can evaluate u
- to put the equation into a form that will produce a linear graph – see Chapter 6
- to combine two or more equations to produce new relationships.

What is an *equation*? What does it mean? The important symbol to understand is the *equals* [or *equality*] *sign*, =. This sign, which was invented in 1557 by the Welsh mathematician, Robert Record[2], indicates that the expressions on either side of it are stated to have the same value.

If the left-hand side has a value of 25.7 N, so does the right-hand side. It is the mathematical equivalent of an old-fashioned balance. For balance, the quantity in the left-hand pan must equal the quantity in the right-hand pan[3]. In the first equation, in the set above, how can we change it to read u = <an expression>?

We can:

- add or subtract the same quantity to or from both sides of the equation; if $a = b + c$, $a - c = b$
- multiply or divide both sides of the equation by the same quantity; if $a = bc$, $\dfrac{a}{c} = b$
- square both sides, or, if we are careful, we can also take the square root[4]; if $a = \sqrt{b + c}$, $a^2 = b + c$
- take the reciprocal of both sides of the equation – if $a = b$, $1/a = 1/b$ [unless $a = b = 0$]. WARNING: We have to take the reciprocal of the whole of both sides of the equation together, not the individual terms:

  e.g. If $\dfrac{1}{a} = b + c$, then $a = \dfrac{1}{b + c}$ is CORRECT but $a = \dfrac{1}{b} + \dfrac{1}{c}$ is INCORRECT.

- add or subtract another equation; if $a = b$ and $c = d$, then $a + c = b + d$ [see Section 3.3].
- [For A2: take a function of both sides, e.g. if $a = b + c$, $\sin a = \sin(b + c)$ and $e^a = e^{(b + c)}$.]

 quickfire 2.7

Add 2 to both sides of the equation $x - 2 = 4y$

quickfire 2.8

Divide both sides of this equation by 3: $3x = 12y - 15$

quickfire 2.9

Square both sides of this equation: $\sqrt{x - 6} = 2y$ and then add 6 to both sides.

---

[2] He also invented the *plus* sign, +.
[3] We use the word *balance* in relation to chemical and nuclear equations.
[4] The need for care arises because, e.g. both $(-3)^2 = 9$ and $3^2 = 9$.

The strategy

The equation $E^2 = p^2c^2 + m^2c^4$ arises in particle physics. E is the total energy of a particle, p is its relativistic momentum, m is its mass and c the speed of light. Particle detectors will measure E and p. We can find m if we can rearrange the equation into the form $m = $ <an expression>.

What is the strategy? We need to see how other quantities are combined with the m and somehow undo the combination. Remember:

- Addition and subtraction are inverse operations – one undoes the other.
- Multiplication and division are inverse operations.
- Squaring and taking the square root are inverse operations.

It is usually easiest to start by picking off additions and subtractions first, then undoing any multiplications and division and finally sorting out powers – reverse BODMAS:

quickfire 2.10

A negatively charged particle has an energy of 3.200×10^{-10} J and a momentum of 9.414×10^{-19} N s. Find the mass of the particle. Can you identify it?

[$c = 2.997 \times 10^8\,\mathrm{m\,s^{-1}}$]

Example F: Finding m from $E^2 = p^2c^2 + m^2c^4$

Subtract p^2c^2 **from both sides**: $\qquad E^2 - p^2c^2 = m^2c^4$

Now get rid of that c^4 by dividing **both sides** by c^4 $\qquad \dfrac{E^2 - p^2c^2}{c^4} = m^2$

Now take the square root because $\sqrt{m^2} = m$ $\qquad \sqrt{\dfrac{E^2 - p^2c^2}{c^4}} = m$

Note – it doesn't matter that the m is on the right; we can always write it $m = \sqrt{\dfrac{E^2 - p^2c^2}{c^4}}$ if we feel strongly about it! So now, it's just a matter of plugging in the values of E, p and c.

See Quickfire 2.10

2.4.2 Handling fractions

This is not difficult; it just needs a bit of care, especially adding and subtracting fractions.

Multiplying and dividing are straightforward we just need to remember a few basic ideas:

$$\frac{a}{b} \times \frac{c}{d} = \frac{ac}{bd} \qquad\qquad \frac{xy}{xz} = \frac{y}{z} \text{ [unless } x = 0] \qquad\qquad \div x \text{ is the same as } \times \frac{1}{x}$$

Adding and subtracting: we can only do this easily for fractions with the same denominator[5]:

e.g. 3 sevenths + 2 sevenths = 5 sevenths.

In general: $\dfrac{a}{x} + \dfrac{b}{x} = \dfrac{a+b}{x}$

But if we have, say, 3 sevenths and 2 tenths, how do we add? Let's look at it in algebra.

Can we make $\dfrac{a}{x} + \dfrac{b}{y}$ into a single fraction? We have to give the two fractions a common denominator, i.e the bottom lines must be the same.

Look at these: $\dfrac{a}{x} = \dfrac{ay}{xy}$ and $\dfrac{b}{y} = \dfrac{bx}{xy}$, so $\dfrac{a}{x} + \dfrac{b}{y} = \dfrac{ay + bx}{xy}$ – the common denominator is xy.

quickfire 2.11

Express $\dfrac{3}{5}$ as a fraction with a denominator of 20.

Similarly: $\dfrac{a}{x} - \dfrac{b}{y} = \dfrac{ay - bx}{xy}$

---

[5] In a fraction, $\dfrac{x}{y}$, x is called the *numerator* and y the *denominator*.

Example G: Evaluate $\frac{3}{7} + \frac{2}{10}$

$\frac{3}{7}$ is the same as $\frac{3 \times 10}{7 \times 10} = \frac{30}{70}$. Also $+\frac{2}{10}$ is the same as $\frac{2 \times 7}{10 \times 7} = \frac{14}{70}$.

So
$$\frac{3}{7} + \frac{2}{10} = \frac{30}{70} + \frac{14}{70} = \frac{30 + 14}{70} = \frac{44}{70}$$

Of course, if it's a straight numerical example, it is probably easier to use the calculator, like this

$$\frac{3}{7} + \frac{2}{10} = 0.4286 + 0.2 = 0.6286, \text{ which you can check is equal to } \frac{44}{70}.$$

quickfire ▶ 2.12

Evaluate $\frac{3}{5} + \frac{7}{20}$.

2.4.3 Equations with brackets

Consider the equation $y = a(bx + c) - d$. How can we make x the subject?

Remember the last advice to use a reverse BODMAS? This advice works here, too.

Start with the undoing the subtraction, i.e. add d to both sides: $y + d = a(bx + c)$

Next, undo the multiply by a, i.e. divide both sides by a: $\frac{y + d}{a} = (bx + c)$

We don't need the brackets any more: $\frac{y + d}{a} = bx + c$

Now subtract c from both sides: $\frac{y + d}{a} - c = bx$

Finally divide both sides by b: $\frac{y + d}{ab} - \frac{c}{b} = x$ or [because it looks nicer!]: $x = \frac{y + d}{ab} - \frac{c}{b}$.

Note: We could also write this as $x = \frac{y + d - ac}{ab}$, or even $x = \frac{\frac{y+d}{a} - c}{b}$ but that looks dire!

Test Yourself 2.2

Make the bracketed symbol the subject of the equation; e.g. in question 1, write the equation in the form $m = \dots$.

① $E = mc^2$ (m) ② $P = \frac{V^2}{R}$ (R) ③ $R = \frac{\rho l}{A}$ (ρ) ④ $c = f\lambda$ (f)

⑤ $I = 4\pi r^2 \sigma T^4$ (r) ⑥ $p = \frac{1}{3}\rho c^2$ (c) ⑦ $v = u + at$ (t) ⑧ $v^2 = u^2 + 2as$ (u)

⑨ $s = \frac{1}{2}(u + v)t$ (t) ⑩ $I = nAve$ (v) ⑪ $E = \frac{1}{2}kx^2$ (x) ⑫ $T = 2\pi\sqrt{\frac{l}{g}}$ (g)

⑬ $\frac{1}{2}mv^2 = mgh$ (v) ⑭ $F = \frac{m(v - u)}{t}$ (m) ⑮ $s = vt - \frac{1}{2}at^2$ (v) ⑯ $E_{k\,max} = hf - \phi$ (h)

⑰ $F = \frac{GM_1M_2}{r^2}$ (M_2) ⑱ $T^2 = \frac{4\pi^2 a^3}{GM}$ (M) ⑲ $Z = \sqrt{X^2 + R^2}$ (X) ⑳ $m = \frac{m_0}{\sqrt{1 - \beta^2}}$ (β)

㉑ $\frac{1}{C} = \frac{1}{C_1} + \frac{1}{C_2}$ (C) ㉒ $V = \frac{ER}{R + r}$ (r) ㉓ $r_1 = \frac{M_2 d}{M_1 + M_2}$ (M_1) ㉔ $r_1 = \frac{M_2 d}{M_1 + M_2}$ (M_2)

㉕ $T = 2\pi\sqrt{\frac{d^3}{G(M_1 + M_2)}}$ (M_1)

2.5 Multiplying brackets

We have seen that $a(b + c) = ab + ac$. Notice that a multiplies b and c separately.

Similarly $(x - y)z = xz - yz$: z is multiplied by x and y separately. Remember the minus sign.

Example H: $3 \times (2.5 + 7)$: There are two ways of handling this:

1   $3 \times (2.5 + 7) = 3 \times 9.5$ [i.e. work out the bracket first] $= 28.5$

2   $3 \times (2.5 + 7) = 3 \times 2.5 + 3 \times 7$ [multiply out the bracket first] $= 7.5 + 21 = 28.5$

Of course they give the same answers. That's the point – the brackets rule works.

Consider the expression $(a + b)(c + d)$: These brackets multiply out as follows:
$(a + b)(c + d) = ac + ad + bc + bd$. Notice that **both** a and b multiply **both** c and d. Of course the order of the terms doesn't matter but it is sensible to multiply out in a systematic way. We can extend this to any number of terms in either bracket;

e.g. $\qquad\qquad (a + b)(c + d + e) = ac + ad + ae + bc + bd + be$

If we have minus signs, the usual rules hold: e.g. minus × minus = plus.

e.g. $\qquad\qquad (a - b)(c + d - e) = ac + ad - ae - bc - bd + be$

Pointer

Multiplying brackets:

all terms in the 1st bracket multiply all terms in the 2nd:

A couple of cases to note

1   $(a + b)^2 = (a + b)(a + b) = aa + ab + ab + bb$

But $aa = a^2$ and $bb = b^2$

So $(a + b)^2 = a^2 + 2ab + b^2$

Similarly $(a - b)^2 = a^2 - 2ab + b^2$. Note that it is $+b^2$ not $-b^2$!

2   $(a + b)(a - b) = a^2 + ab - ab - b^2 = a^2 - b^2$

Both these two rules give you quick ways of doing some calculations in your head without using your calculator.

quickfire ➤ 2.13

Without using a calculator, calculate:

(a) $101^2 - 99^2$

(b) 101^2 [i.e. $(100 + 1)^2$] ,

(c) 99^2,

(d) 950^2,

(e) $42^2 - 39^2$

Example I: Calculate 23^2 in your head:

$\qquad 23^2 = (20 + 3)^2 = 20^2 + 2 \times 20 \times 3 + 3^2 = 400 + 120 + 9 = 529$

Example J: Calculate $100^2 - 99^2$:

$\qquad 100^2 - 99^2 = (100 + 99)(100 - 99) = 199 \times 1 = 199$

Test Yourself 2.3

Multiply out the following expressions and reduce to the simplest form:

① $3(x + 2)$
② $4(5x + 6)$
③ $\frac{1}{2}(2a - 6)$
④ $(4 + 2a + 3b) \times 5$

⑤ $(x + 3)(y - 2)$
⑥ $(x + 2y)(x - 2y)$
⑦ $(x + 5)^2$
⑧ $(2 \quad y)^2$

⑨ $(2p + 3q)(p - q)$
⑩ $(5a - 6b)^2$
⑪ $(3 - x)(x - 3)$
⑫ $a(x - b)$

⑬ $(x - a)(x + a)$
⑭ $(x - 2a)^2$
⑮ $(z + b)^2 - 2zb$
⑯ $(z - b)^2 + 2zb$

⑰ $(z + b)^2 - (z - b)^2$
⑱ $(t^2 + 1)^2$
⑲ $(l^2 - 1)(t^2 + 1)$
⑳ $(t^2 + 1)(t - 2)$
㉑ $(a^2 - b^2)(a + b)$

Simplify the following expressions:

㉒ $\dfrac{a^2 - b^2}{a + b}$
㉓ $\dfrac{a^2 - b^2}{a - b}$
㉔ $\dfrac{(x - a)^2 + 2xa}{x^2 + a^2}$
㉕ $\dfrac{(x + c)^2 - 2xc - 2c^2}{x + c}$

2.6 Solving equations

Solving an equation means finding the value of an unknown number which makes the equation correct. If the unknown quantity is the subject of the equation then all we need to do is to evaluate the expression on the other side of the equation. To do this we use the techniques discussed above.

Example K:

A spring with constant, k, 25 N m^{-1} is extended by 40 cm. Calculate the energy stored:

Equation: $E = \frac{1}{2}kx^2$. $k = 25$ N m^{-1}, $x = 0.4$ m

Substituting: $E = \frac{1}{2} \times 25 \times 0.4^2 = 2.0$ J

If the unknown quantity is not the subject of the equation, then we need to manipulate the equation. There are two ways of approaching this:

1 Put the numbers in and then manipulate.

2 Manipulate the equation, to change the subject and then put the numbers in.

Example L:

A spring with a spring constant, k, of 50 N m^{-1} is stretched. The energy, E, stored is 6.0 J, calculate the extension, x, of the spring. $E = \frac{1}{2}kx^2$.

The two approaches are compared:

Numbers first		Manipulate first	
Equation:	$E = \frac{1}{2}kx^2$	Equation:	$E = \frac{1}{2}kx^2$
Insert the numbers:	$6.0 = \frac{1}{2} \times 50 \times x^2$	$\times 2 \div k$ (both sides)	$x^2 = \dfrac{2E}{k}$
Simplify:	$6.0 = 25 \times x^2$		
÷ both sides by 25:	$x^2 = \dfrac{6.0}{25} = 0.24$	Insert the numbers	$x^2 = \dfrac{2 \times 6.0}{50} = 0.24$
Square root	$x = \sqrt{0.24} = 0.49$ m	Square root	$x = \sqrt{0.24} = 0.49$ m

The technique to use is up to you. Physicists will generally do the algebraic manipulation first but examiners will often give the first mark for a correct substitution into a correct equation. With some equations it is slightly perverse to do the manipulation first,

e.g finding v_2 from $m_1u_1 + m_2u_2 = m_1v_1 + m_2v_2$.

Not many people would write $v_2 = \dfrac{m_1u_1 + m_2u_2 - m_1v_1}{m_2}$ first.

In the following two examples, the numbers are substituted first.

quickfire 2.14

Solve $x - 2 = 10$

Example M: A car accelerates at $a = 3.0$ m s^{-2} for time , $t = 4.0$ s. If it travels 64 m (s) in this time, what was its initial velocity, u?

Equation	$s = ut + \frac{1}{2}at^2$
Insert the numbers	$64 = 4.0u + 0.5 \times 3.0 \times 4.0^2$
Simplify (BODMAS)	$64 = 4.0u + 24$
Subtract 24	$64 - 24 = 4.0u$
Simplify	$40 = 4.0u$
Divide by 4.0	$\dfrac{40}{4.0} = u$ i.e. $u = 10$ m s^{-1}

quickfire 2.15

Solve $3x = 15$

quickfire 2.16

Solve $10x + 5 = 75$

Many people, including the authors, like putting the units of the quantities into the calculation. It provides a check. Using this approach the above working would be [after step 2]

Insert the quantities	$64\,m = (4.0\,s) \times u + 0.5 \times (3.0\,m\,s^{-2}) \times (4.0\,s)^2$
Simplify	$64\,m = (4.0\,s) \times u + 24\,m$ $[m\,s^{-2} \times s^2 = m]$
Subtract 24 m	$64\,m - 24\,m = (4.0\,s)u$

[Note the dimensions check: $64\,m - 24\,m\ \checkmark$]

Simplify	$40\,m = (4.0\,s)u$
Divide by 4.0 s	$\dfrac{40\,m}{4.0\,s} = u$ i.e. $u = 10$ m s^{-1}

Pointer

If the equation involves fractions, remember the WARNING on page 19.

In example N,

$R \neq 12 + 33!$

Example N: If the equation involves fractions, it is almost always easier to put the numbers in first:

e.g. Use $\dfrac{1}{R} = \dfrac{1}{R_1} + \dfrac{1}{R_2}$ to find the combined resistance of a 12 kΩ and a 33 kΩ resistor in parallel.

Insert the quantities $\dfrac{1}{R} = \dfrac{1}{12} + \dfrac{1}{33}$

[Note: we can keep the resistances in kΩ for this calculation – the answer will come out in kΩ]

Calculate the fractions and add $\dfrac{1}{R} = 0.0833 + 0.0303 = 0.1136$

Take the reciprocal of both sides $R = \dfrac{1}{0.1136} = 8.80$ kΩ

Test Yourself 2.4

Find the unknown quantity in these equations:

1 $10.0 = 12.0 - 0.37r$

2 $0.36 = \dfrac{4.5}{R}$

3 $60 = \dfrac{240^2}{R}$

4 $53 = 41 + 2.7t$

5 $20^2 = 10^2 + 2a \times 15$

6 $150 = 10 \times 3 + \tfrac{1}{2} a \times 3^2$

7 $0.2 \times 15 - 0.1 \times 20 = 0.3v_2$

8 $25 = \dfrac{10 + v}{2} \times 3$

9 $\dfrac{1}{f} = (1.5 - 1)\left(\dfrac{1}{60} + \dfrac{1}{20}\right)$

10 $1.01 \times 10^5 = \tfrac{1}{3} \times 1.28 \times c^2$

11 $\dfrac{1}{4} = \dfrac{1}{3} - \dfrac{1}{R}$

12 $9.81 = \dfrac{6.67 \times 10^{-11} M}{(6.37 \times 10^6)^2}$

13 $590 \times 10^{-9} = \dfrac{0.5 \times 10^{-3} y}{1.5}$

14 $20 = \dfrac{\rho \times 0.80}{\pi \times (0.5 \times 10^{-3})^2}$

15 $12 = \tfrac{1}{2} \times 5 \times v^2$

16 $83 = \dfrac{P_{OUT}}{1500} \times 100$

17 $125 = \left(\dfrac{\omega}{2\pi}\right)^2 \times 0.05$

18 $3.5 \times 10^{-27} = \dfrac{6.63 \times 10^{-34}}{\lambda}$

19 $0.6 = n \times 4\pi \times 0.0005^2 \times 1.2 \times 10^{-3} \times 1.6 \times 10^{-19}$

20 $36 = \sqrt{25^2 + F^2}$

21 $4.7 \times 10^{-7} = \dfrac{1.0 \times 10^{-6} R}{5.3}$

22 $8.6 = \dfrac{9.5 \times 10}{10 + r}$

23 $\dfrac{1}{30} = \dfrac{1}{60} + \dfrac{1}{C + 40}$

24 $\dfrac{1}{24} + \dfrac{1}{v} = \dfrac{1}{12}$

25 $80 = \dfrac{60}{\sqrt{1 - \dfrac{v^2}{9.00 \times 10^{16}}}}$

Chapter 3

Further Algebra

3.1 Introduction

Chapter 2 covered basic linear algebra. In this chapter we are going to look at equations with squared terms, i.e. quadratic equations, situations in which we need to solve equations with more than one variable, and we introduce the binomial theorem.

3.2 Quadratic equations

In quadratic equations the unknown quantity, e.g. x, is present as x^2 – and often as x as well. The general form of this equation can be written:

$$ax^2 + bx + c = 0,$$

where a, b and c are known constants and x is the unknown quantity [often the unknown is t, time].

Before we look at the difficult cases, we'll look at some special cases.

Pointer

Quadratic equations must be homogeneous.
So, in $ax^2 + bx + c = 0$,
$[ax^2] = [bx] = [c]$.

3.2.1 Quadratic equations with $b = 0$

An example of this is: Calculate the velocity, v, of an object of mass 8 kg with a kinetic energy of 144 J.

Substituting into the equation: $E_k = \frac{1}{2}mv^2 \rightarrow 144 = 4 \times v^2$

$$\therefore \qquad v^2 = 36$$

$$\therefore \qquad v = \sqrt{36} = \pm 6 \text{ m s}^{-1}$$

Why ±6 not just 6? Because $(-6)^2 = 36$ and $6^2 = 36$, so we don't know which solution is correct – it could be either. Another way of saying this is the kinetic energy of an object depends on its mass and speed but not its direction of motion. We'll see that **quadratic equations usually have two solutions**.

quickfire 3.1

If $v^2 = 64$, what are the two possible values of v?

quickfire 3.2

If $R^2 - 12 = 0$, what is R? [i.e. solve the equation for R]

3.2.2 Quadratic equations with $c = 0$

We'll do this algebraically this time:

If $c = 0$, $\qquad\qquad ax^2 + bx = 0$

which can be written $\qquad (ax + b)x = 0$

So we have two expressions, $(ax + b)$ and x, multiplied together to give 0. This can only be true if either $\qquad ax + b = 0$

or $\qquad\qquad\qquad\qquad x = 0$

So the two solutions are: $x = 0$ and $x = -\dfrac{b}{a}$.

Example A:

If a stone is thrown upwards from the ground at time $t = 0$ with an initial velocity, u, of 25 m s^{-1}, calculate the time, t, at which the stone hits the ground. Take g to be 9.8 m s^{-2}.

Substituting into $s = ut + \frac{1}{2}at^2$, $\qquad 0 = 25t - 4.9t^2$ $\qquad$ [– sign because g is downwards]

Factorising $\qquad\qquad\qquad 0 = (25 - 4.9t)t$

So, either $t = 0$ or $25 - 4.9t = 0 \rightarrow t = \dfrac{25}{4.9} = 5.1$ s.

So which solution is the one we want, $t = 0$ or $t = 5.1$ s? Clearly $t = 0$ refers to the starting time so the answer we want is 5.1 s.

3.2.3 Quadratic equations of the form $(x + p)^2 = 0$

Actually, you'll hardly ever see one but it is going to be important – so stick with it.

If $(x + p)^2 = 0$ then, taking the square root, $x + p = 0$, so the solution is $x = -p$.

Now, if $(x + p)^2 = 0$ then $\qquad (x + p)(x + p) = 0$

Multiplying the brackets out: $\qquad x^2 + 2px + p^2 = 0$

We're going to leave it there – why? If we have a quadratic equation that has the form, $x^2 + 2px + p^2 = 0$ we can write it $(x + p)^2 = 0$, so we'll be able to solve it.

Grade boost

If $xy = 0$, then either $x = 0$ or $y = 0$ [or both!].

3.2.4 The general solution of $ax^2 + bx + c = 0$

We're going to derive a general solution to $ax^2 + bx + c = 0$ using the result of 3.2.3.

Step 1: Divide by a: $\qquad x^2 + \dfrac{b}{a}x + \dfrac{c}{a} = 0$

Step 2: Subtract $\dfrac{c}{a}$ $\qquad x^2 + \dfrac{b}{a}x = -\dfrac{c}{a}$

Step 3: Add $\dfrac{b^2}{4a^2}$ $\qquad x^2 + \dfrac{b}{a}x + \dfrac{b^2}{4a^2} = \dfrac{b^2}{4a^2} - \dfrac{c}{a}$

Look at $x^2 + 2px + p^2 = 0$ in 3.2.3: If $p = \dfrac{b}{2a}$, $2p = \dfrac{b}{a}$ and $p^2 = \dfrac{b^2}{4a^2}$, so ...

Step 4: Factorise the LHS and put the RHS over a common denominator of $4a^2$

$$\left(x + \dfrac{b}{2a}\right)^2 = \dfrac{b^2 - 4ac}{4a^2}$$

Step 5: Take the square root: $\qquad x + \dfrac{b}{2a} = \pm\dfrac{\sqrt{b^2 - 4ac}}{2a}$

Step 6: Subtract $\dfrac{b}{2a}$ $\qquad x = \dfrac{-b \pm \sqrt{b^2 - 4ac}}{2a}$. This is the general solution.

The solutions to the general quadratic are sometimes needed in projectiles questions.

Grade boost

If $\dfrac{p}{q} = 0$, then $p = 0$.

Grade boost

If $\dfrac{1}{ab} = 0$, you've done something wrong [unless a or b is infinitely large].

Example B:

A stone is thrown down a 100 m deep mine shaft, with initial velocity 10 m s^{-1}. How long does it take to reach the bottom? [Take $g = 9.8$ m s^{-2}]

Step 1: Equation $\qquad s = ut + \tfrac{1}{2}at^2$

Step 2: Substitution $\qquad 100 = 10t + 4.9t^2$

Step 3: Rearrange $\quad 4.9t^2 + 10t - 100 = 0 \qquad$ This is of the form: $ax^2 + bx + c = 0$

Step 4: Identify a, b, c: $\qquad a = 4.9$ m s^{-2}, $b = 10$ m s^{-1}, $c = -100$ m

Step 5: Solve $\qquad t = \pm\dfrac{-10 \pm \sqrt{10^2 - 4 \times 4.9 \times (-100)}}{9.8} = \dfrac{-10 \pm 45.4}{9.8}$

Step 6: Solutions $\qquad t = -5.7$ s or $t = 3.6$ s

Step 7: Identify the correct solution: The time of impact cannot be before we throw it, so we can ignore the $t = -5.7$ s solution. $\therefore$ Time taken is 3.6 s.

quickfire 3.3.

Solve $(l - 0.5)^2 = 4$.

quickfire 3.4

What is the physical significance of the -5.7 s solution in Example B?

quickfire 3.5

$t = \dfrac{-10 \pm \sqrt{10^2 - 4 \times 4.9 \times (-100)}}{9.8}$

is the solution to Example B. Put units into this equation and show that it is homogeneous. Hint: the 10 is the velocity, u, so its unit is m s^{-1}.

We'll see that quadratic equations also crop up when solving some simultaneous equations.

UXBRIDGE COLLEGE
LEARNING CENTRE

Test Yourself 3.1

In questions 1–16, find the values of the unknown:

1 $24 = \frac{1}{2} \times 3x^2$

2 $100 = \frac{1}{2} \times 5000x^2$

3 $12t^2 - 84t = 0$

4 $25t^2 - 750t = 0$

5 $100t - 9.8t^2 = 0$

6 $600 = \frac{1}{2} \times 0.2v^2$

7 $3 \times 10^6 = \frac{1}{2} \times 0.5v^2$

8 $5x^2 + 2 = 247$

9 $72 = \frac{1}{2} \times 5 \times (l - 0.24)^2$ [Hint: treat $(l - 0.24)$ as the variable)]

10 $500 = \frac{1}{2} \times 0.2(v + 50)^2$

11 $80 = \frac{1}{2} \times 0.25 \, (v - 5)^2$

12 $x^2 + x - 2 = 0$

13 $3x^2 + 10x + 6 = 0$

14 $\frac{1}{2}t^2 - 7t + 5 = 0$

15 $25 = 60t - 4.9t^2$

16 $-100 = +0.8t^2 - 20t$

17   The work done, W, in extending a spring, with a spring constant k, is given by $W = \frac{1}{2}kx^2$.

Find the extension, x, if $W = 50\,\text{J}$ and $k = 25\,\text{N m}^{-1}$.

18   Find the velocity, v, of a body of mass 2 kg, with a kinetic energy of 1 MJ.

$E_k = \frac{1}{2}mv^2$.

19   A stone is thrown upwards with a velocity, u, of $10\,\text{m s}^{-1}$. If $g = 9.8\,\text{m s}^{-2}$, calculate the time, t, at which the stone returns to the ground. $s = ut + \frac{1}{2}at^2$, where s is the height above the ground.

[The acceleration is downwards, so $a = -9.8\,\text{m s}^{-2}$].

20   A small asteroid of radius, $r = 5\,\text{m}$ and density, $\rho = 2500\,\text{kg m}^{-3}$ impacts the Earth with an energy equivalent of 0.5 megatonnes of TNT. Estimate its speed of impact.

Data: 1 tonne of TNT $\equiv 4.2\,\text{GJ}$ energy; $\rho = \dfrac{M}{V}$; for a sphere, $V = \frac{4}{3}\pi r^3$; $E_k = \frac{1}{2}mv^2$

21   An astronaut on the Moon dropped a hammer and a piece of paper from a height of 1.5 m. How long did they take to reach the Moon's surface? $g = 1.62\,\text{m s}^{-2}$. $s = ut + \frac{1}{2}at^2$.

22   The range, R, of an artillery gun which fires a shell with a velocity u, at an angle θ to the horizontal can be found from the equation

$R^2 - \left(\dfrac{u^2}{g} \sin 2\theta\right)R = 0$. Find the range for $u = 200\,\text{m s}^{-1}$ and $\theta = 30°$.

23   Find the height, h, above the Earth's surface at which the acceleration due to gravity is $3.0\,\text{m s}^{-2}$.

The radius of the Earth is 6380 km. g at the Earth's surface $= 9.8\,\text{m s}^{-2}$.

$g = \dfrac{k}{r^2}$, where r is the distance from the centre of the Earth.

24   A car brakes to a halt with a deceleration, $-a$, of $2.0\,\text{m s}^{-2}$ over a distance, s, of 100 m. What was its initial velocity, u?

$v^2 = u^2 + 2as$, where v = the final velocity = 0.

25   A ball is dropped onto a hard surface from a height of 10 m. It rebounds to a height of 8 m. Calculate the time it takes to reach the rebound height. [Ignore the duration of the collision with the ground.] $g = 9.8\,\text{m s}^{-1}$. $s = ut + \frac{1}{2}at^2$

3.3 Simultaneous equations

In many physical situations a single equation will not do. We have two or more unknowns, at the same time. As long as we have the same number of equations as the number of unknowns an answer can be found. The skills involved will be also be useful in the sections where we will derive some equations.

Pointer

An example of a situation with two unknowns is measuring the current and pd provided by a cell.

$V = E - Ir$

E and r are unknown.

3.3.1 Linear simultaneous equations

The box with the pulley on page 29 gives a physics example with two unknown quantities, T and a. There are two equations, but neither is enough on its own to find either of the forces. Before we solve it look at the following equations:

$$a + b = 0 \tag{1}$$

$$2a - b = 6 \tag{2}$$

Let's add the two equations together! Are we allowed to? Sure – the left and right sides of an equation are the same size [that's what an equation means] and we can add the same thing to both sides of an equation.

What do we get?

(1) + (2) gives $\quad\quad\quad a + 2a + b - b = 6$

Simplifying gives $\quad\quad\quad\quad\quad 3a = 6 \quad\quad \therefore a = 2.$

So now we know that $a = 2$. How do we find b?

Just substitute the value $a = 2$ in **either** of the two equations: e.g. putting $a = 2$ into equation (1). This gives $2 + b = 0$. $\therefore b = -2$.

Now have a look at the problem with the pulley in the box.

First the physics: $\quad\quad\quad\quad\quad \Sigma F = ma$

For the 3 kg mass: $\quad\quad\quad 3 \times 9.81 - T = 3a$

Rearranging: $\quad\quad\quad\quad\quad T + 3a = 29.43 \quad\quad$ (3)

For the 2 kg mass: $\quad\quad\quad T - 2 \times 9.81 = 2a$

Rearranging: $\quad\quad\quad\quad\quad T - 2a = 19.62 \quad\quad$ (4)

We could eliminate T from the equations by subtracting (4) from (3). Let's do it another way:

Notice that (3) has $3a$ and (4) has $2a$. We'll multiply (3) by 2 and multiply (4) by 3:

$$(3) \times 2 \rightarrow 2T + 6a = 58.86$$
$$(4) \times 3 \rightarrow 3T - 6a = 58.86$$

Adding these two eliminates the a and gives $5T = 117.72$, so $T = \dfrac{117.72}{5} = 23.44\,\text{N}$

[Remember to put the units in. T is a force $\therefore$ N]

Now all we need to do to find a, is to put T into either (3) or (4) to find a.

3.3.2 Non-linear simultaneous equations

Consider the following problem: Two unknown resistors of value R_1 and R_2 are connected together. In series their combined resistance is 25 Ω; in parallel it is 6 Ω. Determine R_1 and R_2.

Looking at the relevant equations: $\quad\quad R_1 + R_2 = 25 \quad\quad$ (1) $\quad$ Resistors in series

$$\frac{1}{R_1} + \frac{1}{R_2} = \frac{1}{6} \quad\quad (2) \quad \text{Resistors in parallel}$$

The presence of the reciprocals means that the technique used in 3.3.1 will not work. Instead we will use substitution. This problem will illustrate this technique.

From equation (1), $R_2 = 25 - R_1$. We will write $25 - R_1$ instead of R_2 in equation (2). This gives:

$$\frac{1}{R_1} + \frac{1}{25 - R_1} = \frac{1}{6}.$$

Following substitution, we have an equation with one unknown. It is just a matter of solving it.

If we multiply by $6R_1(25 - R_1)$ we will get rid of the fractions:

$$6[(25 - R_1) + R_1] = R_1(25 - R_1)$$

Multiplying the bracket and re-arranging gives $R_1{}^2 - 25R_1 + 150 = 0$, which we can solve to give $R_1 = 10\,\Omega$ or $15\,\Omega$. Equation (1) tells us that if $R_1 = 10\,\Omega$ then $R_2 = 15\,\Omega$ and *vice versa*. The question doesn't specify which resistor is which!

quickfire 3.6

Multiply the equation, $3x + y = 2$, by 2

quickfire 3.7

Multiply $5a - 3b = 6$ by -2

Practice

Instead of substituting $a = 2$ into (1), try putting $a = 2$ into equation (2). You should find you get the same answer for b.

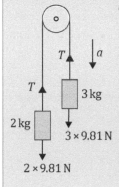

Two objects of mass 2 kg and 3 kg are connected by a thread over a pulley. Calculate the tension, T, in the thread and the acceleration, a, of the objects. Ignore friction and the mass of the thread and pulley.

Note: The two masses have the same acceleration, but if the 3 kg is accelerating downwards, the 2 kg accelerates upwards.

Practice

(a) By substituting $T = 23.44\,\text{N}$ into equation (3), show that $a = 2.0\,\text{m s}^{-2}$.

(b) Repeat this for equation (4).

(c) Solve the whole problem from the beginning by subtracting (4) from (3) to start with.

quickfire 3.8

Add the equations:
$5a - 3b = 7$
$3a + 3b = 5$

quickfire 3.9

Find a and b in Quickfire 3.8.

quickfire 3.10

$a + b = 10$; $a - b = 5$.
Find a and b.

Test Yourself 3.2

In questions 1–8, solve the equations for the given unknowns. For the remaining questions, substitute pairs of values into the given algebraic equation and solve the resulting equations:

1 $24 = u + 4a$

$45 = u + 10a$

2 $1.5 = E - 1.0r$

$1.0 = E - 2.0r$

3 $11 = 2u + 2a$

$51 = 6u + 18a$

4 $27 - 4.5r = 6E$

$36 - 3.0r = 12E$

5 $70 = 5v - 12.5a$

$64 = 8v - 32a$

6 $\frac{1}{2}mv^2 = 1125$

$mv = 150$

7 $5 = 0.4k - kl_0$

$15 = 0.8k - kl_0$

[Hint: write kl_0 as x, find k and x then find l_0]

8 $8^2 = u^2 + 2 \times a \times 7$

$12^2 = u^2 + 2 \times a \times 27$

[Hint: Simplify to start with, solve for u^2 and a, then find the square root of u^2]

9 A car with initial velocity u, undergoing uniform acceleration, a, has a velocity, v, of 10 m s^{-1} after a time, t, of 10 s. Substitute these values into $v = u + at$.

After 16 s its velocity is 14.5 m s^{-1}. Substitute these values into $v = u + at$.

Solve the two equations to find the initial velocity and acceleration.

10 An accelerating car has an initial velocity u and acceleration a. Use the equation $v^2 = u^2 + 2as$ to find u and a given the following values of v and s:

when the displacement $s = 20$ m, the velocity $v = 8$ m s^{-1}

when the displacement $s = 60$ m, the velocity $v = 10$ m s^{-1}

11 A power supply has an emf, E, and internal resistance, r. When the battery delivers a current (I) of 0.8 A, the terminal pd (V) is 4.8 V. When $I = 1.4$ A, $V = 3.9$ V.

Use the equation $V = E - Ir$ to find the emf and internal resistance.

12 An accelerating car travels a distance, $s = 102$ m after a time, $t = 6.0$ s. After 10 s it has travelled 230 m. Use the equation $s = ut + \frac{1}{2}at^2$ to find the initial velocity, u, and the acceleration, a.

13 The currents in the circuit can be found by applying Kirchhoff's laws.

Applying K2 to the left loop gives:

$2.0 - 1.5 = 1.0I_1 + 5I_1 - 2.0I_2$ (1)

Applying K2 to the right loop gives:

$1.5 = 10(I_1 + I_2) + 2.0I_2$ (2)

(a) Simplify and solve these equations for I_1 and I_2.

(b) Use the equation $V = E - Ir$ to find the pd across each power supply.

(c) Use $V = IR$ to find the pd across the 10 Ω resistor; comment on your answer.

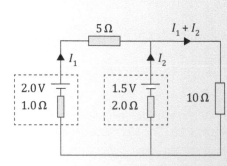

⑭ A power supply has emf, E, and internal resistance, r. When a resistor of resistance $R = 12\,\Omega$ is connected across it, the terminal pd , $V = 6.0$ V. When $R = 24\,\Omega$, $V = 8.0$ V.

Use the equation, $V = \dfrac{ER}{R + r}$ with the above values, to find E and r.

⑮ Two bodies of mass 2 kg and 1 kg travel along the same straight line with velocities v_1 and v_2 respectively. The total momentum and kinetic energy of the pair are 18 N s and 57 J respectively. Find values for v_1 and v_2.

Momentum = mv and kinetic energy = $\frac{1}{2}mv^2$.

[There are two sets of possible values.]

⑯ A body of mass 3 kg, travelling at $4\,\text{m s}^{-1}$, collides elastically* head on with a stationary body of mass 6 kg. Find the velocities of the two bodies after the collision.

Hint: Find the total momentum and kinetic energy before the collision first, then apply the principles of conservation of momentum and energy.

* Elastically = the total kinetic energy is unchanged in the collision.

⑰ A voltmeter and ammeter are used to measure the resistance, R, of a resistor. Their readings are V and I. Unfortunately the voltmeter has a zero error, ε, of unknown size, so that $V = IR + \varepsilon$. When $I = 0.450$ A, $V = 3.058$ V; when $I = 0.750$ A, $V = 5.112$ V. Find R and ε.

⑱ As in Q17, but this time the ammeter has a zero error, so that the relevant equation is $V = (I + \varepsilon)R$. When $I = 0.273$ A, $V = 1.353$ V; when $I = 0.482$ A, $V = 2.341$ V. Find R and ε.

⑲ In an experiment to find the spring constant, k, two different masses, m, are suspended from the spring and the period, T, measured. The masses are attached to a hanger of unknown mass, μ, so that the period is given by:

$T = 2\pi\sqrt{\dfrac{m + \mu}{k}}$. Results: 0.100 kg, 0.490 s; 0.300 kg, 0.744 s. Find k and μ.

⑳ In an experiment to determine g, a pendulum bob is suspended from the ceiling of height h above the floor of a laboratory. When the height, x, of the bob above the floor was 0.253 m, the period, T, was 3.025 s. With $x = 1.279$ m, $T = 2.243$ s.

Given that $T = 2\pi\sqrt{\dfrac{h - x}{g}}$, find values for g and h.

㉑ Two sets of students make measurement on an accelerating car. The first set notes that after 15 s its velocity is $40\,\text{m s}^{-1}$. The other records the distance travelled after 10 s to be 200 m. Assuming constant acceleration, find its initial velocity, u, and acceleration, a.

Use the equations $v = u + at$ and $s = ut + \frac{1}{2}at^2$.

㉒ Another two groups of equally disorganised students repeat the task in Q21. The first group notes that after 4 s the car has a displacement of 100 m; the second notes that the car reaches a velocity of $25\,\text{m s}^{-1}$ after a displacement of 40 m. Find the initial velocity and acceleration.

Use the equations $s = ut + \frac{1}{2}at^2$ and $v^2 = u^2 + 2as$.

NB. There are two valid solutions to this question. Describe the motion in each.

㉓ A student records that the pd, V, across a power supply with an external resistance, R, of $22\,\Omega$ is 22 V. The power, P, supplied to an external resistance of $10\,\Omega$ is 40 W. Find the emf, E, and internal resistance, r, of the power supply.

Use the equations $V = \dfrac{ER}{R + r}$ and $P = \dfrac{E^2 R}{(R + r)^2}$.

NB. There are two algebraic solutions to this problem, only one of which is valid. Give the valid solution.

㉔ The period of oscillations, T, of an object on a spring is given by $T = 2\pi\sqrt{\dfrac{m}{k}}$, where m is the mass and k the spring constant. The period, T_1, of an unknown mass, M_1, is measured. An additional mass, M_2, is added and the period T_2, measured.

(a) Show that $T_2{}^2 - T_1{}^2 = 4\pi^2\dfrac{M_2}{k}$.

(b) Given that $T_1 = 0.662$ s, $T_2 = 1.047$ s and $M_2 = 0.300$ kg, determine values for k and M_1.

㉕ The period, T, of a simple pendulum of length l is given by $T = 2\pi\sqrt{\dfrac{l}{g}}$.

An extraterrestrial on its own planet determines the period of oscillation of a pendulum to be 3.376 s. It shortens the length by 0.500 m and finds the new period to be 3.020 s. Find the value of g and the original length of the pendulum.

3.4 The binomial series

The following expression arises quite frequently in maths and physics: $(1 + x)^n$. This section investigates this expression for the case when n is a positive integer, i.e. we're going to look at $(1 + x)^2$, $(1 + x)^3$, ... $(1 + x)^{10}$... .

Let's look at the expansion of $(1 + x)^n$ for a few low values of n. You should be able to show that the following are correct:

```
           1
          1 1
         1 2 1
        1 3 3 1
       1 4 6 4 1
     1 5 10 10 5 1
   1 6 15 20 15 6 1
         etc.
```

Fig 3.1

$(1 + x)^0$:	1
$(1 + x)^1$	$1 + x$
$(1 + x)^2 = (1 + x)(1 + x)$	$1 + 2x + x^2$
$(1 + x)^3 = (1 + x)^2(1 + x)$	$1 + 3x + 3x^2 + x^3$
$(1 + x)^4 = (1 + x)^3(1 + x)$	$1 + 4x + 6x^2 + 4x^3 + x^4$

Figure 3.1 is the familiar Pascal's triangle: the numbers are the same as the coefficients[1] in the expansions of $(1 + x)^n$. Each row is obtained by adding two neighbouring numbers in the row above, including 0 on the ends of each row.

Because this pattern is so simple there must be a general formula. It turns out to be:

$$(1 + x)^n = 1 + nx + \frac{n(n-1)}{2!}x^2 + \frac{n(n-1)(n-2)}{3!}x^3 + ... \frac{n(n-1)(n-2) ... (n-k+1)}{k!}x^k + ...$$

up to x^n.

Try it for $n = 4$ and you should obtain the values, 1, 4, 6, 4 and 1

The expression on the right of the equation is called a *series*. The usefulness of this particular series to physics arises from Newton's realisation that it is also valid for values of n other than positive integers, in particular for **negative and fractional values of n.** Two potential problems need stressing for negative and fractional values of n:

- the series becomes an **infinite** series, i.e. it doesn't have a final term, because none of the $n - 1$, $n - 2$, etc., is zero;

- the series only converges[2] for values of x between −1 and 1, i.e. $|x| < 1$.

Neither of these is a real problem for physics.

Example C:

What results does the binomial series give for $\sqrt{1.5}$ i.e. $(1 + 0.5)^{\frac{1}{2}}$?

Let's see. The binomial series for $(1 + x)^{\frac{1}{2}}$ is:

$$(1 + x)^{\frac{1}{2}} = 1 + \frac{1}{2}x + \frac{\frac{1}{2}\left(\frac{1}{2} - 1\right)}{2!}x^2 + \frac{\frac{1}{2}\left(\frac{1}{2} - 1\right)\left(\frac{1}{2} - 2\right)}{3!}x^3 + \frac{\frac{1}{2}\left(\frac{1}{2} - 1\right)\left(\frac{1}{2} - 2\right)\left(\frac{1}{2} - 3\right)}{4!}x^4...$$

$$= 1 + \frac{1}{2}x - \frac{1}{8}x^2 + \frac{1}{16}x^3 - \frac{5}{128}x^4 ...$$

Putting $x = 0.5$ into this equation: $(1 + 0.5)^{\frac{1}{2}} = 1 + \frac{1}{2} \times 0.5 - \frac{1}{8} \times 0.5^2 + \frac{1}{16} \times 0.5^3 - \frac{5}{128} \times 0.5^4 ...$

$$= 1 + 0.25 - 0.03125 + 0.0078125 - 0.0024414 + ...$$

If we just take the 1st term (1), we get the so-called *zero order approximation* = 1.

If we add the 2nd term (0.25) we get the first-order approximation = 1.25

---

[1]   Here the word *coefficient* means the number in front of the x^n terms.

[2]   An infinite series *converges* if it gets closer and closer to a final value as more and more terms are added together. NB this is not a proper mathematical definition of convergence.

Carrying on: the 2nd order approx. = 1.21875

3rd order approx. = 1.22656

4th order approx. = 1.22412

This sequence of approximations appears to be approaching the calculator value of 1.22474...

Now do Quickfire 3.11

The important result:

Notice how 'good' the 1st order approximations are in Example C and Quickfires 3.11 and 3.12. And they get better, the smaller x is. Why is this?

Look again at the first few terms of binomial series;

$$(1 + x)^n = 1 + nx + \frac{n(n - 1)}{2!}x^2 + \frac{n(n - 1)(n - 2)}{3!}x^3 + ...$$

If $|x|$ is a lot less than 1 $[|x| \ll 1]$, then x^2 will be tiny and x^3 miniscule, so as long as n isn't very big we can write:

$$(1 + x)^n \approx 1 + nx$$

So, for small x, $\sqrt{1 + x} \approx 1 + \frac{1}{2}x$ and $\frac{1}{1 + x} \approx 1 - x$ are good approximations, and get better as x gets smaller. For an example of how useful it is, look at the derivation of the Young Slits formula in Chapter 12. It will also turn up again when we look at calculus. Questions 18–22 in Test Yourself 3.3 prepare the way for the Young Slits result.

quickfire 3.11

What are the 1st, 2nd and 3rd order binomial approximations to $\sqrt{1.21}$? [If you don't know the true answer, check it on your calculator and then kick yourself!]

quickfire 3.12

Show that $\frac{1}{1 - x} = 1 + x + x^2 + x^3 + ...$ and compare the 1st, 2nd, 3rd order approximations for $\frac{1}{0.9}$ with the correct answer of 1.1111 ... .

Test Yourself 3.3

The first few questions involve the series for $\sqrt{(1 + x)^3}$, i.e. $(1 + x)^{\frac{3}{2}}$.

1. Show that the first few terms [up to the 4th order] of the binomial series for $\sqrt{(1 + x)^3}$ are:

   $$\sqrt{(1 + x)^3} = 1 + \frac{3}{2}x + \frac{3}{8}x^2 - \frac{1}{16}x^3 + \frac{3}{128}x^4$$

2. Use your calculator to find the value of $1.5^{1.5}$ [i.e. $(1+0.5)^{\frac{3}{2}}$]

3. Use the series in question 1, with $x = 0.5$, to find the value of each term, up to the 4th order, of the binomial series for $\sqrt{1.5^3}$.

4. Hence find the 1st, 2nd, 3rd and 4th order approximations to $\sqrt{1.5^3}$. What would be the % error in just using (a) the 1st order approximation and (b) the 2nd order approximation?

5. Repeat Questions 2–4 using $x = 0.1$, i.e. investigating $\sqrt{1.1^3}$

In Questions 6–10, use the equation, $(1 + x)^n \approx 1 + nx$ to find the 1st order binomial approximations for the given numbers, **without using a calculator!**

6. 1.01^3

7. 0.99^{-3}

8. 1.02^{-3}

9. $1.1^{1.5}$

10. $0.8^{-0.5}$

11. Find the 1st and 2nd order binomial approximations to $\sqrt{4.5}$.

    Hint: Write 4.5 as $4 \times (1.125)$.

12. Using the 1st order binomial approximations only, find $\sqrt[3]{1100}$. [Hint: see Q11]

⑬ Work out the binomial series for $\dfrac{1}{\sqrt{1+x}}$ up to the 4th order.

⑭ Use your answer to Q13 to work out the 1st, 2nd, 3rd and 4th order approximations to $0.8^{-0.5}$ and compare your results with the calculator value.

⑮ Show that, to 1st order, $(1+x)^n - (1-x)^n = 2nx$.

⑯ Find the 1st order approximation to $\sqrt{1+x} - \sqrt{1-x}$.

⑰ Find the 1st order approximation to $(1+x)^n - \dfrac{1}{(1+x)^n}$.

⑱ Show that, if $a \ll x$, $(x+a)^n = x^n + nax^{n-1}$ to a good approximation.

Hint: Write $(x+a)$ as $x\left(1 + \dfrac{a}{x}\right)$.

⑲ From Q18, write the 1st order approximation of the expression: $(x+a)^n - x^n$.

⑳ Find the length AC in the right-angled triangle shown,

    (a) using a 1st order binomial approximation

    (b) using the square root function on a calculator.

[Hint: Pythagoras' Theorem]

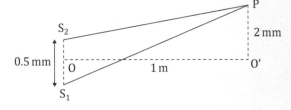

㉑ Find the value of $S_1P - S_2P$

    (a) using a 1st order binomial approximation;

    (b) to 3 s.f. using a calculator square root function.

㉒ Using the diagram from Q21, find the value of $S_1P - S_2P$ using a 1st order binomial approximation with the distances as follows:

$S_1S_2 = d$; $OO' = D$; $O'P = x$.

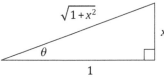

㉓ Show that to **2nd order** $\sqrt{1+x} + \dfrac{1}{\sqrt{1+x}} = 2 + \tfrac{1}{4}x^2$ and find the % error in using this approximation when $x = 0.1$

㉔ Find the **2nd order** approximation to $(1+x)^n + (1+x)^{-n}$ and use this to estimate $1.1^4 + \dfrac{1}{1.1^4}$, **without using a calculator!**

㉕ In the triangle opposite, find the **3rd order** approximations to $\sin\theta$, $\cos\theta$, and $\tan\theta$ in terms of x.

Chapter 4

Indices and Logarithms

4.1 Introduction This comparatively short chapter covers two important areas of maths which are used frequently in A-level Physics. AS candidates may need the content of Section 4.2 only – this will depend upon the specification. Questions 1–10 of Test Yourself 4.1 relate to Section 4.2.

4.2 Indices

a^4 is a compact abbreviation for $a \times a \times a \times a$ in which a can be any number. We pronounce a^4 as 'a to the *power* 4', or just 'a to the 4'. The number 4 is called the *exponent* or the *index*. In this context, the plural of index is *indices*.

The number a is the same as a^1 – the index tells you how many a's are multiplied together: in this case there is only one a.

Indices have a vital role in Physics, for example in expressing very large or very small quantities in standard SI units. Thus, to three figures, the mass of the hydrogen nucleus can be written as 2.38×10^{27} kg, the gravitational constant $G = 6.67 \times 10^{-11}$ kg^{-1} m^3 s^{-2} and the solar mass as 1.99×10^{30} kg (try writing that out in non-indexed form!). It is therefore crucial to be able to perform calculations involving quantities expressed in this way using the laws which follow.

4.2.1 The laws of indices

1. What is the result if we multiply a^4 by a^3?

   $a^4 \times a^3 = (a \times a \times a \times a) \times (a \times a \times a) = a \times a \times a \times a \times a \times a \times a = a^7$

   So, in general, $a^m \times a^n = a^{(m+n)}$ Law 1

   Thus, in order to **multiply** two numbers, we **add** the indices.

2. What if we divide a^4 by a^3? $\dfrac{a \times a \times a \times a}{a \times a \times a} = a = a^1$

   So, in general, $\dfrac{a^m}{a^n} = a^{(m-n)}$ Law 2

3. Finally, what is the third power of a^4?

   $(a^4)^3 = (a \times a \times a \times a) \times (a \times a \times a \times a) \times (a \times a \times a \times a) = a^{12}$

   So, in general, $(a^m)^n = a^{mn}$.   Law 3

Pointer

a^{3^2} means a to the power of 3^2 i.e. a^9.

quickfire ▶ 4.1

Calculate $5^2 \times 2^5$

quickfire ▶ 4.2

Calculate: (a) $(3^4)^2$ and (b) 3^{4^2}.

Example A: Calculate $(1.5^3)^2$.

$(1.5^3)^2 = 1.5^{3 \times 2} = 1.5^6 = 11.39$ (4 s.f.)

4.2.2 Negative and zero indices

We know that $\dfrac{a^m}{a^n} = a^{(m-n)}$ but we can also write $\dfrac{a^m}{a^n}$ as the product $a^m \times \dfrac{1}{a^n}$. To get the right answer using the *first* law of indices, we need to write $\dfrac{1}{a^n} = a^{-n}$.

Pointer

When using laws of indices remember that x can be written as x^1.

Pointer

The expression $a^x b^y$ cannot be simplified. We calculate a^x and b^y separately and multiply them together.

quickfire 4.3

Express 4^{-2} as a decimal.

quickfire 4.4

Calculate $2^{-4} \times 3^2$ and express the answer as a decimal.

Pointer

Remember these cube roots:

$\sqrt[3]{8} = 8^{\frac{1}{3}} = 2$

$\sqrt[3]{27} = 27^{\frac{1}{3}} = 3$

$\sqrt[3]{64} = 64^{\frac{1}{3}} = 4$

$\sqrt[3]{125} = 125^{\frac{1}{3}} = 5$

quickfire 4.5

Without using a calculator, express (a) $64^{\frac{2}{3}}$ and (b) $64^{\frac{3}{2}}$ as numbers.

quickfire 4.6

Without using a calculator, express $4^{-\frac{3}{2}}$ as a number.

quickfire 4.7

(a) Express 72 as $a^m b^n$, in which a and b are prime numbers.
(b) Use the third law of indices to express $(72)^4$ in the same way.

quickfire 4.8

Express $\dfrac{125}{\sqrt{5}}$ as 5^P.

quickfire 4.9

Express $27^{-\frac{4}{3}}$ more simply without using a calculator.

For example, $\frac{1}{2} = 2^{-1}$, so $\frac{1}{2} \times 8 = 2^{-1} \times 2^3 = 2^{(-1+3)} = 2^2 = 4$, which is good! In other words, our new understanding of what a^{-n} means gives us what we know to be the right answer.

What we're now doing is letting the formal laws of indices guide us to assign meanings to a^m and a^n, even when m and n are not positive whole numbers – for which the laws were first written. We continue this assignment of meaning by putting $n = 0$ in the first two laws, giving

$$a^m \times a^0 = a^{(m+0)} = a^m$$

and

$$\frac{a^m}{a^0} = a^{(m-0)} = a^m$$

So multiplying or dividing by a^0 has no effect on a^m. We conclude that, for any a, $a^0 = 1$.

4.2.3 Fractional indices

Put $m = n = \frac{1}{2}$ into the first law. Then: $\quad a^{\frac{1}{2}} \times a^{\frac{1}{2}} = a^1 = a$

But $\sqrt{a}$ is defined by $\qquad\qquad \sqrt{a} \times \sqrt{a} = a$

We conclude that: $a^{\frac{1}{2}} = \sqrt{a}$. And, in general, $\quad a^{\frac{1}{n}} = \sqrt[n]{a}$

What about $a^{\frac{m}{n}}$? Now $\left(a^{\frac{m}{n}}\right)^n = a^{\frac{m}{n} \times n} = a^m$, so $\quad a^{\frac{m}{n}} = \sqrt[n]{a^m}$.

You should be able to show that this can be written $\left(\sqrt[n]{a}\right)^m$. This is left as an exercise.

We can now interpret numbers with decimal indices, for example $2^{0.4}$.

$2^{0.4} = 2^{\frac{4}{10}} = \sqrt[10]{2^4}$. We could equally well write this as $\sqrt[5]{2^2}$.

Example B:

Express $\dfrac{1}{4\sqrt{2}}$ as 2^x.

$$\frac{1}{4\sqrt{2}} = \frac{1}{2^2 \times 2^{\frac{1}{2}}} = \frac{1}{2^{\left(2+\frac{1}{2}\right)}} = \frac{1}{2^{\frac{5}{2}}} = 2^{-\frac{5}{2}}$$

This could equally well be written $2^{-2.5}$.

It is sensible to consider the order of the calculation when simplifying numbers with fractional indices. For example, what is $27^{\frac{4}{3}}$?

We could write this as $(27^4)^{\frac{1}{3}}$: $27^4 = 27 \times 27 \times 27 \times 27 = 531441$

Then $531441^{\frac{1}{3}} = \sqrt[3]{531441} = 81$. That is definitely a calculator job.

But we could write $27^{\frac{4}{3}}$ as $\left(27^{\frac{1}{3}}\right)^4 = \left(\sqrt[3]{27}\right)^4 = 3^4 = 81$, which can be done in your head!

4.3 The 'natural number' e

This section looks like a digression, but it is very important for the logarithms section that follows. It starts by looking at a number called e, which is sometimes known as Euler's constant. Sections 4.3.1 and 4.3.2 could be omitted at an initial reading but will repay study at a later date.

4.3.1 What is e?

We begin with an innocent-looking data exercise on indices. Look at Data Exercise 4.1.

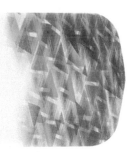

Data Exercise 4.1

Use your calculator or a spreadsheet to plot a graph of y against p for the function $y = (1 + p)^{\frac{1}{p}}$ for $-\frac{1}{2} \le p \le 1$, in other words, for p between $-\frac{1}{2}$ and $+1$. Suggested initial values of p are: $-\frac{1}{2}$, $-\frac{1}{4}$, $\frac{1}{4}$, $\frac{1}{2}$ and 1. Don't try $p = 0$; well you can try!

In Data Exercise 4.1, you should have found the values given in Table 4.1. Most of the values of $(1 + p)^{\frac{1}{p}}$ in the table were found using a calculator, and *you should check them!*[1]

The graph of $(1 + p)^{\frac{1}{p}}$ against p is Figure 4.1. It appears to cross the vertical axis ($p = 0$) at just over 2.7. The exact value is the important 'natural number', known as e. Why didn't we evaluate e directly, by including $p = 0$ in the table above? You may have found out when doing Data Exercise 4.1! Instead we have to sneak up on $p = 0$.

Table 4.2 shows the results when we use smaller and smaller positive values for p.

Table 4.1

p	$(1 + p)^{\frac{1}{p}}$
−0.50	4.00
−0.25	3.16
0.25	2.44
0.50	2.25
1.00	2.00

Table 4.2

p	0.001	0.0001	0.00001	0.000001
$(1 + p)^{\frac{1}{p}}$	2.71692	2.71814	2.71827	2.71828

Note the smaller and smaller changes in $(1 + p)^{\frac{1}{p}}$ as we decrease p. We say that is homing in on a *limiting value* or *limit*, which is the natural number e. We write:

$$\lim_{p \to 0} (1 + p)^{\frac{1}{p}} = e$$

Like π, the number e is irrational: it can't be expressed as a ratio of two whole numbers. Its value is 2.718 to four significant figures, but more will be given by your calculator, using the function e^x (with $x = 1$). Another way of calculating e is to use the series:

$$1 + 1 + \frac{1}{2!} + \frac{1}{3!} + \frac{1}{4!} + \dots$$

It converges on, i.e. it homes in on, e. Try it. 7 terms gives 2.718. But how do we know that this series will converge to e? We'll use the binomial expansion from Chapter 3.

$(1 + x)^n = 1 + nx + \frac{n(n-1)}{2!}x^2 + \dots$, which converges as long as $|x| < 1$. Putting $x = p$ and $n = \frac{1}{p}$:

$$(1 + p)^{\frac{1}{p}} = 1 + \frac{1}{p}p + \frac{\frac{1}{p}\left(\frac{1}{p} - 1\right)}{2!}p^2 + \frac{\frac{1}{p}\left(\frac{1}{p} - 1\right)\left(\frac{1}{p} - 2\right)}{3!}p^3 + \dots .$$

The first two terms are $1 + 1$. The 3rd term is, multiplying it out: $\frac{1 - p}{2!}$, which tends to $\frac{1}{2!}$ as $p \to 0$. Similarly, the 4th term tends to $\frac{1}{3!}$, etc.

So we can write $\qquad e = 1 + 1 + \frac{1}{2!} + \frac{1}{3!} + \frac{1}{4!} + \dots .$

We've made a lot of fuss about e, because you will meet it again – often.

---

[1] Some of the values in Table 4.1 don't need a calculator, e.g. when $p = \frac{1}{2}$, a bit of manipulation gives $y = 4$.

Fig 4.1

To find e using your calculator use the e^x button [on the author's calculator this is accessed using SHIFT + ln] with $x = 1$.

quickfire 4.10

Use a calculator to find (a) $(1 + 0.1)^{10}$ and (b) $(1 + 0.01)^{100}$.

Data Exercise 4.2

Use a spreadsheet and the function

$\exp(x) = 1 + x + \dfrac{x^2}{2!} + \dfrac{x^3}{3!} + \dfrac{x^4}{4!} + \dots,$

to work out the value of $\exp(1.5)$ to 4 significant figures and compare your answer with using the e^x button on your calculator. On many calculators, the e^x function is accessed using inv ln or shift ln, so the key strokes for $e^{1.5}$ are:

1 . 5 inv ln or 1 . 5. shift ln

See footnote: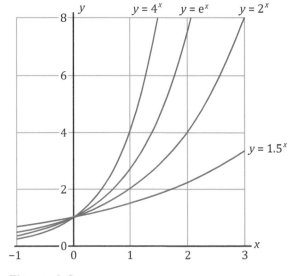

4.3.2 The exponential function, exp(x)

The function $\exp(x)$ is defined by: $\exp(x) = \lim_{p \to 0} (1 + xp)^{\frac{1}{p}}$. This looks very familiar. Using the same process as in 4.3.1 you should be able to show that

$$\exp(x) = 1 + x + \frac{x^2}{2!} + \frac{x^3}{3!} + \frac{x^4}{4!} + \dots \qquad (1)$$

This is the same as e with the addition of the powers of x. How does it relate to e? Clearly $e = \exp(1)$, but what about $\exp(2)$, $\exp(2.5)$, etc.? How do they relate to e?

We get a big clue if we consider the product $\exp(a) \times \exp(b)$.

Using equation (1):

$$\exp(a) \times \exp(b) = \left(1 + a + \frac{a^2}{2!} + \frac{a^3}{3!} + \dots\right)\left(1 + b + \frac{b^2}{2!} + \frac{b^3}{3!} + \dots\right)$$

There are a lot of terms to multiply out here (an infinite number!) but let's make a start and gather together all the terms of order 1, all the terms of order 2, etc.

$$\exp(a) \times \exp(b) = 1 + (a + b) + \left(\frac{a^2}{2!} + ab + \frac{b^2}{2!}\right) + \left(\frac{a^3}{3!} + \frac{a^2 b}{2!} + \frac{ab^2}{2!} + \frac{b^3}{3!}\right) + \dots$$

$$= 1 + (a + b) + \frac{1}{2!}\left(a^2 + 2ab + b^2\right) + \frac{1}{3!}\left(a^3 + 3a^2 b + 3ab^2 + b^3\right) + \dots$$

$$= 1 + (a + b) + \frac{(a + b)^2}{2!} + \frac{(a + b)^3}{3!} + \dots$$

$$= \exp(a + b)$$

So we see that $\exp(1) = e^1$ and $\exp(a) \times \exp(b) = \exp(a + b)$, which means that $\exp(a) = e^a$.

quickfire 4.11

Use your calculator to determine (a) e^2, (b) e^{-2} and (c) $\sqrt{e}$.

Calculator warning:

The **EXP** button on your calculator does not give the $\exp(x)$ function. The **EXP** button is short for "$\times 10^x$", so the key strokes 5 EXP 3 enter the number 5×10^3. The reason is that the **EXP** here is short for *exponent*, which is the power (in this case) of 10.

quickfire 4.12

Write the numbers in QF 4.11 in the style $\exp(x)$.

4.3.3 e^x – the growth function

Figure 4.2 shows graphs of the functions 1.5^x, 2^x, e^x and 4^x. Their common characteristics, as with all other functions a^x, with $a > 1$, are:

- they all pass through $(0, 1)$
- they all tend to 0 as $x \to -\infty$
- their gradients all increase with x.
- their gradients are all proportional to the value of the function.

The last bullet point is not obvious. We need to do some work on it. It is proved in a formal way in Chapter 12, but an example will illustrate it. In fact the gradient of the function e^x at a point is **equal** to the value of e^x at that point. Because of this, e^x [aka $\exp(x)$] is often referred to as the *growth function*. See Example C.

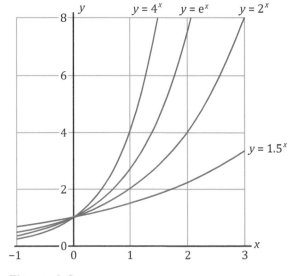

Figure 4.2

Successive partial sums of the infinite series are: 1, 2.5, 3.625, 4.1875, 4.3984, 4.4617, 4.4775, 4.4809, 4.4816. These compare with the $e^{1.5}$ result of 4.482 (4 s.f.). Thus the answer is correct to 4 s.f. after the 8th order term.

Example C:

Justify, by calculation, the assertion that the gradient of e^x is equal to the value of e^x.

Consider the two points, $x = 1$ and $x = 2$. We'll calculate the mean gradients within ± 0.1 of these values of x. The table shows the significant values of e^x.

x	0.9	1.0	1.1	1.9	2.0	2.1
e^x	2.460	**2.718**	3.004	6.686	**7.389**	8.166

Consider $x = 1$: $e^x = 2.718$. Mean gradient around this point $= \dfrac{3.004 - 2.460}{0.2} = 2.72$

Consider $x = 2$: $e^x = 7.389$. Mean gradient around this point $= \dfrac{8.166 - 6.686}{0.2} = 7.40$

In both cases the values of gradient are within 0.15% of the value of e^x which is a reasonable justification. It is suggested that the reader repeat these calculations for other values of x and for smaller ranges, e.g. ± 0.01.

4.4 Logarithms

4.4.1 What are logarithms?

We start with two uncontroversial statements: $64 = 2^6$ and $64 = 4^3$.

What relationship do the 6 and the 3 have to 64? They are, of course, the *powers* to which we have to raise 2 and 4, in order to get 64.

In this context, the 2 and the 4 are called **bases**. The 6 is called *the* **logarithm** *of* 64 *to the base* 2. We write $6 = \log_2 64$. The 3 is called *the logarithm of* 64 *to the base* 4: $3 = \log_4 64$

Thus, if $X = b^p$ then, by definition, $p = \log_b X$.

quickfire ▶ 4.13

Find:
(a) $\log_3 81$
(b) $\log_{81} 3$

Example D:

$243 = 3^5$ and $64 = 3^{3.7856}$ (approx.). Express these relationships in terms of logarithms.

(a) $243 = 3^5 \therefore 5 = \log_3 243$.   (b) $64 = 3^{3.7856} \therefore 3.7856 = \log_3 64$.

quickfire ▶ 4.14

Evaluate
(a) $\log_3 \sqrt{3}$ (b) $\log_3 9\sqrt{3}$
(c) $\log_3 \dfrac{1}{3}$ (d) $\log_3 \dfrac{1}{\sqrt{3}}$

In what follows, we shall assume that the base is greater than 1.

Note these two fairly obvious identities. Whatever the value of b:

$\log_b 1 = 0$ (because $b^0 = 1$) and $\log_b b = 1$ (because $b^1 = b$).

Also $\log_b 0$ does not exist, because we'd have to find a number x such that $b^x = 0$. Similarly we cannot have $\log_b (-1)$ or any other negative number.

quickfire ▶ 4.15

$81 = 27^{\frac{4}{3}}$. What is $\log_{27} 81$?

4.4.2 Popular bases for logarithms

There are only two popular bases: 10 and e (the natural number 2.71828...). Other bases are seldom used in Physics – except in books like this, to help you to understand what logarithms are all about!

$\log_{10} X$ is often written simply as $\log X$. 'log' is probably what you'll find on your calculator button. Base 10 logarithms have the nice feature that $\log_{10} 0.1 = -1$, $\log_{10} 1 = 0$, $\log_{10} 10 = 1$, etc. Sound levels in *decibels* (dB) and star 'brightnesses' in *magnitudes* are both defined in terms of the base 10 logarithms of certain ratios of measurable quantities.

$\log_e X$ is usually written as $\ln X$. 'ln' signifies *natural logarithm*. Natural logarithms are used a great deal in Physics. You'll see why later on.

Pointer

There's no such thing (in the realm of real numbers) as the logarithm of a negative number, e.g. what is $\log_2(-8)$? [If tempted by -3, remember that $2^{-3} = \frac{1}{8}$.]

4.4.3 The laws of logarithms

These are just the laws of indices written in a different way. All the same, they're worth learning in the new form...

(a) $\log_b XY = \log_b X + \log_b Y$ Law 1

This is equivalent to the 'add indices' rule for multiplication and we can derive it from this rule:

Suppose $X = b^p$ and $Y = b^q$: then by definition $\log_b X = p$ and $\log_b Y = q$.

But $XY = b^{p+q}$, $\therefore \log_b XY = p + q = \log_b X + \log_b Y$ QED

Example E:

Given that $\log 2 = 0.3010$, without using your calculator calculate $\log 20$ [Remember $\log 2$ is short for $\log_{10} 2$, etc.]

$\log 20 = \log (2 \times 10) = \log 2 + \log 10 = 0.3010 + 1.0000 = 1.3010$

Now use your calculator to check this.

(b) $\log_b \dfrac{X}{Y} = \log_b X - \log_b Y$ Law 2

This is equivalent to the 'subtract indices' rule for division and can be derived in a similar way to the first law.

(c) $\log_b X^n = n \log_b X$ Law 3

Suppose $X = b^m$ then, by definition, $\log_b X = m$.

And $X^n = b^{mn}$, so $\log_b X^n = mn = n \log_b X$ QED

Example F:

$\ln 100 = 4.605$ [4 s.f.]. Without using the ln button, calculate $\ln 10$.

$\ln 10 = \ln 100^{\frac{1}{2}} = \frac{1}{2} \ln 100 = \frac{1}{2} \times 4.605 = 2.303$

Check: Calculator gives $\ln 10 = 2.303$ [4 s.f.]

If we put $n = -1$ into Law 3, we see that $\log_b \dfrac{1}{X} = -\log_b X$. We can also derive this result from Law 2 by putting $X = 1$ and remembering that $\log_b 1 = 0$.

The following two laws are presented for completeness but you will rarely come across them in A-level Physics.

(d) $\log_a X = \log_a b \times \log_b X$ Law 4

The derivation is left as an exercise. Hint: start by putting $X = b^p$ and $b = a^q$.

As an example: $\ln X = \ln 10 \times \log X = 2.303 \log X$

To make this clearer: $\log_e X = \log_e 10 \times \log_{10} X = 2.303 \log_{10} X$

The 2.303 is, then, the conversion factor between logarithms to base 10 and natural logarithms.

(e) $\log_a b = \dfrac{1}{\log_b a}$ Law 5

Hint: to derive this, put $X = a$ into Law 4.

4.4.4 Comparison log and exponential functions

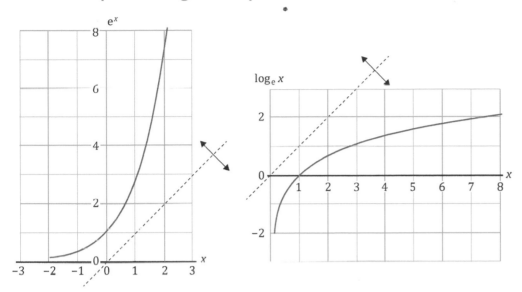

Fig 4.3

Figure 4.3 shows the functions e^x and $\ln x$. Each function maps into the other by reflection in the line $y = x$. This is because each of these functions is the *inverse function* of the other. This means that if we find e^x for any value of x and then find $\log_e$ of the result, the result is x.

This is because: $\ln e^x = x \ln e$ [Law 3 of logs].

But $\ln e = 1$, $\therefore$ $\ln e^x = x$.

Similarly $e^{\ln x} = x$.

This is why e^x is on the same calculator button as $\ln x$ but requires the SHIFT or INV button.

4.4.5 Using log graphs for data display.

If we examine a $\log_b x$ against x graph, e.g the $\log_e$ graph in Fig 4.3, we see that the numbers between 1 and b on the x scale map into numbers 0 and 1 and the $\log_b x$ scale; numbers between b and b^2 map into numbers between 1 and 2 on the $\log_b x$ scale; $b^2 - b^3$ map onto 2 – 3. Thus, taking logarithms has a 'compressing' effect on a range of numbers, the more so the larger the numbers.

This is useful when we need to plot a large range of data on a graph; we may choose to plot logarithms of the numbers rather than to use an ordinary 'linear' scale. We often use $\log_{10}$ when displaying data in this way.[2]

Example G:

The graph in Figure 4.4 displays the atmospheric opacity for electromagnetic radiation. This is the fraction of the radiation which is absorbed by the atmosphere.

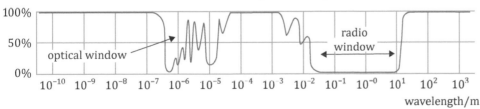

Fig 4.4

[2]   It also seems to be the way our senses handle 'inputs'; for example, if a sound wave is increased in *intensity* by (say) a factor of 10, we judge the increase in loudness to be roughly the same whether the first sound is loud or soft. The (logarithmic) *decibel* scale reflects this feature of our perception.

The horizontal axis is a logarithmic scale: every step is a factor of 10. This way of presenting the scale is equivalent to:

−10	−9	−8	−7	−6	−5	−4	−3	−2	−1	0	1	2	3

$\log_{10}(\text{wavelength} / \text{m})$

This method of presenting data is essential if we want to make sense of differences over a large range of sizes. If the above scale were linear, with a maximum of 10^3 m, all the data below 10^0 m would be compressed into the vertical axis. As it is, we can see that important things happen in the range 10^{-7} to 10^{-4} m which covers the lower ultraviolet, the visible and the near infra-red and again between 10^{-3} and 10^1 m which covers the microwave and VHF radio.

Data Exercise 4.3

The diagram shows a *low-pass filter*, an electronic circuit which is designed to allow low frequency signals through but block high frequencies. V_{OUT} is given by:

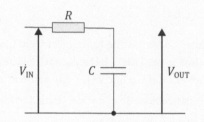

$$V_{OUT} = V_{IN} \times \frac{1}{\sqrt{4\pi^2 f^2 C^2 R^2 + 1}}$$

where f is the frequency, and C and R the values of the capacitor and resistor respectively.

Use a spreadsheet to investigate this relationship, i.e. how V_{OUT} varies with f. Use log scales for both axes.

Suggested initial values: $V_{IN} = 10$V; $R = 100\,\Omega$; $C = 1\,\mu$F; frequency range (in Hz) 10, 30, 100, 300, 1000.....3×10^6, 1×10^7.

Supplementary exercises:

(a) investigate a *high-pass filter*.

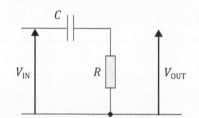

$$V_{OUT} = V_{IN} \times \frac{1}{\sqrt{1 + \frac{1}{4\pi^2 f^2 C^2 R^2}}}$$

(b) investigate a *band-pass filter*, which is a filter designed to allow a range of frequencies through. The output from a low-pass filter is connected to the input of a high-pass filter. The two filters will have different values of R and C so that there is a range of frequencies which are allowed through by both.

4.4.6 Using logs to test power law relationships

Suppose a pair of variables, x and y, are related by an equation of the form $y = Ax^n$, where A and n are constants. This is referred to as a *power law relationship*. Using logs we can cast this equation into the form $y = mx + c$.

Taking logs of both sides of the relationship $y = Ax^n$, to any base b, we get:

$$\log_b y = \log_b (Ax^n) = n \log_b x + \log_b A$$

This equation is of the form

$$y = m \ x \ + \ c$$

with the variables $\log_b y$ and $\log_b x$ replacing y and x; the constants n replaces m and $\log_b A$ replaces c. So, if we have a series of pairs of experimental values for variables x and y and plot a graph of $\log y$ against $\log x$, a straight-line graph will confirm that the relationship is of the form $y = Ax^n$. The value of n will be the gradient and the intercept on the vertical axis will be $\log A$. See Example H.

Example H:

Use the graph of $\log P$ against $\log T$ to find the relationship between P and T.

If $P = aT^b$, $\log P = b \log T + \log a$

Gradient $= \dfrac{8.1 - 6.2}{3.2 - 2.7} = 3.8 = b$

To find the intercept apply $y = mx + c$ with the calculated value of $m = 3.8$ and the point $(2.9, 7.0)$.

$7.0 = 3.8 \times 2.9 + c$

$\therefore$ intercept $= -4.02$.

$\therefore \log a = -4.02 \therefore a = 10^{-4.02} = 9.5 \times 10^{-5}$.

$\therefore$ The relationship is $P = 9.5 \times 10^{-5} T^{3.8}$.

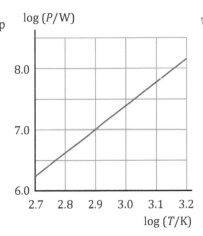

Pointer

We can't take the logarithm of a quantity with *units*, as there's no power to which we can raise a base to get, say, 3.0 m or 1.5 A. We *can* take the logarithm of just the numerical part (3.0 or 1.5).

This is why, where it matters, such as labelling graph axes, we write, for example, ln (T/s), if T is a time. The '/s' means *divide by* s, so T/s is a pure number. If $T = 1.1$ s, then T/s = 1.1.

4.4.7 Using logs to test exponential relationships

Relationships of the form $x = x_0 e^{kt}$ in which x_0 and k are constants, are known as exponential relationships. If the relationship is of the form $x = x_0 e^{-kt}$, where k is a positive constant, the value of x decreases with time and the relationship is called an *exponential decay*. Examples of exponential decays are radioactive decay, capacitor discharge and damped oscillations. Most of these relationships are variations with time but the penetration of gamma rays into a material, for example, is described by the equation $I = I_0 e^{-\mu x}$, where I is the intensity and x the penetration distance.

Exponential decay relationships have a characteristic constant *half-life*, $t_{\frac{1}{2}}$, which is the time over which the decaying quantity halves. Taking radioactive decay as an example, the activity A is given by $A = A_0 e^{-\lambda t}$, where λ is the *decay constant*.

Similarly the number, N, of radioactive nuclei remaining is given by $N = N_0 e^{-\lambda t}$, where λ is the same constant.

We can relate the half-life to the decay constant by substituting $A = \frac{1}{2} A_0$ into $A = A_0 e^{-\lambda t}$.

This gives $2e^{-\lambda t} = 1$; so, taking natural logs, $\ln 2 - \lambda t = 0$.

$$\therefore \qquad t_{\frac{1}{2}} = \frac{\ln 2}{\lambda}. \qquad (1)$$

We can use logs to linearise the exponential decay equation and turn it into a straight line relationship.

Taking logs of the equation $A = A_0 e^{-\lambda t}$, we get:
$$\ln A = \ln A_0 - \lambda t \qquad (2)$$

Compare with the linear equation:
$$y = m \ x \ + \ c$$

quickfire 4.16

λ for a radioactive decay is given by $\lambda = 0.11$ s^{-1}. Calculate the half life.

quickfire 4.17

Determine $2^{-2.5}$.

quickfire 4.18

What fraction of the nuclei of a radioactive material remains after 4.7 half-lives?

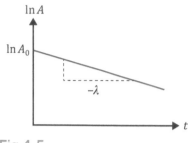

Fig 4.5

The variables in this relationship are A and t. Comparing the two equations, if we plot $\ln A$ against t, we should get a straight line graph of gradient $-\lambda$ and an intercept of $\ln A_0$ on the $\ln A$-axis (see Figure 4.5). This type of graph is called a *semi-log* or a *log-linear* graph.

An equivalent, and very useful, way of writing the decay equation is $A = A_0 2^{-n}$, where n is the number of half-lives: see Example I.

Example I:

Show that the radioactive decay equation can also be written as $A = A_0 2^{-n}$.

n is the number of half-lives. $\therefore\ t = n t_{\frac{1}{2}}$

$\therefore$ From equation (1) in 4.4.7, $t = \dfrac{n \ln 2}{\lambda}$

Substitute into equation (2) in 4.4.7: $\ln A = \ln A_0 - n \ln 2$

$\therefore\ \ln A = \ln (A_0 2^{-n})$ using laws 1 and 3 of logs (see Section 4.4.3)

$\therefore\ A = A_0 2^{-n}$ QED

Test Yourself 4.1

Questions 1–10 relate to indices only.

1 Express as a number or fraction, (a) $125^{\frac{1}{3}}$, (b) $125^{\frac{2}{3}}$, (c) $125^{-\frac{1}{3}}$, (d) $125^{-\frac{2}{3}}$, (e) $125^{\frac{4}{3}}$

2 Express as a number or fraction, (a) $16^{\frac{1}{2}}$, (b) $16^{-\frac{1}{2}}$, (c) $16^{\frac{3}{4}}$, (d) $16^{\frac{7}{4}}$, (e) $16^{-\frac{3}{4}}$

3 Express in the form a^p, (a) $\sqrt[4]{a}$,, (b) $\dfrac{1}{\sqrt[4]{a}}$, (c) $\dfrac{a}{\sqrt[3]{a}}$, (d) $\sqrt[5]{a^2}$, (e) $\left(\dfrac{1}{\sqrt[4]{a^3}}\right)^2$

4 Evaluate, (a) $\left(\dfrac{900}{4}\right)^{\frac{1}{2}}$, (b) $\dfrac{\sqrt{900}}{\sqrt{4}}$, (c) $\left(\dfrac{16}{625}\right)^{\frac{1}{2}}$, (d) $\dfrac{\sqrt[4]{625}}{\sqrt[4]{16}}$, without using a calculator.

5 The intensity, I, of radiation at distance r from a star is given by $I = Kr^p$. I falls by a factor of 4 when r doubles. What is p?

6 The square of the period, T, of revolution of a planet around the Sun is proportional to the cube of its mean orbital radius, a. This can be expressed in the form $T = ka^p$. State the value of p.

7 The volume, V of a sphere can be expressed in terms of the sphere's surface area by $V = KA^p$. Determine the constant, k, and the index p. [Hint: Start with the usual formulae for volume and area of a sphere, and eliminate the radius r.]

8 The resistance, R, of a wire is given by $R = \dfrac{\rho l}{A}$, where ρ is the resistivity, l the length and A the cross-sectional area. A volume, V, of metal is to be made into a wire but the diameter, d, of the wire can be any value. Write the relationship between R and d in the form $R = kd^n$, determining the values of k and n.

9 The luminosity, L, of a star, that is its total emitted power depends upon its temperature and surface area according to Stefan's law: $L = \sigma A T^4$, where σ is a constant. The luminosity of the Sun, $L_\odot = 4 \times 10^{26}$ W. Calculate the luminosity of, (a) a red giant star with a temperature $\frac{2}{3}$ times and a radius 100 times those of the Sun and (b) a white dwarf star with a temperature 3 and a radius $\frac{1}{100}$ times those of the Sun.

10 The current, I, through a non-ohmic resistor varies with pd, V, according to $I = kV^3$, in which $k = 8.0 \times 10^{-3}$ A V^{-3}. Express the resistance, R, of the device $\left[\text{defined by } R = \dfrac{V}{I}\right]$ in terms of the current. Hint: Start with $R = cI^n$ and determine the values of c and n.

11 Given that $\log 2 = 0.3010$ use the laws of logarithms to determine:

(a) $\log 4$, (b) $\log 0.04$, (c) $\log 8$, (d) $\log 200$, (e) $\log 2.5$.

[Hint: $\log_b b^n = n$]

⑫ Given that $\log_2 3 = 1.585$, use the laws of logarithms to find:

(a) $\log_2 9$, (b) $\log_2 \frac{1}{3}$, (c) $\log_2 6$, (d) $\log_2 1.5$, (e) $\log_3 4$

⑬ Calculate: (a) $\log_3 9$, (b) $\log_3 \frac{1}{3}$, (c) $\log_3 \sqrt{3}$, (d) $\log_3 \sqrt{27}$, (e) $\log_3 \frac{1}{\sqrt[4]{243}}$

⑭ Calculate: (a) $\log_4 2$, (b) $\log_4 32$, (c) $\log_4 \frac{1}{64}$, (d) $\log_4 \sqrt{2}$, (e) $\log_4 20$ [given $\log 2 = 0.3010$]

⑮ Express as a multiple of $\log 2$:

(a) $\log 4 + \log 8$, (b) $\log 4 - \log 8$, (c) $\log 2 + \log \frac{1}{2}$, (d) $\log 2 + \log \frac{1}{4}$

⑯. Express in terms of $\ln 2$:

(a) $\ln 4 + \ln e$, (b) $\ln 8e$, (c) $\ln 32 - \ln e$, (d) $\ln \frac{16}{e}$, (e) $\ln \frac{\sqrt{2}}{e^2}$

⑰ Use a calculator to solve the following equations for x:

(a) $e^{2x} = 6$, (b) $e^{2x} = \frac{1}{6}$, (c) $0.1 = 10e^{-x}$, (d) $20 = 5 \times 10^3 \times 2^{-x}$, (e) $\ln \sqrt{x} = 3$

⑱ (a) Show that $a^x = e^{x \ln a}$. [Note this is how we define a^x, for $a > 0$ and irrational x.]

(b) Use the above result to calculate 2^π, without using the x^y button on your calculator.

⑲ Solve the following:

(a) $\log_2 x = 4$, (b) $\log_2 x^2 = 6$, (c) $\log_4 \sqrt[3]{x} = 6$, (d) $\log_4 x^2 = -1$, (e) $\log_6 \frac{1}{x} = -2$

⑳ The sound intensity level, in 'dB SIL' is defined by

$$L_1 = 10 \log \frac{\text{sound intensity}}{10^{-11} \text{ W m}^{-2}} \text{ dB SIL}$$

[10^{-12} W m^{-2} is roughly the threshold of human hearing.]

(a) Calculate the sound intensity level in dB SIL of a sound of intensity 1 W m^{-2} (dangerous to hearing).

(b) Show that an increase of 3 dB SIL represents an increase in sound intensity by a *factor* of 2.

㉑ The activity, A, in becquerel, of a radioactive nuclide varies with time according to $A = A_0 e^{-\lambda t}$, where $A_0 = 6$ MBq and $\lambda = 3.5 \times 10^{-7}$ s^{-1}. Calculate:

(a) the half-life of the decay,

(h) the activity after 1 year and

(c) the time taken for the activity to drop to 100 kBq.

㉒ The frequency, f, of oscillation of a loaded cantilever depends upon its projection length, l, according to the equation $f = kl^n$. In an experiment to investigate this relationship a student timed 20 oscillations for two different lengths and obtained the following results:

For $l = 35$ cm, time = 12.9 s.

For $l = 45$ cm, time = 18.9 s.

(a) Use the results to calculate values of f.

(b) Show that n is approximately -1.5 and k is approximately 0.3 [with l in m].

(c) If the student had obtained a series of values for l and f what graph should she plot to test the relationship? State how values k and n would be obtained from the graph.

㉓ A gamma source is shielded by a 0.50 cm thick sheet of lead. A G-M tube outside the shielding registers radiation. A medical physicist adds additional lead layers and obtains the following results, which are corrected for background:

Total thickness / cm	0.5	1.0	1.5	2.0	2.5	3.0	3.5	4.0
Count rate / min^{-1}	415	350	250	195	165	115	100	77

(a) Assuming that the count rate, C, is related to the thickness x by an equation of the form $C = C_0 e^{-\left(\frac{x}{L}\right)}$, where L is called the characteristic length of the relationship, plot a suitable graph and use it to find values for C_0 and L.

(b) If the safe level of radiation outside the box emanating from the source within is deemed to be 25 min^{-1}, calculate the thickness of lead shielding required.

24 The pd, V, across a filament lamp and the current, I, obey the relationship $I = kV^n$.

A student obtains the following results:

V / V	2.0	4.0	6.0	8.0	10.0	12.0	14.0	16.0
I / A	0.70	1.05	1.30	1.45	1.70	1.90	2.05	2.20

(a) Plot a suitable graph and use it to obtain values for k and n.

(b) The relationship between the resistance, R, and V is $R = cV^m$. State the values of c and m.

25 The half-life of a radioactive source is 8 days. The initial activity, A_0, is 800 kBq.

(a) Use the equation $A = A_0 2^{-n}$, where n is the number of half-lives, to calculate the activity after 60 days. Show your working.

(b) Use the equation $A = A_0 e^{-\lambda t}$, where λ is the decay constant $\left[t_{\frac{1}{2}} = \frac{\ln 2}{\lambda}\right]$ to calculate the activity after 100 days. Show your working.

(c) Compare the appearance of the two graphs (i) $\ln A$ against n and (ii) $\ln A$ against t.

Geometry and Trigonometry

5.1 Introduction

This chapter deals with shapes. It deals with the length of sides of plane figures, the angles between the sides, the areas and volumes and the relationships between these quantities. Together with algebra, indices and logarithms, these concepts form the basis most of the calculations in physics.

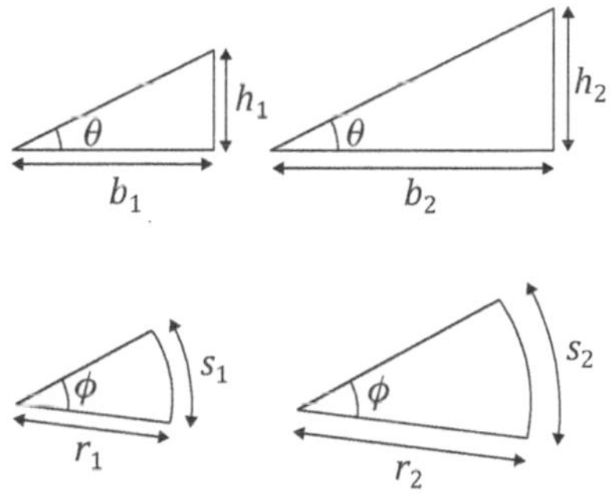

5.2 Similar figures

Similar figures are those which have the same shape but (usually) have a different size. Having the same shape means, among other things that there are the same number of edges (and faces, if the objects are 3 dimensional) and that the angles between corresponding edges (and faces) are the same.

5.2.1 Ratios of sides of similar plane (flat) figures

Consider the following pairs of similar figures:

- two similar right-angled triangles
- two similar sectors

Having the same shape implies that:

1. angles (such as θ and ϕ in Figure 5.1) between corresponding sides are the same
2. corresponding lengths (sides, arc lengths, etc.) are in the same <u>ratio</u>

e.g. for the similar sectors: if $\frac{r_1}{r_2} = \lambda$ then $\frac{s_1}{s_2} = \lambda$,

so $\frac{r_1}{r_2} = \frac{s_1}{s_2}$ or alternatively, rearranging, $\frac{s_1}{r_1} = \frac{s_2}{r_2}$.

These relationships hold for figures with any number of sides of any shape.

Consider these two similar right-angled triangles: Now do Quickfires 5.1, 5.2 and 5.3

Fig 5.1

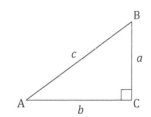

quickfire 5.1

Calculate x in Figure 5.2
[Hint: use Pythagoras' theorem – see Section 5.2.2]

quickfire 5.2

Calculate y using similarity.

Fig 5.2

quickfire 5.3

Calculate z.

5.2.2 Pythagoras' theorem

Pythagoras' theorem has been known for thousands of years and was used by the ancient Egyptians to help lay out their fields following the annual flooding of the River Nile. Consider the triangle ABC in Figure 5.3.

Pythagoras' theorem can be expressed as: $a^2 + b^2 = c^2$

It can be proved using similar triangles.

Fig 5.3

ⓘ Trigonometry is usually abbreviated to 'trig'.

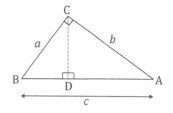

Fig 5.4

quickfire 5.4

The hypotenuse of a right-angled triangle is 20 cm long and another side is 10 cm long. What is the length of the third side?

To do this we'll rotate the triangle and draw a perpendicular line from the apex, C, to the hypotenuse at D (Figure 5.4).

The three triangles, ABC, BCD and CAD are similar – their angles are all the same. This means that the ratios of corresponding sides are equal.

So: $\frac{BD}{a} = \frac{a}{c}$ ∴ $BD = \frac{a^2}{c}$. Also $\frac{DA}{b} = \frac{b}{c}$ ∴ $DA = \frac{b^2}{c}$

But $c = BD + DA$, so $c = \frac{a^2}{c} + \frac{b^2}{c}$. Multiplying this equation by c gives $c^2 = a^2 + b^2$.   QED.

5.2.3 Ratios of areas of similar figures

If the ratio of the corresponding lengths is λ, the ratio of areas of the similar figures is λ^2. We shall demonstrate this for the pairs of similar figures in Figure 5.1.

- For the similar triangles, since Area = $\frac{1}{2}$ × base × height

$$\frac{\text{Area of right-hand triangle}}{\text{Area of left-hand triangle}} = \frac{\frac{1}{2}b_2 h_2}{\frac{1}{2}b_1 h_1} = \frac{(\lambda b_1)(\lambda h_1)}{b_1 h_1} = \lambda^2$$

- For the similar sectors, each has the same angle ϕ, so is the same fraction, f, of the circle from which it is cut.

So $$\frac{\text{Area of right-hand sector}}{\text{Area of left-hand sector}} = \frac{f\pi r_1^2}{f\pi r_2^2} = \frac{r_1^2}{r_2^2} = \left(\frac{r_1}{r_2}\right)^2 = \lambda^2$$

Example A:

Triangles 1 and 2 are similar. Show that the area of triangle 2 is 2.25 times that of triangle 1.

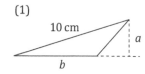

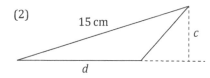

$c = 1.5a$ and $d = 1.5b$

$$\frac{\text{Area of }\Delta 2}{\text{Area of }\Delta 1} = \frac{\frac{1}{2}dc}{\frac{1}{2}ba} = \frac{(1.5b)(1.5a)}{ba} = 1.5 \times 1.5 = 2.25. \therefore \text{Area of }\Delta 2 = 2.25 \times \text{Area of }\Delta 1. \quad \text{QED}$$

It is reasonable to suppose that this rule holds for any arbitrary shape. We can show this is the case as follows. Consider the two similar shapes in Figure 5.5. The length and breadth of the lower shape is λ times as big as those of the upper shape.

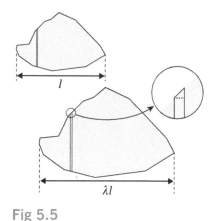

Fig 5.5

Divide up the figures into the same large number of thin strips. These strips are composed of a rectangle with a small triangle at each end – see inset. Both the height and width of each strip will be increased by a factor of λ as we go from the small figure to the larger one. This is true of the rectangle and the end triangles, so the areas of the corresponding strips will be λ^2 times that of the smaller figure.

quickfire 5.5

A cone has a base diameter of 12 cm and surface area of 360 cm². What is the surface area of a **similar** cone with a base diameter of 4 cm?

5.2.4 Ratios of volumes of similar figures

If the sides of two similar 3-dimensional figures are in the ratio λ:1, the ratio of the volumes of the two figures is λ^3:1.

This is most easily demonstrated with cubes. Consider a 2-cube (see Figure 5.6):

The number of 1-cubes = 2 × 2 × 2 = 8.

With a 3-cube, the number of 1-cubes = 3 × 3 × 3 = 27

quickfire 5.6

A cone has a base diameter of 12 cm. and a volume of 405 cm³. What is the volume of a **similar** cone with a base diameter of 4 cm?

Ratio of the volumes = $\frac{27}{8}$ = 3.375 = 1.5³ = (ratio of sides)³.

Fig 5.6

5.3 Miscellaneous facts about angles

Look carefully at the following diagrams (Figure 5.7). They all contain facts about angles that should be familiar. You should make sure that you understand the facts and can apply them.

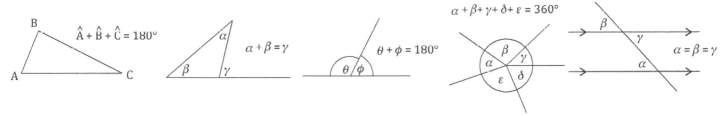

Fig 5.7

5.4 Angles in radians

We're used to expressing angles in degrees, knowing that there are 360 degrees (360°) in one revolution. But 360, though a lovely number with lots of factors (2, 3, 4, 5, 6, 8, 9, 10, 12, 15, 18, 20, 24, 30, 36, 40, 45, 60, 72, 90, 120 and 180), is an arbitrary choice.

By contrast, the *radian*, is a 'natural' unit. If we draw an arc of a circle, centred on θ, where the 'arms' of the angle meet, then the angle θ in radians is defined by:

$$\theta = \frac{\text{arc length}}{\text{radius}}, \text{ i.e. } \theta = \frac{s}{r} \text{ (see Figure 5.9)}$$

A larger radius will give a proportionately larger arc length (see Section 5.2.1) so we'll get the same value for θ.

What is 360° in radians?

For one complete revolution, $\quad \theta = \frac{s}{r} = \frac{2\pi r}{r} = 2\pi$ (see Figure 5.10).

So 360° = 2π rad; 180° = π rad; 90° = $\frac{\pi}{2}$ rad, etc.

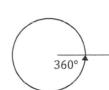

Fig 5.8

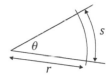

Fig 5.9

Example B:

How do we convert between degrees and radians?

$$180° = \pi \text{ rad, so } \theta \text{ / rad} = (\theta \text{ / }°) \times \frac{\pi}{180}$$

Read this as: θ in radians = θ in degrees × π over 180

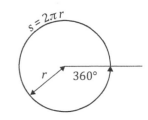

Fig 5.10

In cases like π rad, we can omit the 'rad'; the distinctive 'π' shows the angle to be in radians. So we can write $\frac{3\pi}{2}$ rad simply as $\frac{3\pi}{2}$, but if we choose to evaluate $\frac{3\pi}{2}$ (= 4.71), we must write 4.71 rad, to avoid confusion with 4.71°. In AS Physics we normally express angles in degrees; radians become important when dealing with rotations and vibrations in A2. Sections 5.5–5.7 will use degrees exclusively and we'll pick up radians again in Chapter 8.

 **5.7**

Calculate ϕ.

140°

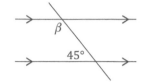 **5.8**

Calculate β.

β

45°

quickfire **5.9**

Find the values of all the angles in the figure below. Assume that the dotted lines are either horizontal or vertical as appropriate.

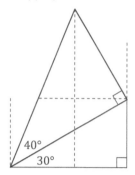

40°
30°

quickfire **5.10**

Express 1 radian in degrees.

quickfire **5.11**

Express 1° in radians: (a) as a multiple of π, (b) as a number.

quickfire **5.12**

What do the angles in a triangle add up to, expressed in radians?

5.5 Right-angled triangles

Right-angled triangles – ones in which one of the angles is 90° – are fundamental to trigonometry. Any triangle can be considered to be formed from two right-angled triangles (look back at Figure 5.4).

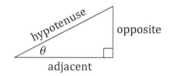 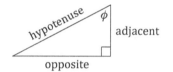

hypotenuse — opposite
θ
adjacent

hypotenuse — ϕ — adjacent
opposite

Abbreviations:
hyp; opp; adj

Fig 5.11

The longest side of a right-angled triangle (the side opposite the largest angle – that is the right angle) is called the *hypotenuse*. If we now choose one of the other angles – θ or ϕ in the diagrams – we label the other two sides *opposite* and *adjacent* accordingly.

5.5.1 Trig ratios

Pointer

By remembering that $\phi = 90° - \theta$, we see that
$\sin\theta = \cos(90° - \theta)$;
$\cos\theta = \sin(90° - \theta)$;
$\tan\theta = \cot(90° - \theta)$

If we pick a value of θ, e.g. 40° / 0.70 rad, then all right-angled triangles with this as one of the angles are similar: the ratio of corresponding sides is the same for all these triangles, whatever their size. This means that in a right-angled triangle, the ratios of the sides depend upon only one angle (θ, say), since the other angles are fixed as 90° and (90° − θ).

The names for these ratios are (relating to the left-hand diagram in Figure 5.11):

quickfire **5.13**

Write the above pointer in radians.

$$\text{sine}(\theta) = \frac{\text{opp}}{\text{hyp}} \qquad \text{usually written} \qquad \sin\theta = \frac{\text{opp}}{\text{hyp}}$$

$$\text{cosine}(\theta) = \frac{\text{adj}}{\text{hyp}} \qquad \text{usually written} \qquad \cos\theta = \frac{\text{adj}}{\text{hyp}}$$

quickfire **5.14**

Show – and commit to memory! – that $\tan\theta = \frac{\sin\theta}{\cos\theta}$.

$$\text{tangent}(\theta) = \frac{\text{opp}}{\text{adj}} \qquad \text{usually written} \qquad \tan\theta = \frac{\text{opp}}{\text{adj}}$$

The notation sine(θ) pronounced 'sine of θ' or more usually just 'sine θ' emphasises the dependency of the ratio $\frac{\text{opp}}{\text{hyp}}$ on the angle θ. We are, in fact using the function notation, $f(\theta)$, with the name 'sine' given to the function f. Similarly with cosine (θ) and tangent (θ).

Example C:

Use the equilateral triangle to calculate sin 60°.

Consider the right-angled triangle with sides 2,1 and x:

Using Pythagoras' theorem, $x = \sqrt{2^2 - 1^2} = \sqrt{3}$

So $\sin 60° = \dfrac{\text{opp}}{\text{hyp}} = \dfrac{\sqrt{3}}{2} = 0.8660$.

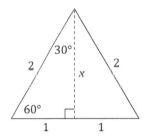

quickfire 5.15

Use the diagram in Example C to work out sin 30°, cos 30°, tan 30°, cos 60° and tan 60°.

Pointer

Working from the hypotenuse, $x = a\cos\theta$ and $y = a\sin\theta$.

Use cos if you move through the angle to get from the hypotenuse to the side you want.

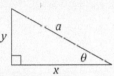

5.5.2 Reciprocal trig ratios

The names 'cosecant', 'secant' and 'cotangent' are given to the reciprocals of sine, cosine and tangent respectively:

$$\csc\theta = \frac{1}{\sin\theta} = \frac{\text{hyp}}{\text{opp}}; \qquad \sec\theta = \frac{1}{\cos\theta} = \frac{\text{hyp}}{\text{adj}}; \qquad \cot\theta = \frac{1}{\tan\theta} = \frac{\text{adj}}{\text{opp}}$$

You are unlikely to find these on your calculator; to calculate $\cot\theta$, for example, find $\tan\theta$ and take the reciprocal.

Pointer

Trig ratios whose names begin with *co* decrease as θ goes from 0 to 90°; if their names don't start with *co* they *increase* as θ goes from 0 to 90°.

Example D:

Use a calculator to find cot 60°.

Using a calculator, $\tan 60° = 1.732$. $\therefore \cot 60° = \dfrac{1}{1.732} = 0.5774$

5.5.3 Calculators and trig ratios

If you want your calculator to handle trig ratios correctly, you need to tell it whether your angles are expressed in degrees or radians[2]. Before doing a calculation you should check angle mode. One way of doing this is to put in an angle of known sine. We have seen that sin 30° = 0.5 [Quickfire 5.15] but sin 30 rad = −0.99 [don't worry about negative values of $\sin\theta$, we'll deal with them later]. So entering sin 30 will confirm which mode you are in.

Pointer

Another calculator check: $\sin\dfrac{\pi}{2} = 1$ but sin 1.57° = 0.027.

quickfire 5.16

What are (a) tan 45°, (b) tan 45 rad?

5.5.4 Pythagoras relationships

In the right-angled triangle in Figure 5.12, Pythagoras' theorem tells us that

$$a^2 + b^2 = c^2$$

So $\qquad\qquad (c\sin\theta)^2 + (c\cos\theta)^2 = c^2$

$\therefore$ Dividing by $c^2 \qquad\qquad (\sin\theta)^2 + (\cos\theta)^2 = 1$

This is normally written as: $\qquad \sin^2\theta + \cos^2\theta = 1$. $\qquad\qquad$ (1)

This equation is equivalent to Pythagoras' theorem. It is another equation to remember!

Fig 5.12

---

[2] Many calculators can also handle angles expressed in *grad*: 1 right angle = 100 grad.

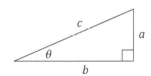

Pointer

$\sin^2\theta$ means $(\sin\theta)^2$.

quickfire ▶ **5.17**

$\cos\phi = 0.4$. Using only the $\sqrt{}$ and x^2 function buttons, calculate (a) $\cos^2\phi$, (b) $\sin\phi$ and (c) $\tan\phi$.

Example E:

If $\sin x = 0.6$, what is $\cos x$?

$$\sin^2 x + \cos^2 x = 1. \therefore 0.6^2 + \cos^2 x = 1. \therefore \cos x = \sqrt{1 - 0.6^2} = \sqrt{0.64} = 0.8$$

NB. Actually this is not the only possibility: $\cos x = -0.8$ is also possible. We'll deal with negative values of $\cos x$ later.

There are other ways of writing the trig form of Pythagoras' theorem:

$$\sin^2\theta + \cos^2\theta = 1 \tag{1}$$

Dividing both sides by $\cos^2\theta$ gives

$$\frac{\sin^2\theta}{\cos^2\theta} + 1 = \frac{1}{\cos^2\theta}$$

But $\dfrac{\sin\theta}{\cos\theta} = \tan\theta$ and $\sec\theta = \dfrac{1}{\cos\theta}$ $\therefore$

$$\tan^2\theta + 1 = \sec^2\theta \tag{2}$$

Dividing (1) by $\sin^2\theta$ gives

$$1 + \cot^2\theta = \mathrm{cosec}^2\theta \tag{3}$$

Equations (2) and (3) are also forms of Pythagoras' theorem. You are advised either to remember them or to know how to derive them.

5.5.5 Finding the angle from the trig ratio

Consider the triangle in Figure 5.13. What is the value of the angle δ?

Clearly

$$\sin\delta = \frac{\mathrm{opp}}{\mathrm{hyp}} = \frac{40}{100} = 0.4$$

So δ is the angle whose sine is 0.4. We write this as $\delta = \sin^{-1}(0.4)$, or we usually leave out the brackets and write $\delta = \sin^{-1} 0.4$, and pronounce this 'delta equals sine to the minus one 0.4'.[a] To work this out on the calculator we use the SHIFT button to access the $\sin^{-1}$ function. Try this. Your answer should be 23.6°, if your calculator is set to degrees mode (if you get 0.412 it is set to radians). As an exercise, work out the base of the triangle using Pythagoras' theorem and check that you get the same answer using the $\cos^{-1}$ and the $\tan^{-1}$ functions.

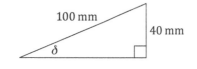

Fig 5.13

Example F:

A hiker walks 10 km N, then 10 km E, then 10 km 40° South of East. What are her distance and bearing from the starting point?

The starting and end points are A and E.

We first calculate AB and BE:

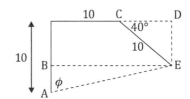

$$AB = 10 - DE = 10 - 10\sin 40° = 3.57 \text{ km}$$

$$BE = 10 + CD = 10 + 10\cos 40° = 17.66 \text{ km}.$$

$\therefore$ Using Pythagoras' theorem $\quad AE = \sqrt{AB^2 + BE^2} = \sqrt{3.57^2 + 17.66^2} = 18.0$ km.

$\phi = \tan^{-1}\left(\dfrac{BE}{AB}\right) = \tan^{-1}\left(\dfrac{17.66}{3.57}\right) = 78.6°$. So the end point is 18.0 km on a bearing 78.6° E of N.

quickfire ▶ **5.18**

Find θ if

(a) $\theta = \sin^{-1} 0.80$

(b) $\theta = \cos^{-1} 0.80$

(c) $\theta = \tan^{-1} 0.80$.

[a] There are two other ways of writing this, (i) $\delta = \arcsin 0.4$, or (ii) $\delta = \mathrm{invsin}\, 0.4$ but most calculators use the $\sin^{-1}$ symbol.

Warning

The standard notation $\sin^{-1}$ does not mean $\dfrac{1}{\sin}$. Do not be confused by this. To write $\dfrac{1}{\sin\theta}$ using index notation, you would have to write $(\sin\theta)^{-1}$. However $\sin^2\theta$ **does mean the same as $(\sin\theta)^2$! Sorry, but that's the way it is!**

5.5.6 Snell's law

Figure 5.14 shows a light ray being refracted as it crosses a boundary from material 1, in which its speed is c_1, into material 2 with speed c_2. The normal is a line perpendicular to the boundary.

The Law of Refraction, usually called Snell's law[4] can be written, for a given pair of materials the ratio $\dfrac{\sin\theta_1}{\sin\theta_2}$ is a constant.

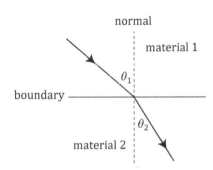

We show in Chapter 12 that this ratio is the ratio of the velocities of light in the two materials, i.e.

$$\frac{\sin\theta_1}{\sin\theta_2} = \frac{c_1}{c_2} \qquad (1)$$

Fig 5.14

The *refractive index*, n, of a material is defined as the ratio of the speed of light in a vacuum, c, to the speed of light in the material.

$\therefore$ for material 1, $n_1 = \dfrac{c}{c_1}$ and for material 2, $n_2 = \dfrac{c}{c_2}$.

Substituting in equation (1) for c_1 and c_2 gives the usual refraction formula:
$n_1\sin\theta_1 = n_2\sin\theta_2$. This equation can also be written in the form $n\sin\theta = $ constant, which can be applied to situations in which the refractive varies continuously with position.

5.6 General definitions of trig ratios

Angles, other than the right angle, within a right-angled triangle are always within the range $0 < \theta < 90°$ $[0 < \theta < \frac{\pi}{2}]$ Trig ratios are also defined for angles outside this range. This is done in a manner which is consistent with the definitions above using the co-ordinates of a point on a circle.

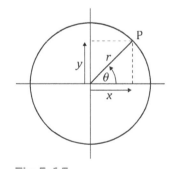

Point **P** has co-ordinates (x, y). It is a distance r from the origin. The angle θ is the angle between the radius r and the positive x axis, measured anticlockwise (see diagram).

We define: $\sin\theta = \dfrac{y}{r}$, $\cos\theta = \dfrac{x}{r}$ and $\tan\theta = \dfrac{y}{x}$.

Fig 5.15

These definitions are the same as we have used before, using the right-angled triangle including θ. **P** can move around the circle, into any of the other 4 quadrants of the circle.

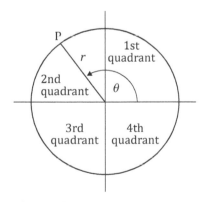

Fig 5.16

---

[4] This is after the 17th century Dutch astronomer Willebrord Snellius, but it was discovered over 600 years earlier by the Persian physicist and astronomer Ibn Sahl.

Figure 5.16 shows **P** in the *second quadrant*. In this position, θ is between 90° and 180° [$\frac{\pi}{2}$ and π rad]. In this quadrant, the *x* co-ordinate of **P** is negative and *y* is positive, so, using the same definitions:

$$\sin\theta > 0, \ \cos\theta < 0 \ \text{ and } \ \tan\theta < 0.$$

Note that *r* is a length and is always positive.

quickfire ▶ 5.19

Show whether sin, cos and tan are positive or negative for angles between 180° and 270°.

Example G:

Show whether sin, cos and tan are positive or negative for angles between 270° and 360°?

Between these angles, **P** is in the 4th quadrant so $x > 0$ and $y < 0$.

So: $\sin\theta = \dfrac{y}{r} < 0$ $\qquad \cos\theta = \dfrac{x}{r} > 0$ $\qquad \tan\theta = \dfrac{y}{x} < 0$ $\left[\text{Alternatively: } \tan\theta = \dfrac{\sin\theta}{\cos\theta} < 0\right]$

5.6.1 Finding the angle from the trig ratio (a 2nd look)

If the angle can have any value, i.e it is not restricted to between 0° and 90°, then how do we find the value of the angle from the trig ratio?

For example, if $\cos\theta = 0.5$, what is θ? Referring to Figures 5.15 and 5.16, $x > 0$, so there are two possibilities for the position of **P**. The points $\mathbf{P}_1$ and $\mathbf{P}_2$ in Figure 5.17 have the same values of *x* and *r*, so $\cos\theta_1$ and $\cos\theta_2$ are both 0.5.

The calculator, set to degrees, returns a value for θ of 60°. From the diagram 360° – 60° = 300° is also a possibility. In order to solve the equation $\cos\theta = 0.5$ we need more information. θ could also be outside the range 0–360°. We shall return to this.

Table 5.1 gives values of sin, cos and tan θ for some significant values of θ.

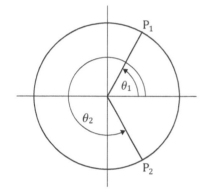

Fig 5.17

quickfire ▶ 5.20

$\sin\alpha = 0.7$. Find two values of α between 0 and 360° which are solutions to this equation.

Table 5.1

$\theta\,/\,°$	$\theta\,/\,\text{rad}$	$\sin\theta$	$\cos\theta$	$\tan\theta$
0	0	0	1	0
30	$\dfrac{\pi}{6}$	0.5	$\dfrac{\sqrt{3}}{2} = 0.866$	$\dfrac{1}{\sqrt{3}} = 0.577$
45	$\dfrac{\pi}{4}$	$\dfrac{1}{\sqrt{2}} = 0.707$	$\dfrac{1}{\sqrt{2}} = 0.707$	1
60	$\dfrac{\pi}{3}$	$\dfrac{\sqrt{3}}{2} = 0.866$	0.5	$\sqrt{3} = 1.732$
90	$\dfrac{\pi}{2}$	1	0	∞
120	$\dfrac{2\pi}{3}$	$\dfrac{\sqrt{3}}{2} = 0.866$	–0.5	$-\sqrt{3} = -1.732$
135	$\dfrac{3\pi}{4}$	$\dfrac{1}{\sqrt{2}} = 0.707$	$-\dfrac{1}{\sqrt{2}} = -0.707$	–1
150	$\dfrac{5\pi}{6}$	0.5	$-\dfrac{\sqrt{3}}{2} = -0.866$	$-\dfrac{1}{\sqrt{3}} = -0.577$
180	π	0	–1	0

5.7 General triangles

Sometimes we need to work with triangles which are not right-angled. We consider two rules which help us in this. We work from this triangle ABC, its angles, Â, B̂ and Ĉ and sides a, b and c. The dotted line is a perpendicular from C to the side AB. See Figure 5.18.

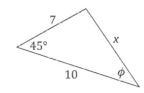

Fig 5.18

5.7.1 The cosine rule

Applying Pythagoras' theorem to the two right-angled triangles in Figure 5.18:

$$b^2 = x^2 + y^2 \qquad (1)$$

$$a^2 = x^2 + (c - y)^2 \qquad (2)$$

Expanding equation (2) and substituting for $x^2 + y^2$ from (1) gives:

$$a^2 = b^2 + c^2 - 2cy \qquad (3)$$

But $y = b \cos Â$. Substituting for y in (3) gives:

$$a^2 = b^2 + c^2 - 2bc \cos Â \qquad \text{This is the \textbf{cosine rule}.}$$

5.7.2 The sine rule

Using the 2 right-angled triangles containing the dotted side, x : $x = b \sin Â$ and $x = a \sin B̂$.

From these two equations: $\qquad b \sin Â = a \sin B̂$

$$\therefore \qquad \frac{\sin Â}{a} = \frac{\sin B̂}{b}$$

By choosing a perpendicular from B to side AC and repeating this we get: $\dfrac{\sin Â}{a} = \dfrac{\sin Ĉ}{c}$.

So we can write: $\dfrac{\sin Â}{a} = \dfrac{\sin B̂}{b} = \dfrac{\sin Ĉ}{c}$ $\qquad$ This is the **sine rule**.

quickfire ▶ **5.21**

Find ϕ and x.
Show your working.

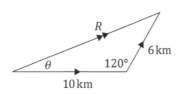

5.7.3 Applying the sine and cosine rules

In A-level Physics, we most often apply these rules in the context of adding or subtracting vectors, which is dealt with in Chapter 7. We usually have to apply both rules. See Example H.

Example H:

Calculate R and the angle θ.

Apply the cosine rule: $\qquad\qquad R^2 = 10^2 + 6^2 - 2 \times 10 \times 6 \cos 120°$

$$R^2 = 196, \qquad \therefore \underline{R = 14 \, \text{km}}.$$

Apply the sine rule with $R = 14$ km: $\dfrac{\sin 120°}{14} = \dfrac{\sin \theta}{6}$ $\quad \therefore \sin \theta = 0.371$

$\therefore \theta = \sin^{-1} 0.371 = 21.8°$. Note: $\sin 158.2°$ [$= \sin(180° - 21.8°)$] $= 0.371$ as well, but θ is clearly an acute angle.

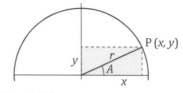

5.8 Compound angle formulae

If we combine two angles, A and B, it is often useful to be able to express sin (A + B) and cos (A + B) in terms of A and B separately.

Consider the point **P** as before on the circle of radius r (figure 5.19)

Fig 5.19

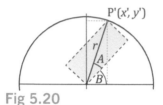

Then
$$x = r \cos A \tag{1}$$

and
$$y = r \sin A \tag{2}$$

Now we'll rotate **P** through a further angle, B, anti-clockwise. In fact we'll rotate the whole rectangle through angle B (Figure 5.20).

Fig 5.20

For angle (A + B) we consider the co-ordinates of P'.

So:
$$x' = r \cos (A + B) \tag{3}$$

and
$$y' = r \sin (A + B) \tag{4}$$

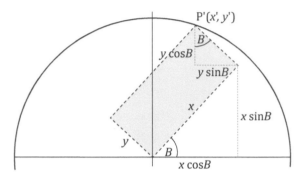

Fig 5.21

Figure 5.21 is an enlarged version of 5.20 with some detail removed. Now check the displacements marked on the third diagram and how they add in pairs to give x' and y' in equations (5) and (6)

$$x' = x \cos B - y \sin B \tag{5}$$

and
$$y' = x \sin B + y \cos B \tag{6}$$

If we substitute the expressions for x and y from equations (1) and (2) and expressions for x' and y' from equations (3) and (4) we get:

$$r \cos (A + B) = r \cos A \cos B - r \sin A \sin B$$

and

$$r \sin (A + B) = r \sin A \cos B + r \cos A \sin B$$

∴ Dividing by r
$$\cos (A + B) = \cos A \cos B - \sin A \sin B$$
and
$$\sin (A + B) = \sin A \cos B + \cos A \sin B$$

Note the minus sign in the cos (A + B) formula: this should not be surprising in view of the fact that the value of $\cos \theta$ decreases with θ between 0 and 90°.

Similarly
$$\cos (A - B) = \cos A \cos B + \sin A \sin B$$
and
$$\sin (A - B) = \sin A \cos B - \cos A \sin B$$

These can be derived in a similar way to the addition formulae or can be derived from them using the relationships cos (−B) = cos B and sin (−B) = − sin B [see Sections 8.2.1 and 8.2.2]

Example I:

Use the formulae for sin $(\theta + \phi)$ and cos $(\theta + \phi)$ to show that $\tan 2\theta = \dfrac{2 \tan \theta}{1 - \tan^2 \theta}$ and use the result to evaluate tan 22.5° given that tan 45° = 1.

$$\tan 2\theta = \frac{\sin 2\theta}{\cos 2\theta} = \frac{\sin (\theta + \theta)}{\cos (\theta + \theta)} = \frac{2 \sin \theta \cos \theta}{\cos^2 \theta - \sin^2 \theta}$$

Dividing top and bottom by $\cos^2 \theta$ and using $\dfrac{\sin \theta}{\cos \theta} = \tan \theta$ gives $\tan 2\theta = \dfrac{2 \tan \theta}{1 - \tan^2 \theta}$.   QED

Putting $2\theta = 45°$, $\tan 45° = \dfrac{2 \tan 22.5°}{1 - \tan^2 22.5°}$.

Rearranging and putting tan 45° = 1, gives $\tan^2 22.5° + 2 \tan 22.5° - 1 = 0$.

This is a quadratic equation in tan 22.5°, we we can solve using the quadratic formula (see Section 3.2.4):

$\tan 22.5° = \dfrac{-2 \pm \sqrt{4 + 4}}{2} = -1 \pm \sqrt{2}$. We can ignore the negative root as we know that

$\tan 22.5 > 0$, so $\tan 22.5° = -1 + \sqrt{2} = 0.4142$ (4 s.f.)

quickfire 5.22

tan 225° = 1. Use the working of Example I to write down the value of tan 112.5°.

Test Yourself 5.1

In Questions 1–5 find the values of all the angles.

[Assume that a line that appears horizontal or vertical is so.]

1 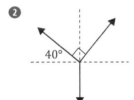   25°

2    40°

3 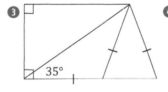   35°

4

5 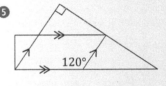   120°

Questions 6–10 refer to the diagram:

6 If c = 200 mm and θ = 30°, calculate (a) a, (b) b.

7 If b = 40 m and θ = 40° calculate (a) a, (b) c.

8 If a = 30 cm and θ = 50° calculate (a) b, (b) c.

9 If b = 150 mm and a = 100 mm, calculate (a) c, (b) θ.

10 If a = 20 m and c = 30 m, calculate (a) θ, (b) b.

11 A student walks x m due East, then y m due North. She ends up 300 m at 30° East of North from her starting point. Find x and y.

12 (a) A man measures the angle of elevation (i.e. to the horizontal) of a cliff-top as 35° from a point 200 m from the foot of the cliff on horizontal ground extending to the foot of the cliff. Calculate the height of the cliff.

  (b) How far would he have to be from the foot of the cliff for the angle of elevation to be 25°?

13 Light travels though a 1000 m long optical fibre by the zigzag path shown. Calculate the distance travelled by the light.

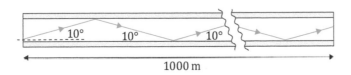

10°   10°   10°

1000 m

⑭ A light ray passes from medium 1 to medium 2 as shown. The refractive indices
are: $n_1 = 1.52$ and $n_2 = 1.33$. Calculate:

(a) θ_2 when $\theta_1 = 30°$; [$n_1 \sin \theta_1 = n_2 \sin \theta_2$ or $n \sin \theta = $ const]

(b) θ_1 when $\theta_2 = 60°$

(c) θ_1 when $\theta_2 = 90°$

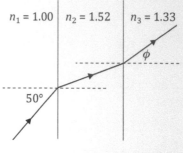

⑮ The diagram shows a light ray passing from air, through a parallel sides glass
sheet into water in a fish tank.

(a) Calculate ϕ.

(b) Which piece of information in the diagram is irrelevant and why?

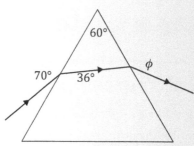

⑯ The diagram shows a light ray passing through a glass prism. Using the
information in the diagram, calculate

(a) the refractive index of the glass;

(b) the angle ϕ.

$n_{air} = 1.00$

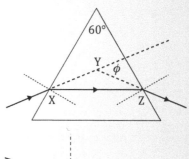

⑰ A light ray passes symmetrically through a triangular glass prism as shown. Its
direction changes by angle $\phi = 44.4°$.

Determine the refractive index of the glass of the prism.

[Hint: Use the isosceles triangle XYZ to help find the angle of incidence at X]

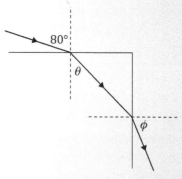

Questions 18–20 concern a light ray which passed though the corner of a transparent
plastic block surrounded by air of refractive index 1.00.

⑱ If $\theta = 45°$ calculate the refractive index of the plastic.

⑲ If $\phi = 85°$ calculate the refractive index of the plastic.

⑳ Calculate the maximum refractive index of the plastic for a light ray to be able to
pass through the corner.

Use the equations, $\sin (\theta + \phi) = \sin \theta \cos \phi + \cos \theta \sin \phi$,
$\cos (\theta + \phi) = \cos \theta \cos \phi - \sin \theta \sin \phi$ and $\sin^2 \theta + \cos^2 \theta = 1$ to answer Questions 21–23.
Show your working.

㉑ If $\sin \alpha = 0.8$ calculate (a) $\cos \alpha$, (b) $\tan \alpha$.

㉒ Show that $\cos 2\beta = 2 \cos^2 \beta - 1$

㉓ If $\sin \chi = x$, write the following in terms of x:

(a) $\cos \chi$, (b) $\cos (180° + \chi)$ (c) $\tan (360° - \chi)$

㉔ Determine x and y.

Show your working.

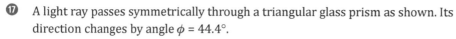

㉕ Triangle ABC has the following
sides: AB = 10 cm, BC = 14 cm.
Angle Ĉ = 45°. Find the two
possible lengths of side CA.
Show your working.

Chapter 6

Graphs

6.1 Introduction

Many fields of study use charts and graphs to display data. They are useful to us because we often find it easier to see patterns in visual rather than in numerically presented results. The graphs that we meet in Physics are of a special kind: physicists often propose theories in which there is an algebraic relationship between variables. Because of this we can use graphs to make predictions and to test the theories themselves.

In this chapter we are going to examine the construction of graphs and compare the graphical and algebraic ways of analysing relationships between variables. We will look at both theoretical graphs and those drawn from experimental data.

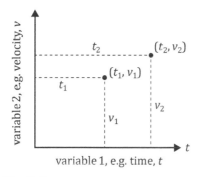

Fig 6.1

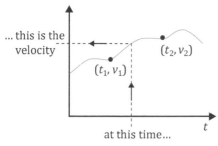

Fig 6.2

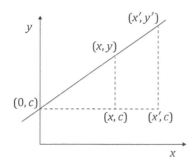

Fig 6.3

6.2 Axes, points and graphs

We use graphs to represent how one variable depends upon another. Here are two examples:

- how the velocity of a vehicle depends upon the time
- how the pd across the terminals of a power supply depends upon the current.

Notice the phrase *depends upon* in the above examples. We could substitute the phrase *is determined by*.

We plot the values of the variables as distances along one axis or up another one – see Figure 6.1. Two points are plotted, labelled (t_1, v_1) and (t_2, v_2). (t_1, v_1) and (t_2, v_2) are referred to as the *co-ordinates* of the points. The horizontal axis is often called the *x-axis* and the vertical axis is the *y-axis*. [①]

If we know how the velocity varies with time, we represent this as a line on the two axes. We call this line the *graph of velocity against time*. Note the order of this: 'graph of [y variable] against [x variable]'. The advantage of a graph over a series of readings of velocity and time is that we can use the graph to infer the velocity at times other than those given in the data. See Figure 6.2.

6.3 Axis scales and graphs of linear functions

A *linear* function is one of the form: $y = ax + b$, where y and x are the variables and a and b are constants. Two examples are:

- $v = u + at$, where t and v are the variables
- $V = E - Ir$, where I and V are the variables.

A *linear* graph is a straight-line graph. We'll now show that a linear function is represented by a linear graph.

Figure 6.3 shows a straight line that passes through the point $(0, c)$, i.e. its intercept on the y-axis is c. (x, y) is one point on the line and (x', y') is another.

---

① The correct names are *abscissa* (for the *x-axis*) and *ordinate* (for the *y-axis*).

The **slope** or **gradient** of a graph, m, is defined by:

$$m = \frac{\text{increase in } y \text{ value}}{\text{increase in } x \text{ value}} = \frac{y - c}{x}.$$

Rearranging the algebra:

$$y = mx + c$$

Because it is a straight line, the gradient of the graph is always the same, so we can also write

$$m = \frac{\text{increase in } y \text{ value}}{\text{increase in } x \text{ value}} = \frac{y' - c}{x'}.$$ So $y' = mx' + c$ [2] and, for **any** (x, y) on the graph: $y = mx + c$.

In other words, the equation $y = mx + c$ represents the straight line, where

- it is an equation which is correct for any pair of values (x, y)
- m is the gradient, which is a constant
- c is the intercept on the y-axis.

If $y = ax + b$, in a graph of y against x, the gradient is a and the intercept on the y-axis is b.

In $y = mx + c$, if m is negative the graph slopes downwards.

In $y = mx + c$, if c is negative, the graph intersects the y-axis below the x-axis.

Example A: The velocity-time graph is for a car travelling with a constant acceleration. Find:

(a) the velocity after 6.4 s
(b) the initial velocity
(c) the acceleration
(d) the equation of motion.

Answers: (a) See the dotted line: 12.0 m s^{-1} at $t = 6.4$ s.

(b) Initial velocity is the intercept on the v axis, i.e. 4.0 m s^{-1}.

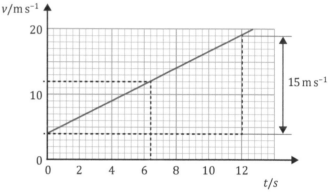

(c) The acceleration = the gradient: see the dotted triangle.
Vertical side = $19.0 - 4.0 = 15 \text{ m s}^{-1}$
Horizontal side = 12.0 s

$\therefore$ Acceleration $= \frac{19.0 - 4.0}{12.0} = \frac{15.0}{12.0} = 1.25 \text{ m s}^{-2}$

(d) The equation of motion is $v = 1.25t + 4.0$.
[We could write: $v = 4.0 + 1.25t$ to fit in with $v = u + at$]

Note

The equation in Example A (d) is incomplete as it doesn't tell us the units in which v and t are expressed. One way to resolve this is to write '$v = 1.25t + 4.0$, with v in m s^{-1} and t in s'. Another way is to write the equation as $(v/\text{m s}^{-1}) = 1.25(t/s) + 4.0$. You are unlikely to be penalised in A-Level Physics for leaving the units out of the equation but you **will** lose marks for leaving the units out of the velocity or acceleration in your final answer.

Definitions

If the graph of y against x is a straight line, y is **linearly related** to x.

If the graph also passes through the origin $(0, 0)$, y is **directly proportional** to x.

---
[2] The two triangles, $(0, c)-(x, y)-(x, c)$ and $(0, c)-(x', y')-(x', c)$, are *similar triangles* [can you see why?] so the ratio of the vertical side to the horizontal side for the 1st Δ is the same as for the 2nd.

Units in graphs – a note for purists

Most mathematicians and physicists regard graphs and algebraic equations as relationships between numbers and not quantities, i.e. numbers with units. This is shown on the labelling of graphical axes. Look again at the v and t axes of the graph in Example A. the vertical axis is labelled '$v/\text{m s}^{-1}$' and the horizontal axis is labelled 't/s'. These labels indicate that for example the velocities are **divided by m s^{-1}**, so that it is pure numbers that are plotted, e.g. the intercept is 4.0. We then have to think as follows:

- the initial velocity, $u/\text{m s}^{-1} = 4.0$
- $\therefore u = 4.0 \times \text{m s}^{-1} = 4.0 \text{ m s}^{-1}$.

Similarly in the calculation of acceleration the thought process is:

- acceleration, $a / \text{m s}^{-2}$ = the gradient $= \dfrac{15}{12} = 1.25$
- $\therefore a = 1.25 \times \text{m s}^{-2} = 1.25 \text{ m s}^{-2}$.

For the purposes of A-Level Physics, you will not be penalised if you write:

- the initial velocity = the intercept = 4.0 m s^{-1} and
- the acceleration = the gradient = 1.25 m s^{-2},

so you can forget this digression if you like! Just remember that, in an answer, you must give quantities, such as acceleration and velocity, their correct units.

quickfire 6.1

In a graph of $y = 3x + 2$, what are:
(a) the gradient
(b) the y-intercept?

quickfire 6.2

In a graph of $v = 45 - 1.5t$, what are:
(a) the gradient
(b) the t-intercept?

quickfire 6.3

In Quickfire 6.2, what are (a) the acceleration and (b) the initial velocity?
[Assume basic SI units.]

6.4 Finding the equation from a section of a graph

Sometimes a graph has only a small range of known values of x, well away from 0. In these cases we may not be able to find the value of c by looking at where the graph crosses the y-axis. See Figure 6.4 (the values on the x-axis are only for illustration). This situation often arises in practical work, especially when using log functions in A2.

We shall examine two cases:

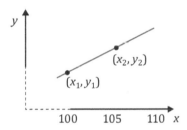

Fig 6.4

6.4.1 Finding the equation from the gradient and one point

Suppose we know the gradient, m, of the graph; we can use one point on the graph to find its equation.

We'll start with the general equation:

$$y = mx + c$$

It is convenient to rearrange this as $y - mx = c$. We'll see why in a moment!

Look at the triangle $(0, c)$, (x_1, y_1), (x_1, c): The gradient, m, is given by

$$m = \frac{y_1 - c}{x_1}$$

Rearranging this gives: $c = y_1 - mx_1$. Substituting this into $y - mx = c$ gives the straight line equation:

$$y - mx = y_1 - mx_1$$

The reason for the rearrangement above is now clear – the resulting equation is more memorable in form!

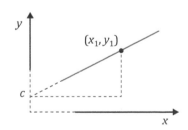

Fig 6.5

Pointer

Finding the unknowns in $y = mx + c$ from two points is essentially the same as solving two simultaneous equations.

Pointer

The expression $\frac{y_2 - y_1}{x_2 - x_1}$ is the gradient, m.

So $y - \frac{y_2 - y_1}{x_2 - x_1}x = y_1 - \frac{y_2 - y_1}{x_2 - x_1}x_1$
is the same as $y - mx = y_1 - mx_1$

Example B:

A straight-line graph has gradient 0.6 and passes through the (112, –85). What is its equation?

If we substitute 0.6 and (112, –85) into $y - mx = y_1 - mx_1$, we get $y - 0.6x = -85 - 0.6 \times 112$.

Rearranging: $y = 0.6x - 152.2$

Pointer

If $\frac{y_1}{x_1} = \frac{y_2}{x_2}$, $c = 0$.

6.4.2 Finding the equation from two points

In practice this is more useful than the gradient and point method. Suppose we know two points, (x_1, y_1) and (x_2, y_2).

From the definition of gradient: $m = \frac{y_2 - y_1}{x_2 - x_1}$

Using the result for c in 6.4.1: $c = y_1 - \frac{y_2 - y_1}{x_2 - x_1}x_1$

Substituting these expressions into $y - mx = c$,

the equation is $y - \frac{y_2 - y_1}{x_2 - x_1}x = y_1 - \frac{y_2 - y_1}{x_2 - x_1}x_1$.

Again, this has a memorable form.

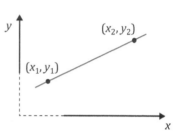

Fig 6.6

quickfire ▶ 6.4

With variables x and y, find the gradient, and then the equation if the line passes through:
(a) (2, 4) and (3, 5),
(b) (2, 10) and (4, 6).

Example C: A straight-line graph passes through the points (24, 9) and (36, –15).

Its equation is: $y - \frac{-15 - 9}{36 - 24}x = 9 - \frac{-15 - 9}{36 - 24} \times 24$

You should be able to show that this leads to $y + 2x = 57$.

We can write this as $y = -2x + 57$, which is the conventional form of the equation.

Test Yourself 6.1

For questions 1–10, prepare a pair of y, x axes with y from –4 to +16 and x from –6 to +12. On these axes, draw the following graphs paying close attention to the points where they cross the axes.

① $y = 2x + 4$ ② $y = -3x + 12$ ③ $y = \frac{1}{2}x + 2$ ④ $y = -x + 10$ ⑤ $y = \frac{1}{3}x - 2$
⑥ $y = x$ ⑦ $2y = x + 8$ ⑧ $y = -x$ ⑨ $y = -\frac{1}{2}x + 2$ ⑩ $y = -\frac{1}{3}x + 8$

In Questions 11–20, find the equation relating the variables:

⑪ y against x: gradient = 1.5, $y = 3$ when $x = 6$.

⑫ y against x: gradient = –0.4, $y = 10$ when $x = 50$.

⑬ V against I: gradient = –0.2, $V = 5.2$ when $I = 4\,A$.

⑭ V against f: gradient = 4.14×10^{-15}, $V = 0$ when $f = 1.69 \times 10^{14}$.

⑮ v against t: gradient = 0.8, $v = 24$ when $t = 10$.

⑯ F against l: gradient = 25, $F = 10$ when $l = 0.6$.

⑰ V against I: $V = 2.4$ when $I = 0.5$; $V = 2.0$ when $I = 0.8$.

⑱ v against t: $v = 20$ when $t = 12$; $v = 18$ when $t = 22$.

⑲ F against l: $F = 2$ when $l = 10$; $F = 6$ when $l = 18$.

⑳ V against f: $V = 3.0$ when $f = 1.0 \times 10^{15}$; $V = 1.0\,V$ when $f = 5.0 \times 10^{14}$.

㉑ A battery has a terminal pd, V, of 8.0 V when it passes a current, I, of 0.40 A. When the current is 0.60 A, the terminal pd is 7.2 V. Sketch a graph of V against I and determine the emf, E, and internal resistance, r. $[V = E - Ir]$.

㉒ When a load, F, of 4.0 N is suspended from a spring, its length, l, is 8.2 cm. With a load of 7.5 N the length is 11.5 cm. Sketch a graph of F against l and determine the spring constant, k, and unstretched length, l_0. $[F = k (l - l_0)]$ Hint: Rewrite the equation as $F = kl - c$.

㉓ A space capsule has a velocity, v, of 12.0 km s^{-1} at a time, t of 50 s. At 150 s, the velocity is 12.8 km s^{-1}. Sketch a graph of v against t and determine the initial velocity, u, and acceleration, a. $[v = u + at]$.

㉔ The stopping voltage, V_s, for a photo-cell is 0.45 V when the frequency, f, of the incident radiation is 2.5×10^{14} Hz. When the frequency is 3.5×10^{14} Hz, the stopping voltage is 0.87 V. Sketch a graph of V_s against f and determine a value for the Planck constant, h and the work function, ϕ. $\left[V_s = \dfrac{h}{e}f - \dfrac{\phi}{e} \right]$ NB. e = charge on the electron = 1.60×10^{-19} C.

6.4.3 Linear graphs from experimental data

Most graphs in Physics arise from experimental data, i.e. each data point is the result of a measurement or combination of measurements. This section of the book will deal with handling experimental plots involving some degree of scatter but without a discussion of error bars and uncertainty.

Consider the experimental plot in Figure 6.7. The first question which needs to be asked is, 'Are these points consistent with a linear relationship?' In order to answer this question we need to consider:

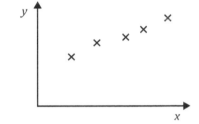

Fig 6.7

- whether the points are considered accurate, i.e. is the uncertainty in each point low, and
- whether there are theoretical reasons for expecting a linear relationship
- whether it is possible to obtain further readings at different values of x

Look at these possible graphs (Figure 6.8), which all have the same original data points.

There are mathematical procedures for establishing a 'best fit' straight line, e.g. applying a simple linear regression. Usually in A-Level Physics, the number of data points and repeat readings is quite low so such a procedure is not justified and it is not required by A-Level specifications. We just use a transparent ruler and move it so that:

- it matches the gradient suggested by the data points and
- the points are scattered equally above and below the line.

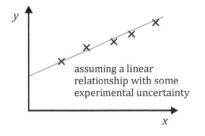
assuming a linear relationship with some experimental uncertainty

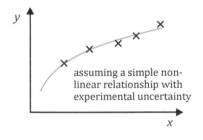
assuming a simple non-linear relationship with experimental uncertainty

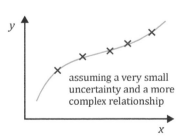
assuming a very small uncertainty and a more complex relationship

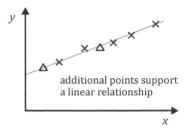
additional points support a linear relationship

Fig 6.8

Pointer

An indicator of possible non-linearity is if the points at either end of the best-fit line are on the same side of the line.

Pointer

When drawing a best-fit line by eye, do not force it through the end points.

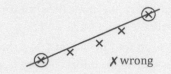

✗ wrong

Pointer

When drawing a best-fit line by eye, do not force it through the origin.

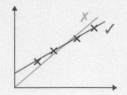

quickfire 6.5

(a) Calculate the centre of mass, $(\bar{x}, \bar{y})$, of these points: (1.0, 0.26), (2.0, 0.38), (3.0, 0.45), (4.0, 0.58), (5.0, 0.66).

(b) Find the equation of the graph.

Use of the 'centre of mass' point

Many people recommend plotting the centre of mass point and drawing the line through it which reflects the gradient of the scattered points:

If we have N points, $(x_1, y_1), (x_2, y_2), \dots (x_N, y_N)$, **which are all equally weighted**, the co-ordinates of the centre of mass point $(\bar{x}, \bar{y})$ are defined by:

$$(\bar{x}, \bar{y}) = \left(\frac{x_1 + x_2 + \dots x_N}{N}, \frac{y_1 + y_2 + \dots y_N}{N} \right),$$ i.e. it is (mean of x-values, mean of y-values).

The caveat, 'if they are all equally weighted', is important. In this case it means that the uncertainties in position of the points are all the same.

6.5 Graphs of non-linear functions

Many relationships in physics involve non-linear equations. Some involve powers and roots, e.g.

$$P = I^2R, \quad v^2 = u^2 + 2as, \quad P = A\sigma T^4, \quad \lambda_{max} = WT^{-1} \quad \text{or} \quad T = 2\pi\sqrt{\frac{l}{g}}$$

A-Level Physics students need to be familiar with the graphs of these relationships and to use them to make measurements and draw conclusions. If these relationships are plotted simply, using one variable plotted against the other, the graphs are curves. A major requirement of A-Level Physics is to linearise these graphs in order to make them easier to analyse.

Other relationships involve so-called *transcendental functions*, e.g. $I = I_0 e^{-t/RC}$, $x = A \sin(\omega t + \varepsilon)$. These relationships are dealt with in Section 4.4.7 and Chapter 8 respectively.

6.5.1 Graphs of equations involving powers and roots

(a) $y \propto x^n$, for $n > 1$

These graphs curve upwards from the origin. The gradient at the origin is zero. For $x > 0$, all the graphs look similar – the greater the value of n, the more rapidly the graph takes off after $x = 1$. The graphs in Figure 6.9 compare $y = x^n$ for $n = 1.5$, 2, 3 and 4. Negative values of x are not often required in A-Level Physics. Examples:

- $P = I^2R$

- $T = \dfrac{2\pi}{\sqrt{GM}} a^{1.5}$ [Kepler's 3rd law]

(b) $y \propto x^n$, for $0 < n < 1$

The graph for $y \propto x^{\frac{1}{2}}$, i.e. $y = \sqrt{x}$ is shown in Figure 6.10. Note the following:

- there are two values of y for every positive value of x: $\sqrt{4} = \pm 2$ [i.e.+ 2 or – 2].

- there are no values of y for $x < 0$.

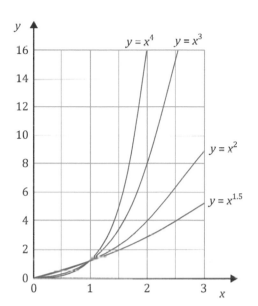

Fig 6.9

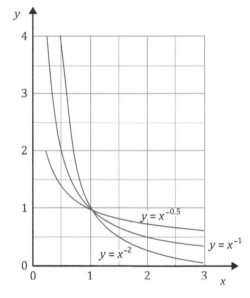

Fig 6.10

Other values of n give similar shapes in the positive quadrant, i.e. $x > 0$ and $y > 0$. The closer n is to zero, the tighter the curve. Example:

▪ $T = 2\pi \sqrt{\dfrac{l}{g}}$ – simple pendulum

▪ $T = 2\pi \sqrt{\dfrac{m}{k}}$ – oscillating mass on spring

(c) $y \propto x^{-n}$ for $n > 0$, i.e. $y \propto \dfrac{1}{x^n}$

These graphs all have a negative gradient which decreases with increasing x. These relationships occur quite frequently in A2 Physics, e.g.

▪ $F = \dfrac{GMm}{r^2}$ – Newton's law of gravity

▪ $v = \sqrt{\dfrac{2GM}{r}}$ – escape velocity

The potential energy, E_p, of two atoms bound by a van der Waals bond at a separation, r, obeys the following equation approximately:

$E_p = \dfrac{A}{r^{12}} - \dfrac{B}{r^6}$ – the so-called '6–12 potential'.

Fig 6.11

Data Exercise 6.1

Use a spreadsheet to plot the value of E_p for the 6–12 potential, with the values of A and B taken to be 1. Estimate the equilibrium separation of the atoms [i.e. where E_p is a minimum]. Suggested range of values of x: 0.96–2.00 but you will need to play around with the size of the steps between the values of x. What is the minimum value of E_p?

6.5.2 Linearising equations

It is very useful to find a way of plotting data which are suspected of satisfying non-linear equations so that the graph is linear. This is for two reasons:

1 The eye is good at detecting departures from linearity and hence we can judge whether data are consistent with the putative relationship.

2 The values of the gradient and intercept of a linear graph can be used to reveal useful values of constants.

(a) Equations of the form $y^m = kx^n$, in which n is known [or suspected]

A graph of y^m against x^n is a straight line of gradient k. There are other possibilities but you should do Data Exercise 6.2 first.

Data Exercise 6.2

A car accelerates from rest (at time, $t = 0$) with constant acceleration. The time it takes to reach 10 m distance posts is measured using a stopwatch with a discrimination of 0.05 s.

The results are as follows:

Distance / m	10	20	30	40	50	60	70
Time / s	2.75	4.00	4.70	5.55	6.15	6.70	7.35

Plot a graph of distance, s, against time², t^2, verify that it satisfies the relationship $s = kt^2$ and hence determine the acceleration. [Hint: $s = ut + \frac{1}{2}at^2$ and $u = 0$]

If $y^m \propto x^n$, then all these are relationships are true:

- $y^{m/n} \propto x$, so a graph of $y^{m/n}$ against x will be a straight line.
- $y \propto x^{n/m}$, so a graph of y against $x^{n/m}$ will be a straight line.
- $y^{1/n} \propto x^{1/m}$, so a graph of $y^{1/n}$ against $x^{1/m}$ will be a straight line.

Why should we consider these alternatives?

Reason 1: If you have completed Data Exercise 6.2, you will have noticed that the data points were equally spaced. Approximate equal spacing is usually desirable. Consider the data in Q6 of Test Yourself 6.2, which is of the same situation but with the data taken with approximate equal spacing in time. You will notice that the fifth distance is greater than the spread over the first four distances, so the points in a graph of s against t^2 will be very bunched at the lower end.

How do we overcome this? If $s \propto t^2$, then $\sqrt{s} \propto t$, so a graph of $\sqrt{s}$ against t should be a straight line, with roughly equally spaced points.

Reason 2: If one of the variables, e.g. x, has a systematic error, ε, of unknown size, then plotting that as the linear variable should still give a straight line and the intercept on the x-axis will be $-\varepsilon$.

For example, simple theory suggests that the resonance frequency, f, of a pipe with one open end is related its the length, l, by the equation

$$f = \frac{c}{4l}$$

so a graph of f against $1/l$ should be a straight line. More complete theory suggests there is an end correction, ε, to be applied to the length. This gives

quickfire 6.6

You are investigating $P = I^2 R$ and have readings of P, for a series of nicely spaced values of I ranging from 0.1 A to 2 A. What graph should you plot and why?

quickfire 6.7

What graphs would give a straight line if you are investigating

$T = 2\pi\sqrt{\dfrac{m}{k}}$ for constant k? Which one would you use if your readings were for $m = 100, 200, 300, 400$ and 500 g?

quickfire 6.8

How would your answer to QF6.7 be different if you suspected that the times T were subject to a systematic error?

$$f = \frac{c}{4(l + \varepsilon)}.$$

If we rearrange the equation: $l = \frac{c}{4f} - \varepsilon$, so a graph of l against $1/f$ should be a straight line whereas a graph of f against $1/l$ is not. [See Test Yourself 6.2 Q9.]

(b) Equations of the form $y^m = kx^n + c$

A graph of y^m against x^n will be a straight line of gradient k and intercept c on the y^m axis. [See Test Yourself 6.2 Q7.]

(c) More complicated relationships

It is not possible here to deal with all the possible relationships but looking at a few will reveal some useful rules. So we'll consider two particular equations.

(i) $s = ut + \frac{1}{2}at^2$, where the variables are s and t.

The problem is that t appears twice on the right-hand side – once as t and once as t^2.

If we divide both sides by t we get: $\frac{s}{t} = u + \frac{1}{2}at$

Comparing this to $y = mx + c$, if we plot $\frac{s}{t}$ on the vertical [y] axis and t on the horizontal axis, we should get a straight line with a gradient $\frac{1}{2}a$ and an intercept of u on the $\frac{s}{t}$-axis. Let's just look at that again:

$$\left(\frac{s}{t}\right) = \frac{1}{2}a\left(t\right) + u$$
$$y = m\,x + c$$

The ovals show how the variables are related in the two equations and the arrows show the gradient and intercept.

(ii) $V = \frac{ER}{R + r}$, where the variables are V and R.

Again the problem is that R appears twice on the right-hand side, once in the top line and once in the bottom.

If we take the reciprocal of both sides we get $\quad \frac{1}{V} = \frac{R + r}{ER}$

Splitting the fraction on the right $\quad \frac{1}{V} = \frac{R}{ER} + \frac{r}{ER}$

Rearranging slightly $\quad \frac{1}{V} = \frac{r}{E} \times \frac{1}{R} + \frac{1}{E}$

So a graph of $\frac{1}{V}$ against $\frac{1}{R}$ should be a straight with a gradient $\frac{r}{E}$ and an intercept of $\frac{1}{E}$ on the $\frac{1}{V}$-axis. From the gradient and intercept, we can find E and r.

Conclusion: If you can re-arrange the equation so that there is only one variable [or cluster of variables] on each side and that variable appears only once on each side, it will then be in a form which can be plotted to give a linear graph.

(iii) A one-off case.

When a light ray passes between two materials, 1 and 2, the angle, θ, to the normal changes and obeys the relationship $n_1 \sin\theta_1 = n_2 \sin\theta_2$, where n is the *refractive index* of a material and is defined by:

$$n = \frac{\text{speed of light in the material}}{\text{speed of light in a vacuum}}.$$

Hence a graph of $\sin\theta_2$ against $\sin\theta_1$ is a straight line through the origin, with a gradient of $\frac{n_1}{n_2}$ [See Test Yourself 6.2 Q16.]

quickfire 6.9

If $y^2 = \frac{ax^2 + b}{x}$, where a and b are constants, what plot should be a straight line?

quickfire 6.10

If $x = \frac{a\sqrt{x^2 + y^2}}{y}$, where a is a constant, what should a graph of $x^2 y^2$ against $x^2 + y^2$ be like?

Test Yourself 6.2

1 The table shows the measured pd, V, across a power supply for various values of the current, I.

I and V are related by the equation: $V = E - Ir$, where E is the emf of the supply and r is its internal resistance.

Plot a graph of V against I. Determine the gradient and intercept, and hence find the values of E and r.

I / A	V / V
0.10	6.10
0.25	5.87
0.35	5.79
0.50	5.60
0.70	5.41
0.80	5.31

2 The table shows the measured velocity, v, at various values of time, t, of a body undergoing uniform acceleration, a, from an initial velocity, u.

v and t are related by the equation: $v = u + at$, where a and u are constants.

Plot a graph of v against t. Determine the gradient and intercept, and hence find the values of a and u.

t / s	v / m s^{-1}
1.5	4.00
4.0	4.39
6.0	4.90
7.5	5.30
9.0	5.54
10.0	5.75

3 The table shows the measured values of the length, l, of a spring for various values of a suspended load, F.

The variables are related by the equation $F = k(l - l_0)$, where l_0 is the unloaded length of the spring and k is the spring constant. Plot a graph of F against l and determine the values of k and l_0.

F / N	l / cm
0.98	9.6
1.96	13.0
2.94	18.2
3.92	21.4
4.91	27.3
5.89	30.3

4 The table shows the measured values of the pressure, p, in a flask of air at various values of the Celsius temperature, θ.

The variables are related by: $p = p_0 + \alpha\theta$. Plot a graph of p against θ, determine p_0 and a value in °C for absolute zero – this is the temperature at which the pressure would be zero.

NB. Find absolute zero by calculation not by drawing.

θ / °C	p / atm
20	1.025
35	1.062
50	1.115
65	1.176
80	1.238
98	1.291

5 As question 1 but:

- the current is in mA
- the range of currents is small.

Taking the current axis from 50 mA to 75 mA and the voltage axis from 7.0 to 8.2 V, find the gradient and calculate the intercept on the V-axis as in 6.4.1. or 6.4.2.

I / mA	V / V
50	8.18
53	8.01
57	7.80
60	7.63
65	7.49
69	7.23
72	7.14

6   A car accelerates from rest with constant acceleration. Its position, s, varies with t as follows:

Time, t / s	2	3	5	7	10	12
Displacement, s / m	4.6	12.5	36.0	68.0	120	195

Plot a graph of $\sqrt{s}$ against t and use it to determine the acceleration. $\left[s = \frac{1}{2}at^2\right]$

7   A train accelerates at a constant acceleration. Its velocity, v, varies with displacement, s, as follows:

Displacement, s / m	500	1000	1500	2000	2500	3000
Velocity, v / m s^{-2}	26.5	30.3	35.8	39.4	41.8	46.0

Given the equation $v^2 = u^2 + 2as$, where a is the acceleration and u the initial velocity, draw a suitable graph and determine a and u.

8   The frequency, f, of standing waves on a stretched wire is inversely proportional to the length, l of the wire. A student investigates this using a sonometer and obtains the following results:

Frequency, f / Hz	512	480	426	384	341.3	320	288	256
Length, l / m	0.204	0.215	0.251	0.275	0.309	0.324	0.358	0.410

The relationship between f and l is: $f = \frac{c}{2l}$, where c is the speed of transverse waves on the wire. Plot a suitable graph to verify the relationship. Comment upon whether the results are consistent with f and l being inversely proportional and determine a value for c.

NB. Consider whether you should take the axes back to 0 or to use the results of Sections 6.4.1 and 6.4.2.

9   A student (possibly the same one as in Q8) uses a resonance tube to determine, c, the speed of sound in air. He determines the resonance length, l, for a range of frequencies, f, produced by a set of tuning forks. The results are:

Frequency / Hz	512	480	426	384	341.3	320	288	256
Length / cm	15.4	16.0	19.2	21.0	24.5	25.4	28.5	31.9

The relationship between f and l is $f = \frac{c}{4(l + \varepsilon)}$. By plotting a suitable graph [see Section 6.5.2], determine values for c and ε.

10 A student uses a simple pendulum to measure the acceleration dues to gravity, g, by measuring the period, T, over a range of values of length, l. The suspension point of the pendulum is not accessible so the true pendulum length is $l + \varepsilon$ where ε is unknown. The results are:

Measured length, l/m	0.200	0.400	0.600	0.800	1.000	1.200
Period, T / s	0.92	1.35	1.58	1.82	2.08	2.22

With the uncertainty in length, the expected relationship is $T = 2\pi\sqrt{\dfrac{l + \varepsilon}{g}}$. Plot a suitable graph to determine values for g and ε.

11 A student in North Wales investigates the inverse square law for gamma radiation. She measures the background radiation as 35.5 counts per minute (cpm).

She measures the count rate, r, with a gamma source at various values of measured distance, d. Her results are as follows:

Distance, d / cm	10	15	20	25	30	50	70
Count rate, r / cpm	460	240	155	115	89	54	47

The true rate, R, corrected for background relates to d by: $R = \dfrac{k}{(d + \varepsilon)^2}$, where ε is a correction to the length: ε arises because neither the position of the source within its holder nor the effective sensitive position in the Geiger–Müller tube is known. Plot a suitable graph to verify the inverse square law and determine values for k and ε, giving suitable units.

12. A torsional pendulum consists of a wooden bar with addition equal loads, m, positioned at equal distances l from the centre of mass. The bar is suspended from a wire and allowed to oscillate in a horizontal plane – see diagram.

The period, T, of oscillation depends upon l according to the equation: $T = \sqrt{\dfrac{I + 2ml^2}{k}}$, where I is a constant called the *moment of inertia* of the bar and k depends upon the torsional stiffness of the wire. A student investigates this, with masses $m = 0.100$ kg and obtains the following results.

Distance, l / m	0.100	0.140	0.180	0.200	0.220	0.240
Period, T / s	9.2	11.9	14.3	15.8	17.5	18.7

Plot a suitable graph to verify the relationship and find values for k and I, giving suitable units.

13. A *compound pendulum* consists of a wooden bar pivoted as shown. By drilling a set of holes, the distance y can be varied. The period of oscillation, T, varies with y as:

$$\frac{T}{2\pi} = \sqrt{\frac{k^2 + y^2}{gy}}$$

where k is a constant called the *radius of gyration* of the bar [note: $mk^2 = I$, the moment of inertia] and g the acceleration due to gravity.

The following results are taken:

y / m	0.200	0.300	0.400	0.500	0.600	0.700
T / s	2.15	1.93	1.87	1.90	1.89	1.98

Plot a suitable graph to verify the relationship and find values for k and g.

14. Various values of resistor, R are connected across a battery and the terminal pd, V, measured.

The relationship between V and R is $V = \dfrac{ER}{R + r}$, where E is the emf and r the internal resistance. The following results are obtained:

R / Ω	1.0	2.2	3.3	4.7	6.8	8.2
V / V	4.15	4.95	5.82	6.50	7.50	7.85

Plot a suitable graph and find values for E and r.

15. The object distance, u, image distance, v, and the focal length, f, of a lens are related by the equation

$$\frac{1}{u} + \frac{1}{v} = \frac{1}{f}$$

A student obtained the following data for a lens:

u / cm	100	50	25	20	16	12	10
v / cm	17.0	21.5	36.0	53.5	147	−60.0	−32.0

Plot a suitable graph to confirm the relationship and find a value for f.

[You can work either in cm or m.]

16. A student measures the angle to the normal of a light ray passing from water into a sample of glass. She varies the angle of incidence and obtains the following results.

θ_1 /°	10	20	30	45	60	75	85
θ_2 /°	8	16	24	35	43	52	53

Plot a graph of $\sin\theta_2$ against $\sin\theta_1$, verify that the relationship is proportional and find a value for the speed of light in the glass.

Data: speed of light in a vacuum = 3.00×10^8 m s⁻¹; refractive index of water = 1.33

6.6 Proportionality

The idea of proportion is very useful in physics and mathematics. If an increase in one quantity by a factor, e.g. × 2, produces an increase by the same factor in another quantity, the two quantities are said to be [*directly*] *proportional*. The word 'directly' is often omitted.

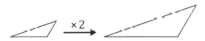

The second triangle is just a scaled-up version of the first, by a factor of 2. In scaling up, the sides expand in proportion to one another. The horizontal side increases by a factor of 2 and so do the other two sides.

A physics example: If a car is travelling at a constant speed, the distance it travels is proportional to the time: if it travels 80 km in 2 hours, it will travel 120 km in 3 hours [both × 1.5]. Another way of looking at this is that the ratio of the two quantities is the same:

In this case: $\dfrac{80\text{ km}}{2\text{ h}} = \dfrac{120\text{ km}}{3\text{ h}} = 40$ km/h [in this case, the ratio is the speed].

Similarly, the mass of a substance is proportional to its volume – the ratio is the density. The symbol '$\propto$' is used to denote proportionality: $m \propto V$ reads 'm is [directly] proportional to V.'

Inverse proportion also occurs. This is where an increase in one quantity by a factor, produces a **decrease** by the same factor in another quantity.

Example: Wavelength and frequency of electromagnetic waves – if the frequency is doubled, the wavelength is halved, i.e. $f \times 2 \rightarrow \lambda \div 2$.

Another way of describing this is to say the frequency is directly proportional to '1 / the wavelength'.

Proportionality and graphs

If x and y are directly proportional, a graph of y against x [or x against y!] is a straight line **through the origin**, i.e. direct proportionality is a special case of a linear relationship.

If x and y are inversely proportional, i.e. $y \propto \dfrac{1}{x}$, a graph of y against x is just the $y = kx^{-1}$ graph that we met in 6.5.1(c). One thing to notice is that all rectangles drawn underneath the graph as shown have the same area because $xy = k$.

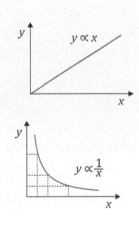

Pointer

If $y = kx^2$, then $y \propto x^2$. If we multiply x by 2, y is multiplied by $2^2 = 4$.

Pointer

If $y \propto \dfrac{1}{x^2}$, multiplying x by 2 will divide y by 4.

quickfire 6.11

Write $y = kx^3$ as a proportionality. What happens to y if x is **halved**?

quickfire 6.12

$y \propto \dfrac{1}{x^4}$. What happens to y if x is divided by 4?

quickfire 6.13

If $y \propto x$ and if $y = 2.5$ when $x = 1.5$, what is the value of y when $x = 6$?

quickfire 6.14

If $y \propto x^{-1}$ and if $y = 10$ when $x = 0.3$, what is the value of y when $x = 0.1$?

Chapter 7

Vectors

7.1 Introduction

Many physical quantities, such as force and motion, are directional. We refer to them as *vector quantities*, or just vectors. Quantities with no direction, such as mass or volume are *scalars*. The rules for handling vectors are different from those that apply to scalars: a force of 3 N and a force of 4 N might combine to give a force of 7 N, or 1 N or anything in between, depending on the directions of the forces. A vector quantity has a magnitude [i.e. a number × a unit] and a direction, e.g.

- a force of 55 N vertically upwards

- an acceleration of 3 m s^{-2} northwards.

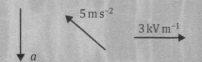

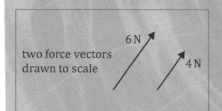

two force vectors drawn to scale

We distinguish between vectors and scalars by writing vectors in **bold** letters, e.g. **F**, **v**, unlike scalars, which will be non-bold *italic* as before, e.g. *m*, *V*. In handwriting you can use a wavy line under a letter, e.g. $\underset{\sim}{F}$ or $\underset{\sim}{v}$. This wavy line is just a printer's mark for a bold letter. The magnitude of a vector quantity is the non-bold italic letter, *F* or *v*.

In diagrams we show vectors as arrows. Sometimes vector diagrams are drawn to scale, in which case the length of the arrow is used to represent the magnitude of the vector. Vectors can have any orientation in 3-dimensional space, though many examples in A-level Physics make use of only one or two spatial dimensions, which makes diagrammatic representation useful.

Before we have a look at the mathematics of combining vector quantities, we need to establish a basic rule for multiplying vectors by scalars:

For any vector, **a**, the vector 2**a** has twice the magnitude and is **in the same direction**. Similarly the vector $\frac{1}{5}$**a** is one fifth as big and in the same direction.

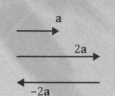

The vector –2**a** is twice as big as **a** and **in the opposite direction**.

e.g. **F** = *m***a**. The equation has two aspects:

1. *F* = *ma*, i.e. the magnitude of **F** = *m* × the magnitude of **a**.

2. The direction of **F** is the same as that of **a**.

7.2 Adding vectors

7.2.1 Triangles and parallelograms

Pointer

Don't use scale drawings to solve vector problems unless the question asks you to.

quickfire 7.1

v = 35 m s^{-1} northeast. What is –10**v**?

The diagram shows two vectors, **u** and **v**. The grid is drawn to enable you to follow the addition process and copy it using graph paper. Assuming that the two vectors are of the same type, e.g. two velocities or two forces, we ask what is their combined effect. We call this the *resultant* and write the process as:

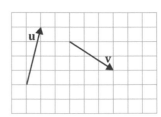

$$R = u + v.$$

The next two diagrams show two ways of finding the resultant vector.

Notice that in both methods, the positions of the two vectors, **u** and **v**, are changed in order to add them up. The vectors' positions on the diagrams don't necessarily correspond to their position in the physical problem – the same goes for the resultant, **R.** The two methods give the same answer and which you use is a matter of taste.

Example A illustrates the two approaches for a simple case.

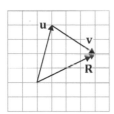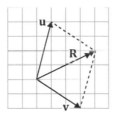

Example A:

Two forces are applied at 90° to each other as shown. What is their resultant?

The two approaches give these diagrams:

From the right-angled triangle:

$R = \sqrt{100^2 + 80^2} = 128$ N

and $\phi = \tan^{-1}\left(\dfrac{80}{100}\right) = 38.7°$

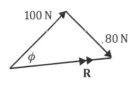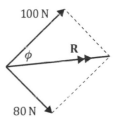

So the resultant is 128 N at an angle of 38.7° below the 100 N force [or 6.3° above the horizontal].

Clearly, R, the magnitude of **R,** can never be greater than $u + v$.

Some special cases:

(a) The two vectors are in **the same direction**:

The magnitudes of the vectors add up, i.e.

$R = u + v$.

The direction is unchanged.

(b) The vectors are in **opposite directions**:

$R = |u - v|$, i.e. the positive difference

The direction of **R** is that of the larger of **u** and **v**.

(c) The vectors are at **right angles**:

The magnitude, R, of the resultant of **u** and **v** (using Pythagoras' theorem) is:

$R = \sqrt{u^2 + v^2}$

The angle θ is given by $\tan \theta = \dfrac{v}{u}$, so we can express the resultant vector, **R** by:

$\mathbf{R} = \sqrt{u^2 + v^2}$ at $\tan^{-1}\dfrac{v}{u}$ to the vector **u.**

(d) Two vectors of equal magnitude at 120°.

Because of the angle and the fact that u and v are equal, the two triangles are equilateral. So

$R = u = v$

The direction of R is 60° to $\boldsymbol{u}$.

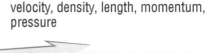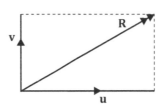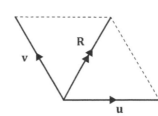

> **Pointer**
>
> Energy is a scalar but potential energy can be either + or –.

> **quickfire** 7.2
>
> Identify the vectors and scalars from: velocity, density, length, momentum, pressure

> **Pointer**
>
> Velocity is a vector – its magnitude is speed.

> **Pointer**
>
> Distance is the magnitude of displacement.

> **quickfire** 7.3
>
> $u = 10\,\mathrm{m\,s^{-1}}$ due North; $v = 4\,\mathrm{m\,s^{-1}}$ due South. What is **u + v**?

To find the resultant of two vectors at an arbitrary angle to each other, we need to apply the cosine and sine rules [see Sections 5.7.1 and 5.7.2]. Example B shows the method using a specific example. There is no point in learning a general formula.

quicKfire 7.4

Find the resultant of 5 N and 12 N if

(a) the forces are in the same direction,

(b) the forces are in opposite directions,

(c) the forces are at right angles.

quicKfire 7.5

Find the resultant force.

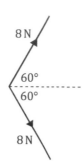

8 N

60°
60°

8 N

quicKfire 7.6

Repeat QF 7.5 if the angles are both 30°.

quicKfire 7.7

The forces are in equilibrium. Use the triangle of forces to find *T* and *F*.

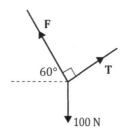

F

60° ⊢ T

100 N

quicKfire 7.8

The forces are in equilibrium. Find **F** and **R**.

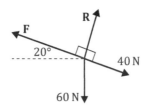

R

F

20°

40 N

60 N

Example B:

Find the resultant, **R**, of the vectors shown.

Working: consider the triangle △ABC:

Side BC = 15 N

Angle $\hat{C}$ = 120°

Applying the cosine rule:

$$R^2 = 10^2 + 15^2 - (2 \times 10 \times 15 \cos 120°)$$

$$\therefore\ R = 21.8 \text{ N to 3 s.f.}$$

Apply the sine rule to find Â: $\dfrac{\sin \hat{A}}{15} = \dfrac{\sin 120°}{21.8}$, $\therefore \hat{A} = \sin^{-1}\left(\dfrac{15 \times \sin 120°}{21.8}\right) = 36.6°$

Answer: The resultant is 21.8 N at an angle of 36.6° to the 10 N force.

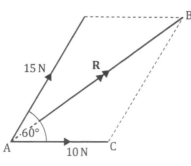

15 N   R   B

.60°

A   10 N   C

7.2.2 Statics – forces in equilibrium

In many practical situations the forces on an object combine to give a zero resultant, so the object is either stationary or moving at a constant velocity, e.g. a stationary building or a skydiver at terminal velocity. The object, and the forces, are said to be *in equilibrium*.

Consider the system of three forces acting on a particle O. Under what conditions would they be in equilibrium?

In equilibrium:

$$\mathbf{F}_1 + \mathbf{F}_2 + \mathbf{F}_3 = 0 \qquad (1)$$

If we use the head-to-tail method of vector addition, this means that the three forces must combine to give a closed triangle. This is known as the *triangle of forces*.

Another way of looking at the problem is to re-arrange equation (1) to give:

$$\mathbf{F}_3 = - (\mathbf{F}_1 + \mathbf{F}_2) \qquad (2)$$

i.e. **F**₃ is minus the resultant of **F**₁ and **F**₂.
Alternatively **F**₂ = – (**F**₁ + **F**₃) etc.

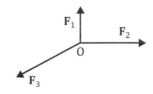

F₁   F₂

O

F₃

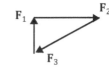

F₁   F₂

F₃

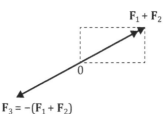

F₁ + F₂

O

F₃ = –(F₁ + F₂)

Example C:

A ball of mass 10 kg is suspended from a wire. What horizontal force will pull the ball to one side so the wire makes an angle of 30° to the vertical?

On the diagram, **W** is the weight of the ball (98.1 N) and **T** is the tension in the wire.

Drawing a triangle of forces: $\tan 30° = \dfrac{F}{98.1}$

$$\therefore\ F = 56.6 \text{ N}$$

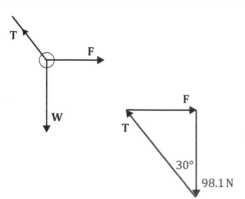

T   F

W

F

T

30°

98.1 N

The two diagrams in Example C are referred to as the *space diagram*, which shows the physical arrangement of the forces, and the *force diagram*, which is for calculating the equilibrium conditions. In this case, it is much easier to solve the problem using the triangle of forces than applying the parallelogram rule.

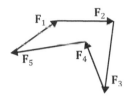

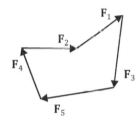

We can use the same idea for the case when a particle is in equilibrium under the action of more than three forces, in which case, the figure is called the *polygon of forces*. The diagrams above illustrate a system of five forces in equilibrium. Note that the order of the forces in the polygon is not significant but it is more convenient to drawn them so the arrows do not cross.

This method of combination is rather cumbersome when more than three forces are involved, (see Example D). In such cases, the powerful tool of resolving the forces into components is a more straightforward approach, as illustrated in Section 7.3.

quickfire 7.9

The forces are in equilibrium. Find T and θ.

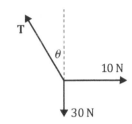

Example D:

A hiker walks 10 km N followed by 10 km E and 10 km SE. What displacement will take the hiker back to the starting point? [Equivalent to a forces-in-equilibrium problem]

The diagram shows the displacements; s is the return vector.

$DB = 10 + 10\sin 45° = 17.07$ km [4 s.f.]

$DE = 10 - 10\cos 45° = 2.93$ km [3 s.f.]

$\therefore \quad s = \sqrt{17.07^2 + 2.93^2} = 17.3$ km [3 s.f.]. $\tan\phi = \dfrac{2.93}{17.07}$, $\therefore \phi = 9.74°$ [3 s.f.].

So the return displacement is 17.3 km 9.74° S of W.

7.2.3 Combining vectors in 3 dimensions

The techniques in 7.2.1 for adding vectors can be extended to three dimensions. A relatively simple example of three vectors at right angles is shown in the diagram.

We can build up the answer in two stages. First we find $\mathbf{u} + \mathbf{v}$ as before. This is shown in the second diagram.

We then add $\mathbf{w}$ to $\mathbf{u} + \mathbf{v}$ using the same process. In this diagram, the fine dotted lines have been drawn in to show that the resultant vector is the diagonal of the 3D box [rectangular parallelepiped] defined by the vectors.

With the three vectors at right angles, the magnitude of the resultant, R, is given by:

$$R^2 = u^2 + v^2 + w^2$$

In fact there are easier ways of combining 3D vectors which also handle any number of vectors. These are developed in the next section.

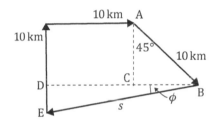

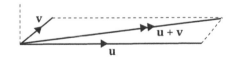

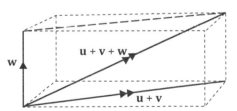

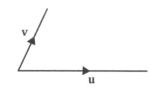

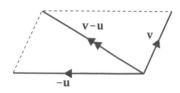

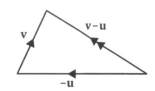

7.2.4 Subtracting vectors

If the volume of a gas changes from V_1 to V_2 then the change in volume is $V_2 - V_1$.

Similarly, if the velocity of an object changes from **u** to **v**, the change in velocity is **v** − **u**.

As in scalar algebra, subtracting is the same thing as adding the negative quantity, i.e. **v** − **u** = **v** + (−**u**).

The vector −**u** has the same magnitude as **u** and is in the opposite direction. The diagonal of the parallelogram in the second diagram is thus **v** − **u**.

You will see that the diagonal in the second diagram has the same length and direction as the diagonal in the third diagram, i.e. the vectors are the same. The second and third diagrams give alternative ways of subtracting **u** from **v**.

Example E involves subtracting two vectors and using the result in a subsequent calculation.

Example E:

The velocity of a microlight plane changes from 30 m s⁻¹ due North to 40 m s⁻¹ due East over a period of 10 s. If the mass of the plane is 300 kg, calculate the mean resultant force on the plane over this period.

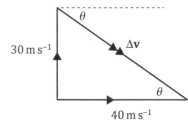

The diagram shows the velocities and Δ**v**, the change in velocity.

Using Pythagoras' theorem: $(\Delta v)^2 = 30^2 + 40^2$

∴ $\Delta v = 50 \text{ m s}^{-1}$.

The direction of Δ**v** is given by $\theta = \tan^{-1}\left(\dfrac{30}{40}\right) = 36.9°$

The mean acceleration $\mathbf{a} = \dfrac{\Delta v}{t} = 5 \text{ m s}^{-2}$. The mean resultant force $\mathbf{F} = m\mathbf{a} = 300 \times 5 = 1500 \text{ N}$. The direction of the resultant force is the same as the direction of Δ**v**, i.e. 36.9° S of E.

quickfire ▶ 7.10

Calculate the change in velocity, $\mathbf{v}_1 - \mathbf{v}_2$.

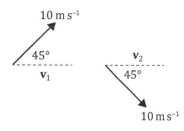

7.2.5 Centripetal acceleration and force

Consider a particle moving with a steady speed, v, in a circle of radius r. The velocity, **v**, is not constant because its direction is constantly changing. In other words the particle is accelerating. We shall show that the magnitude of the acceleration is given by $a = \dfrac{v^2}{r}$ and that the direction of **a** is towards the centre of the circle.

The circumference of the circle is $2\pi r$, so the period $T = \dfrac{2\pi r}{v}$ and the angular speed $\omega = \dfrac{2\pi}{T} = \dfrac{v}{r}$. Note that we are expressing angles in radians.

Consider the change in velocity Δ**v** between **P** and **Q**, at angle θ before and after the vertical position, **O**, in the diagram.

Δ**v** = $2v \sin\theta$ vertically downwards.[●]

The time, t, between **P** and **Q**, $t = \dfrac{2\theta}{\omega} = \dfrac{2\theta r}{v}$.

∴ the mean acceleration $\langle\mathbf{a}\rangle = \dfrac{\Delta v}{t} = 2v\sin\theta \times \dfrac{v}{2\theta r} = \dfrac{v^2}{r}\dfrac{\sin\theta}{\theta}$ vertically downwards.

The ratio $\dfrac{\sin\theta}{\theta} \to 1$ as $\theta \to 0$ [see Section 8.2.4] so the acceleration at **O** itself is given by $a = \dfrac{v^2}{r}$,

---

[●] Note that this is a vector equation – the direction of the vector is vertically downwards.

vertically downwards, i.e. towards the centre of the circle. We call this acceleration *centripetal acceleration*, meaning *acceleration towards the centre*. We conclude that the resultant force, **F**, on an object of mass m moving in a circle of radius r with a constant speed v is given by:

$\mathbf{F} = \dfrac{mv^2}{r}$ towards the centre of the circle – the *centripetal force*.

Example F:

A pendulum bob is suspended from a string of length l and is swung around in a horizontal circle so that the string makes an angle, θ, to the vertical. Show that the period, P, of the motion is given by:

$$P = 2\pi\sqrt{\frac{l\cos\theta}{g}}.$$

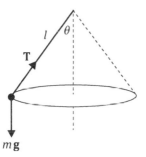

Let the bob have mass m and the radius of the circle be r.

The bob is in equilibrium in a vertical direction. $\therefore T\cos\theta = mg$ (1)

Using the centripetal force formula: $T\sin\theta = mr\omega^2 = m(l\sin\theta)\omega^2$ $\therefore T = ml\omega^2$ (2)

Divide (1) by (2): $\cos\theta = \dfrac{mg}{ml\omega^2}$,   so $\omega = \sqrt{\dfrac{g}{l\cos\theta}}$.

$\therefore$ $P = \dfrac{2\pi}{\omega} = 2\pi\sqrt{\dfrac{l\cos\theta}{g}}$ QED.

7.3 Analysing vectors

This section introduces graphical methods of handling vectors. These methods are very useful in simplifying many physics problems.

7.3.1 Unit vectors

A unit vector is a vector with a magnitude of 1. When analysing vectors in three dimensions, it is useful to define unit vectors along the x, y and z directions.[2] These are identified as **i**, **j** and **k** (some maths books call them $\mathbf{e}_x$, $\mathbf{e}_y$ and $\mathbf{e}_z$ or $\mathbf{e}_1$, $\mathbf{e}_2$ and $\mathbf{e}_3$). For 2D work, we shall just use **i** and **j**.

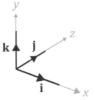

7.3.2 Horizontal and vertical components of vectors

Two vectors at right angles can be added to produce an equivalent single vector, the resultant vector. This was covered in Section 7.2. The opposite process, known as resolution, is also useful.

The first diagram shows a vector **a**, which acts at an angle θ to the horizontal. This vector can be considered to be the sum of two vectors, $\mathbf{a}_x$ and $\mathbf{a}_y$ as shown in the second diagram.

$\mathbf{a} = \mathbf{a}_x + \mathbf{a}_y$

Vector $\mathbf{a}_x$ is called the *horizontal* or *x component* of **a**.

Similarly $\mathbf{a}_y$ is called the *vertical* or *y component* of **a**.

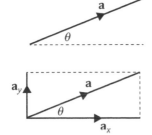

Applying trigonometry to the right angled triangles we get $a_x = a\cos\theta$ and $a_y = a\sin\theta$. The values a_x and a_y are called the *scalar components* of **a**; $\mathbf{a}_x$ and $\mathbf{a}_y$ are the *vector components*.

---

[2]   Note that the system is called the *right-hand Cartesian system*. 'Cartesian' after René Descartes and 'right-handed' because a rotation from x to y makes an imaginary right-handed screw advance along z.

Using the unit vectors we have already introduced: $\mathbf{a} = a_x\mathbf{i} + a_y\mathbf{j}$.

Example G shows how resolving into components can be used to simplify a problem. There are four forces at a variety of angles; finding their components allows them to be added easily. Check that you understand each stage of the calculation.

Example G:

Find the resultant of these forces:

Take the x direction to be horizontal to the right and the y direction vertically upwards.

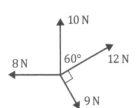

Sum of the x components = $12\cos 30° + 9\cos 60° - 8 = 6.89$ N [3 s.f.]

[Note that the 10 N force has an x component of 0; the 8 N force has an x component of -8 N]

Sum of the y components = $10 + 12\cos 60° - 9\cos 30° = 8.21$ N [3.s.f.]

So the resultant $\mathbf{R} = 6.89\mathbf{i} + 8.21\mathbf{j}$ and, using Pythagoras' theorem:

$$R = \sqrt{6.89^2 + 8.21^2} = 10.7 \text{ N}$$

and the angle to the horizontal is $\tan^{-1}\left(\dfrac{8.21}{6.89}\right) = 50.0°$.

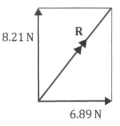

Components can also be used to find the *equilibrant*, the additional force which will produce a system in equilibrium. As in Section 7.2.2, the system is in equilibrium when the resultant is zero. In terms of components that can be restated as, '**a system is in equilibrium when the sum of the components in any direction is zero**'. In Example G, the equilibrant, **F**, must be $-6.89\mathbf{i} - 8.21\mathbf{j}$, i.e. a force of 10.7 N to the left at 50.0° below the horizontal.

7.3.3 Components in other directions

Depending on the physical problem it is often useful to resolve in directions other than horizontal and vertical to define components. For motion entirely in a horizontal plane, for example, it could be appropriate to define East as the x direction and North as the y direction.

Many questions involve motion and/or forces on an inclined plane, in which case it often simplifies the problem to resolve parallel and perpendicular to the plane. The diagram shows forces on an object which is resting on an inclined plane.

W is the weight, **F** the frictional force which is acting up the plane (which means that the object is either at rest or sliding down the slope) and **C** is the contact force acting at right angles to the plane.[3]

What are the components of the forces?

- **C** is in the y direction so $C_y = C$ and $C_x = 0$.
- **F** is in the $-x$ direction so $F_y = 0$ and $F_x = -F$
- **W** is vertical – its angle to the x direction is $90° - \theta$ and its angle to the $-y$ direction is θ, so $W_x = W\sin\theta$ and $W_y = -W\cos\theta$

From this analysis the resultant force, $\mathbf{R} = (-F + W\sin\theta)\mathbf{i} + (C - W\cos\theta)\mathbf{j}$.

This doesn't look particularly simple but Example H shows that is can make a problem very straightforward to solve.

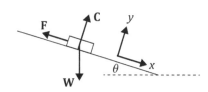

quickfire ▶ 7.11

Calculate the North and East components of the velocity.

quickfire ▶ 7.12

Split the velocity in QF 7.11 into South and East components.

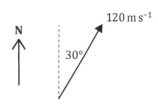

---

[3] The force **C** is often labelled **R** and referred to as the *normal reaction*. The author prefers **C** because of the possible confusion with the Newton 3rd law reaction.

Example H:

Calculate the acceleration down the slope of a sledge of mass 200 kg, which is on a snow slope of 20°, if the frictional force is 360 N [g = 9.81 m s^{-2}].

Resolve parallel to the slope:

Resultant force down the slope = $W \sin 20° - 360 = 200 \times 9.81 \sin 20° - 360 = 311$ N [3 s.f.]

$$\text{Acceleration} = \frac{\text{resultant force}}{\text{mass}} = \frac{311}{200} = 1.56 \text{ m s}^{-2}$$

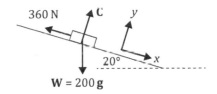

It is worth looking at the physics of Example H. Because the sledge cannot move at right angles to the slope, the components in the y direction must sum to zero (see Quickfire 7.13). It is only the components, which are parallel to the slope, that influence the acceleration; hence we can ignore **C** entirely: resolving in this way allows us to do just that.

quickfire 7.13

By resolving at 90° to the slope, find the force **C** in Example H.

7.4 Vector equations

7.4.1 Principles of vector equations

Many equations in physics are vector equations, i.e. they relate vector quantities, though often we only consider one-dimensional applications and so their vector nature is restricted to + and −.

Example: **F** = m**a**

We can write this equation in terms of the x, y and z components, as follows:

$$F_x\mathbf{i} + F_y\mathbf{j} + F_z\mathbf{k} = m(a_x\mathbf{i} + a_y\mathbf{j} + a_z\mathbf{k})$$

This equation can only be correct if it is so for each of the x, y and z components separately, i.e.

$$F_x = ma_x \quad \text{and} \quad F_y = ma_y \quad \text{and} \quad F_z = ma_z$$

In other words, by writing the equation in terms of the components, we are back in the familiar territory of our one-dimensional equations.

The equations of motion for constant acceleration are also vector equations.[●] We'll write the displacement vector s as $x\mathbf{i} + y\mathbf{j} + z\mathbf{k}$. Two of the equations of motion become:

$$x\mathbf{i} + y\mathbf{j} + z\mathbf{k} = (u_x\mathbf{i} + u_y\mathbf{j} + u_z\mathbf{k})t + \tfrac{1}{2}(a_x\mathbf{i} + a_y\mathbf{j} + a_z\mathbf{k})t^2 \text{ and}$$

$$v_x\mathbf{i} + v_y\mathbf{j} + v_z\mathbf{k} = (u_x\mathbf{i} + u_y\mathbf{j} + u_z\mathbf{k}) + (a_x\mathbf{i} + a_y\mathbf{j} + a_z\mathbf{k})t$$

We'll apply these to the motion of projectiles but first we'll consider a three-dimensional case in Example I. This is just to illustrate the principles involved – you are unlikely to meet this sort of example in an A-level Physics paper.

quickfire 7.14

A stone is thrown at 15 m s^{-1} at an angle of 35° to the horizontal. What are the horizontal and vertical components of this velocity?

quickfire 7.15

Write the velocity in QF7.14 in the form $\mathbf{v} = v_x\mathbf{i} + v_y\mathbf{j}$, where **i** is the horizontal unit vector and **j** the vertical.

quickfire 7.16

$\mathbf{F_1} = 5\mathbf{i} + 8\mathbf{j}$ and $\mathbf{F_2} = 7\mathbf{i} + 8\mathbf{j}$. $\mathbf{F} = \mathbf{F_1} + \mathbf{F_2}$. Find **F**.

quickfire 7.17

For the force **F** in QF7.16, find F and the angle between **F** and **i**.

Example I:

A rocket with a low-thrust ion drive is travelling in the gravitational field of a planet.

The velocity, **u** in m s^{-1}, at time t = 0 is **u** = 500**i** + 400**j** + 200**k**.

The drive produces a constant acceleration in m s^{-2} of **a** = 0.1**i** + 0.1**j** + 0.1**k**.

The gravitational field of the planet produces an acceleration **g** = −0.5**k**.

$g_z = -0.5$ m s^{-2}

Find (a) the velocity, **v** and (b) the position **s** after 1000 s.

(a) **v** = **u** + **a**t, so **v** = (500 + 0.1×1000)**i** + (400 + 0.1×1000)**j** + (200 +(0.1−0.5)×1000)**k**

$$= 600\mathbf{i} + 500\mathbf{j} - 200\mathbf{k}$$

(b) Applying **s** = **u**t + $\tfrac{1}{2}$**a**t^2 gives (in km) **s** = 550**i** + 450**j** , i.e. s_z = 0 at t = 1000 s.

[●] Apart from $v^2 = u^2 + 2as$. This is a scalar equation. It involves the scalar product (see Section 7.6.2) and can be written $v^2 = u^2 + 2\mathbf{a.s}$.

7.4.2 Projectiles

We'll apply the above principles to the standard A-level topic of projectiles, which are objects moving freely under gravity. For dense objects moving relatively slowly air resistance can be ignored.[5]

We choose a co-ordinate system, x, y and z as shown, with the initial velocity in the x,y plane. Because there are no sideways forces, the motion takes places entirely within this plane and the z co-ordinate can be ignored.

If the projectile is thrown with velocity $\mathbf{u}$ at θ to the horizontal, then

$\mathbf{u} = u_x\mathbf{i} + u_y\mathbf{j}$, where $u_x = u\cos\theta$ and $u_y = u\sin\theta$.

The acceleration vector, $\mathbf{a} = -g\mathbf{j}$.

To find the velocity, $\mathbf{v}$, at a later time, we apply $\mathbf{v} = \mathbf{u} + \mathbf{a}t$.

This gives $\mathbf{v} = u_x\mathbf{i} + (u_y - gt)\mathbf{j}$.

It is worth separating out the components:

$\mathbf{i}$ (horizontal) component: $v_x = u_x$, i.e. constant horizontal velocity

$\mathbf{j}$ (vertical) component: $v_y = u_y - gt$, i.e. uniformly accelerated (downwards acceleration)

Example J:

A stone is catapulted with a velocity of $25\ \text{m s}^{-1}$ at an angle of $40°$ to the horizontal. What is its velocity after 2 s?

Initial velocity: $u_x = 25\cos 40° = 19.15\ \text{m s}^{-1}$ [4 s.f.];

$\qquad\qquad\qquad u_y = 25\sin 40° = 16.07\ \text{m s}^{-1}$ [4 s.f.]

$v_x = u_x = 19.15\ \text{m s}^{-1}$; $v_y = u_y - gt = 16.07 - 9.81 \times 2 = -3.55\ \text{m s}^{-1}$
[i.e. downwards $3.55\ \text{m s}^{-1}$]

$\qquad v = \sqrt{v_x^2 + v_y^2} = \sqrt{19.15^2 + (-3.55)^2} = 19.5\ \text{m s}^{-1}$ [3 s.f.]

The direction angle $\phi = \tan^{-1}\left(\dfrac{3.55}{19.15}\right) = 10.5°$

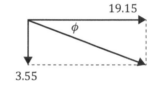

Answer: The velocity is $19.5\ \text{m s}^{-1}$ at an angle of $10.5°$ below the horizontal.

Moving on to the displacement vector, applying $\mathbf{s} = \mathbf{u}t + \frac{1}{2}\mathbf{a}t^2$, we have:

$$x\mathbf{i} + y\mathbf{j} = (u_x\mathbf{i} + u_y\mathbf{j})t + \tfrac{1}{2}(-g\mathbf{j})t^2.$$

$\mathbf{i}$ (horizontal) component: $x = u_x t$, i.e. the projectile moves with constant horizontal velocity.

$\mathbf{j}$ (vertical) component: $y = u_y t - \frac{1}{2}gt^2$

Advice: It is not worth learning equations such as $y = u_y t - \frac{1}{2}gt^2$. It is more sensible to understand the process of deriving them. Example J is extended in the next example.

Example K:

(a) When and (b) where does the projectile in Example J reach its highest point?

(a) The projectile is at its highest point when it is travelling horizontally, i.e. when $v_y = 0$.

$v_y = u_y - gt$, with $u_y = 25\sin 40° = 16.07\ \text{m s}^{-1}$.

$\therefore t = \dfrac{0 - 16.07}{-9.81} = 1.638\ \text{s}$ [4 s.f.]

---

quickfire ▶ 7.18

A stone is projected (in m s^{-1}) at $\mathbf{u} = 15\mathbf{i} + 30\mathbf{j}$. Find $\mathbf{v}$ the velocity at $t = 2\ \text{s}$. [Take $g = 10\ \text{m s}^{-1}$]

⌃ Grade boost

The positive y-direction can be defined as downwards, in which case $y = u_y t + \frac{1}{2}gt^2$.
If $y > 0$, the projectile is then **below** the starting point.
If $y < 0$ the projectile is **above** the starting point.

---

5 Other simplifying assumptions are that the range and maximum altitude of the projectile are small enough that the curvature of the Earth can be neglected; the gravitation field considered uniform and the rotation of the Earth neglected.

(b) At the highest point, $x = u_x t$, where $u_x = 25 \cos 40° = 19.15 \text{ m s}^{-1}$.

$\therefore x = 19.15 \times 1.638 = 31.4 \text{ m [3 s.f.]}$

$y = u_y t - \frac{1}{2}gt^2 = 16.07 \times 1.638 - \frac{1}{2}9.81 \times 1.638^2 = 13.2 \text{ m [3.s.f]}$

So the projectile reaches its highest point at 1.64 s, when its height is 13.2 m and the horizontal distance is 31.4 m from the starting point.

7.4.3 Trajectory and range of projectiles

From the previous section:

$$x = u_x t \tag{1}$$

and

$$y = u_y t - \frac{1}{2}gt^2 \tag{2}$$

Using equation (1), substitute for t in (2), giving $\quad y = u_y \dfrac{x}{u_x} - \dfrac{1}{2}g\left(\dfrac{x}{u_x}\right)^2$.

Substituting $u_x = u \cos \theta$ and $u_y = u \sin \theta$ we have $\quad y = x\dfrac{\sin \theta}{\cos \theta} - \dfrac{1}{2}\dfrac{g}{u^2 \cos^2 \theta}x^2 \tag{3}$

But $\dfrac{\sin \theta}{\cos \theta} = \tan \theta$, so we can write equation (3) as $\quad y = x \tan \theta - \dfrac{1}{2}\dfrac{g}{u^2 \cos^2 \theta}x^2 \tag{4}$

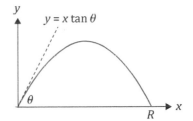

quickfire 7.19

Show that the equation

$y = x\tan\theta - \dfrac{1}{2}\dfrac{g}{u^2\cos^2\theta}x^2$

is homogeneous.

Equation (4) is a quadratic equation in x so it represents a parabola. The dotted graph is the path that the same projectile would take in the absence of gravity.

The range, R, of the projectile is the distance from the point of projection to the point of impact. We can calculate this from equation (3) by putting $y = 0$:

$$0 = R\frac{\sin \theta}{\cos \theta} - \frac{1}{2}\frac{g}{u^2 \cos^2 \theta}R^2$$

Multiplying by $\cos \theta$ and factorising: $R\left(\sin \theta - \dfrac{1}{2}\dfrac{g}{u^2 \cos \theta}R\right) = 0$

The solutions to this equation are $R = 0$ or $\sin \theta - \dfrac{1}{2}\dfrac{g}{u^2 \cos \theta}R = 0$.

The $R = 0$ solution represents the distance to the point of projection which is zero.

So the range is given by: $R = \dfrac{u^2\, 2 \sin \theta \cos \theta}{g} = \dfrac{u^2 \sin 2\theta}{g}$.

quickfire 7.20

Show that the formula for the range of a projectile, $R = \dfrac{u^2 \sin 2\theta}{g}$, is homogeneous.

Example L:

What angle of projection gives the maximum range?

Answer: The maximum value of $\sin 2\theta$ is 1 when $2\theta = 90°$, i.e. $\theta = 45°$. $R_{max} = \dfrac{u^2}{g}$.

7.5 Frames of reference

In these days of very smooth train travel and plane flight we know that, if we close our eyes, we cannot tell whether we are moving or not – as long as the motion is uniform. This means that if we carry out an experiment, such as measuring the time it takes for a ball to fall 1 m, we'll get the same answer if we are at rest, on a train, or on a plane – as long as these are moving with a constant velocity.[6] This means that it might be possible to simplify problems by changing how we are moving when we look at them.

---

[6] This is not quite correct because the acceleration due to gravity decreases very slowly with height [by about 0.03% per km near the surface of the Earth].

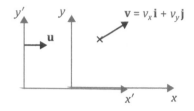

First some theory: we'll stick to two dimensions. Suppose a stationary observer sees an object moving with velocity **v** as shown. We call the x, y co-ordinate system the *frame of reference* of this observer. The velocity, **v′**, of the object as seen by a second observer who is moving at velocity **u** along the x-direction is given by:

$$\mathbf{v'} = (v_x - u)\mathbf{i} + v_y\mathbf{j}$$

If we can find a second observer who is moving steadily in such a way as to simplify a problem, we can now apply the above relationship. Here is a simple example.

Example M:

A perfectly elastic ball travels at 10 m s^{-1} towards a heavy flat object moving in the opposite direction at 20 m s^{-1} as shown.

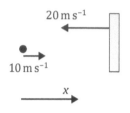

Calculate the velocity of rebound of the ball.

Consider the event, as observed by someone sitting on the wall:

In the observer's frame of reference, the initial velocity of the ball = 10 − (−20) = 30 m s^{-1}.

The ball is elastic so the rebound velocity, as seen from the wall = − 30 m s^{-1}.

Change back to the laboratory frame of reference: Rebound velocity = −30 − 20 = −50 m s^{-1}.

Example M concerned a system in which one of the objects, the wall, was considered to be effectively infinitely massive. A useful frame of reference, where this is not the case, is the *centre of mass* frame.

Consider a system of N particles. The masses of the particles are m_1, m_2 ..., their positions are $\mathbf{r}_1$, $\mathbf{r}_2$ ... and their velocities are $\mathbf{v}_1$, $\mathbf{v}_2$ etc.

The position, **r**, of the centre of mass is given by: $\mathbf{r} = \dfrac{m_1\mathbf{r}_1 + m_2\mathbf{r}_2 + ... m_N\mathbf{r}_N}{m_1 + m_2 + ... m_N}$

Because $\mathbf{v} = \dfrac{\Delta\mathbf{r}}{t}$, the velocity of the centre of mass is $\mathbf{v} = \dfrac{m_1\mathbf{v}_1 + m_2\mathbf{v}_2 + ... m_N\mathbf{v}_N}{m_1 + m_2 + ... m_N}$, i.e. the total momentum divided by the total mass. In the frame of reference which moves with the centre of mass, the total momentum of the particles is zero. Example N shows how this can be used to simplify a problem.

Example N:

A 2 kg object travelling at 10 m s^{-1} and a 5 kg object travelling at 11 m s^{-1} collide elastically head on. Calculate their velocities after colliding.

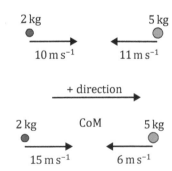

The velocity of the centre of mass $= \dfrac{(2 \times 10) - (5 \times 11)}{7} = -5$ m s^{-1}.

Subtracting −5 m s^{-1} to change to the CoM frame: $u_{2\,kg} = 15$ m s^{-1}; $u_{5\,kg} = -6$ m s^{-1}.

In this frame, let the velocities after collision be **v** and **w** respectively.

Applying conservation of momentum: $\quad\quad\quad 2v + 5w = 0 \quad\quad\quad$ (1)

Considering the kinetic energy: $\quad \frac{1}{2}2v^2 + \frac{1}{2}5w^2 = \frac{1}{2}(2 \times 15^2) + \frac{1}{2}(5 \times 6^2) = 315$ J,

$$\therefore 2v^2 + 5w^2 = 630 \quad\quad\quad (2)$$

Substitute $v = -\frac{5}{2}w$ from (1) into (2) gives: $2(-\frac{5}{2}w)^2 + 5w^2 = 630$, i.e. $17.5w^2 = 630$

$$\therefore w = \pm 6 \text{ m s}^{-1} \text{ in the CoM frame.}$$

Reject the −6 m s^{-1} solution because that is a 'no collision' solution.

$\therefore w = 6$ m s^{-1} and substitution into (1) gives $v = - 15$ ms^{-1}.

Finally, converting back to the laboratory frame [adding −5 m s^{-1} to each velocity] gives:

The 2 kg mass has a velocity of −20 m s^{-1} and the 5 kg mass has a velocity of +1 m s^{-1}.

quickfire ▶ 7.21

A ship is moving at **v** = 15**i** + 18**j**. What is the velocity in a frame of reference which moves with velocity −20**i** + 10**j** ?

Note that, in the centre of mass frame, the total kinetic energy is not the same as in the laboratory frame. In Example N, the total kinetic energy in the laboratory frame is 402.5 J; in the CoM frame it is 315 J. However the **change** of kinetic energy is the same whether we look at it in the 'laboratory frame', the centre of mass frame, or indeed in any other uniformly moving frame. This is investigated in the miscellaneous proofs chapter.

> **Pointer**
>
> In an elastic collision between two objects, the velocity of each object is reversed in the centre of mass frame.

7.6 Multiplication of vectors

We have already seen that the product $k\mathbf{v}$ is a vector of magnitude kv and in the same direction as **v**. We shall briefly investigate two ways in which two vectors can be multiplied together.

7.6.1 Scalar product

The scalar product, **a.b** of two vectors, also called the *dot product*, is a scalar quantity defined by

$$\mathbf{a.b} = ab\cos\theta,$$

where θ is the angle between the vectors.

Because $a\cos\theta$ is the component of a in the direction of b, we can think of this as:

a.b = (the component of **a** in the direction of **b**) × the magnitude of **b**.

Of course this is equally (the component of **b** in the direction of **a**) × the magnitude of **a**.

Example O:

If **i** and **j** are the unit vectors in the x- and y-directions respectively, calculate

(a) **i.i** (b) **i.j**.

(a) The magnitude of **i** = 1 and the angle between **i** and **i** = 0°. $\therefore$ **i.i** = 1 × 1 × cos 0° = 1

(b) The angle between **i** and **j** = 90°, cos 90° = 0. $\therefore$ **i.j** = 0

If we write the vectors a and b in terms of their components:

$$\mathbf{a} = a_x\mathbf{i} + a_y\mathbf{j} + a_z\mathbf{k} \quad \text{and} \quad \mathbf{b} = b_x\mathbf{i} + b_y\mathbf{j} + b_z\mathbf{k}$$

Then
$$\mathbf{a.b} = (a_x\mathbf{i} + a_y\mathbf{j} + a_z\mathbf{k}).(b_x\mathbf{i} + b_y\mathbf{j} + b_z\mathbf{k}).$$

We can multiply this out and remember that **i.i** = 1 etc. and **i.j** = 0 etc:

$\therefore$
$$\mathbf{a.b} = a_xb_x + a_yb_y + a_zb_z$$

If a force, **F**, moves its point of application by a displacement **d**, it does work. The work, W, done by the force is given by: $W = \mathbf{F.d}$ and similarly the power, P, developed by the force moving with velocity $\mathbf{v}$ is given by $P = \mathbf{F.v}$.

Example P:

A force, in newton, **F** = 30**i** + 40**j** pulls a sledge a displacement, in metre, **d** = 400**i** + 300**j**.

(a) Use the components to calculate the work done by **F**.

(b) Show that the formula $W = Fd\cos\theta$ gives the same answer, where θ is the angle between the vectors.

(a) $W = 30{\times}400 + 40{\times}300 = 24\,000$ J.

(b) $\mathbf{F} = \sqrt{30^2 + 40^2} = 50$ N at an angle of $\alpha = \tan^{-1}\left(\dfrac{40}{30}\right) = 53.13°$ to the x-axis.*

 In Example N, the change in kinetic energy is zero in both frames of reference.

$$\mathbf{d} = \sqrt{400^2 + 300^2} = 500 \text{ m at an angle of } \beta = \tan^{-1}\left(\frac{300}{400}\right) = 36.87° \text{ to the } x\text{-axis.}$$

$$\therefore W = 50 \times 500 \cos(53.13° - 36.87°) = 24\,000 \text{ J}$$

* Note: A more elegant way of calculating $\cos\theta$ is:

$$\cos\theta = \cos(\alpha - \beta) = \cos\alpha\cos\beta + \sin\alpha\sin\beta \text{ ; here } \sin\alpha = \cos\beta = 0.8 \text{ and } \cos\alpha = \sin\beta = 0.6$$

$$\therefore \cos\theta = 0.6 \times 0.8 + 0.8 \times 0.6 = 0.96. \therefore W = 50 \times 500 \times 0.96 = 24\,000 \text{ J}$$

Further examples of the use of the scalar product are given in Chapter 8.

7.6.2 Vector product

The vector product $\mathbf{a} \times \mathbf{b}$ of two vectors, also called the *cross product* is a vector quantity defined by $\mathbf{a} \times \mathbf{b} = ab\sin\theta$ in a direction at right angles to $\mathbf{a}$ and $\mathbf{b}$ such that a rotation from $\mathbf{a}$ to $\mathbf{b}$ would cause a right-handed screw to advance along the direction $\mathbf{a} \times \mathbf{b}$.

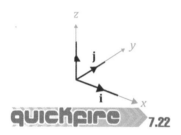

Because $\sin 0 = 0$, $\mathbf{r} \times \mathbf{r} = 0$ for any vector, $\mathbf{r}$. The major use of the cross product in A-level Physics is in the production and detection of magnetic fields, and can be particularly helpful, for example, in understanding and treating torque and the motion of charged particles in magnetic fields. Also it has a crucial role in more advanced physics.

Note that, whilst the dot product is defined for vectors in 1, 2 or 3 dimensions, the cross product only has a 3D definition. If we work with components, it is important to define the directions of the axes carefully. We normally work in *right-handed Cartesian co-ordinates*. If we rotate a right-handed screw from x to y the screw advances along the z-direction. With this co-ordinate system, $\mathbf{i} \times \mathbf{j} = \mathbf{k}$ and $\mathbf{j} \times \mathbf{i} = -\mathbf{k}$.

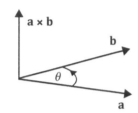

quickfire 7.22

Evaluate $\mathbf{j} \times \mathbf{k}$.

The moment, τ, of a force about a point is also a vector quantity, defined by $\tau = \mathbf{r} \times \mathbf{F}$, where $\mathbf{r}$ is the position vector of the place where the force is applied. For example:

$\mathbf{F} = 5\mathbf{i} - 3\mathbf{j}$ applied at the point $\mathbf{r} = 2\mathbf{i} + 4\mathbf{j}$

$\tau = (2\mathbf{i} + 4\mathbf{j}) \times (5\mathbf{i} - 3\mathbf{j}) = -(6\mathbf{i} \times \mathbf{j}) + (20\mathbf{j} \times \mathbf{i}) = -6\mathbf{k} + 20(-\mathbf{k}) = -26\mathbf{k}$

There are two conditions for a set of forces to be in equilibrium:

1   The resultant force is zero, and

quickfire 7.23

Evaluate $(3\mathbf{i} - 2\mathbf{j}) \times (2\mathbf{i} + 3\mathbf{j})$.

2   The resultant moment **about any point** is zero.

We can use vectors to show that we can take moments about any point, as follows: Consider three forces, $\mathbf{F}_1$, $\mathbf{F}_2$ and $\mathbf{F}_3$ acting at $\mathbf{r}_1$, $\mathbf{r}_2$ and $\mathbf{r}_3$ in equilibrium on a body.

Condition 1 gives us $\mathbf{F}_1 + \mathbf{F}_2 + \mathbf{F}_3 = 0$ (1)

Condition 2 gives us $\mathbf{r}_1 \times \mathbf{F}_1 + \mathbf{r}_2 \times \mathbf{F}_2 + \mathbf{r}_3 \times \mathbf{F}_3 = 0$ (2)

Take moments about the point $\mathbf{x}$.

The total moment $\tau = (\mathbf{r}_1 - \mathbf{x}) \times \mathbf{F}_1 + (\mathbf{r}_2 - \mathbf{x}) \times \mathbf{F}_2 + (\mathbf{r}_3 - \mathbf{x}) \times \mathbf{F}_3 = 0$

Multiplying out the brackets: $\tau = (\mathbf{r}_1 \times \mathbf{F}_1 + \mathbf{r}_2 \times \mathbf{F}_2 + \mathbf{r}_3 \times \mathbf{F}_3) - \mathbf{x} \times (\mathbf{F}_1 + \mathbf{F}_2 + \mathbf{F}_3)$

Both terms in brackets are zero from equations (1) and (2) so the total torque is zero about any point.

Test Yourself 7.1

Questions 1–15 relate to Sections 7.1–7.3

1 Find the resultant vector.

(a)
15 km   10 km

(b)
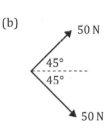
50 N
45°
45°
50 N

(c)
25 N
50 N

(d)
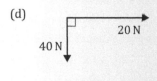
20 N
40 N

(e)
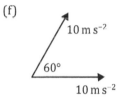
80 N
45 N
NE

(f)
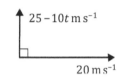
10 m s⁻²
60°
10 m s⁻²

(g)
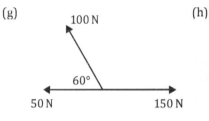
100 N
60°
50 N   150 N

(h)
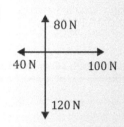
80 N
40 N   100 N
120 N

2 Find the resultant of the two forces at time $t = 2.0$ s

$25 - 10t$ m s⁻¹

20 m s⁻¹

3 Find the components of the vectors in the directions of the dotted lines (which are at right angles).

(a)
10 m s⁻¹
45°

(b)
500 N
25°

(c)
8 km
70°

4 In each of these two cases, the forces are in equilibrium. Find the magnitudes of **F** and **G.**

(a)
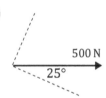
10 N
G
30°
F

(b)
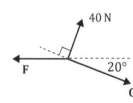
40 N
F
20°
G

5 Find the magnitude and direction of force **F** which is the equilibrant of the other two forces.

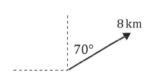
30 N
60°
F   θ   50 N

6 Find the equilibrant of these forces:

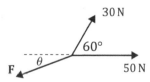
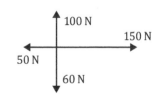
100 N
150 N
50 N
60 N

7 Two forces, in newton, are: $\mathbf{F}_1 = 6\mathbf{i} + 3\mathbf{j}$; $\mathbf{F}_2 = -4\mathbf{i} + 10\mathbf{j}$. Find the equilibrant, $\mathbf{F}$, expressed

 (a) in terms of components and (b) in magnitude and direction.

8 The velocity of a plane, in m s^{-1}, changes from $60\mathbf{i} + 80\mathbf{j}$ to $-80\mathbf{i} + 60\mathbf{j}$ in 5 seconds. Calculate the mean acceleration (a) in terms of components and (b) in magnitude and direction.

9 The displacement, $\mathbf{s}$, of an object is given by $\mathbf{s} = 10t\mathbf{i} + (40t - 2t^2)\mathbf{j}$. Calculate the following after a time, t, of 2 seconds:

 (a) the displacement in terms of components

 (b) the velocity in terms of components

 (c) the magnitude and direction of the velocity.

10 A particle travels at constant speed of 25 m s^{-1} in a circle of radius 5 m.

 (a) Calculate the mean acceleration of the particle over a time interval (i) of 0.2 s and (ii) of 0.02 s.

 (b) Compare these values to the value of instantaneous acceleration given by $a = \dfrac{v^2}{r}$.

11 A sled of mass 150 kg is held on a 15° slope by a rope which is parallel to the slope. If the frictional force, $\mathbf{F}$, up the slope is 200 N calculate the tension, $\mathbf{T}$, in the rope. [$g = 9.8$ m s^{-2}]

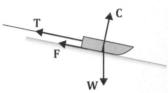

12 A cycle and cyclist of mass 100 kg freewheel up a slope of gradient 5°. Their initial velocity is 10 m s^{-1}. If friction and air resistance can be ignored, calculate:

 (a) the resultant force down the slope and

 (b) the distance travelled up the slope before coming to rest.

13 A box of mass m rests on a plank which is at an angle, θ, to the horizontal.

 (a) Calculate $\mathbf{F}$ and $\mathbf{C}$ in terms of m and θ.

 (b) The magnitude of the maximum frictional force $F_{max} = 0.2C$. Calculate the greatest value of θ to which the plank can be tipped before the box starts to slip.

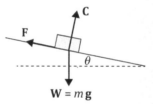

14 For the box in Q13, calculate the acceleration down the slope when $\theta = 20°$. [Assume that $F = 0.2C$ is still valid.]

15 A ball of mass 10 kg is suspended on a string. The ball is pulled to one side by a horizontal force $\mathbf{F}$. The breaking tension in the string is 250 N. Calculate (a) the angle θ between the string and the vertical and (b) the magnitude of force $\mathbf{F}$ just before there string breaks.

16 A ship whose position at time $t = 0$ is the origin $(0,0)$, steams with a velocity, in knots*, $\mathbf{v}_1 = 20\mathbf{i} + 5\mathbf{j}$ for 2 hours and then $\mathbf{v}_2 = 10\mathbf{i} - 18\mathbf{j}$ for 3 hours. Calculate:

 (a) the ship's displacement, $\mathbf{s}(2)$, after 2 hours using components, [i.e. $a\mathbf{i} + b\mathbf{j}$]

 (b) the displacement , $\mathbf{s}(5)$, after 5 hours;

 (c) the speed in each of the legs of the journey

 (d) the mean velocity in terms of components

 (e) the mean velocity in magnitude and direction.

 * Note 1 knot = 1 nautical mile per hour.

17 The initial velocity, $\mathbf{u}$, of a rocket, in m s^{-1}, is given by, $\mathbf{u} = 5000\mathbf{i} + 12\,000\mathbf{j}$. It accelerates with a constant acceleration, in m s^{-2}, of $\mathbf{a} = -0.1\mathbf{j} + 0.2\mathbf{k}$ for 10 hours. Its initial position was $(0, 0, 0)$. Calculate:

 (a) the magnitude of the initial velocity

 (b) the velocity after 10 hours

 (c) the magnitude of the velocity after 10 hours

 (d) the displacement after 10 hours [use $\mathbf{s} = \mathbf{u}t + \frac{1}{2}\mathbf{a}t^2$]

 (e) the distance from the starting point after 10 hours.

18. A stone is thrown from ground level on Mars with a velocity **u** = 30**i** + 40**j**, where **i** and **j** are the horizontal and vertical unit vectors respectively. The acceleration due to gravity is 3.7 m s^{-2}. Calculate:

    (a) the acceleration, velocity and displacement vectors after 10 seconds

    (b) the magnitude and direction of the velocity of the stone after 10 s

    (c) speed and direction of the stone when it hits the ground

    (d) the velocity vector after 10 s as seen in a frame of reference which moves with a velocity 30**i**.

19. A projectile is catapulted at a speed of 40 m s^{-1} at 30° to the horizontal from the top of a 50 m high sea cliff. Calculate:

    (a) its position and velocity at the highest point

    (b) its point and velocity of impact with the sea.

20. Two bodies of mass 3 kg and 5 kg have velocities, in m s^{-1}, of 5**i** + 4**j** and −3**i** + 7**j** respectively. Calculate:

    (a) the total momentum,

    (b) the velocity of the centre of mass

    (c) the total kinetic energy.

21. Repeat the calculations in Q20 as seen from a frame of reference with velocity −3**i** + 7**j**.

22. A body of mass 2 kg has a momentum, in N s, of 3**i** + 5**j**. A force in N of 2**i** +2**j** acts on the body for a period of 10 s. Calculate:

    (a) the momentum after 10 s

    (b) the change of kinetic energy between 0 and 10 s.

23. For the body in Q22, calculate:

    (a) the initial velocity and the acceleration vectors

    (b) the displacement vector after 10 s

    (c) the scalar product of the force and displacement vectors – comment on your answer.

24. A body is free to move. It has an initial kinetic energy of 400 J. A force, in N, **F** = 8**i** + 12**j** acts on the body as it moves from position, in m, **s**$_1$ = −50**i** + 30**j** to **s**$_2$ = 10**i** + 40**j** . Calculate the final kinetic energy of the body.

25. The moment, τ, of a force, **F**, acting at a **r** about a point is given by **r** × **F**.

    (a) Calculate the moment about the origin of each of the following two forces: **F**$_1$ = 10**j** acting at **r**$_1$ = 3**i** + 2**j** and **F**$_2$ = 4**i** − 6**j** acting at **r**$_2$ = 2**i** + **j**.

    (b) According to the Principle of Moments, the resultant moment must be zero for equilibrium. State the moment of a third force, **F**$_3$, which is necessary to produce rotational equilibrium.

    (c) For equilibrium the resultant force must also be zero. State **F**$_3$.

    (d) If **F**$_3$ acts at x**i** + y**j**, show that $x - y = 3.5$. [Hint: form the vector product $(x\mathbf{i} + y\mathbf{j}) \times \mathbf{F}_3$]

Oscillations

8.1 Introduction

This chapter builds upon the work of Chapters 5, 6 and 7 and applies it to oscillations. Topics involving oscillations are mainly to be found at A2. Angles are expressed in radians throughout this chapter.

8.2 Graphs of trignometric functions

8.2.1 Graph of sin θ against θ

The graph can be sketched by considering the y co-ordinate of the point **P** as it rotates anticlockwise about the origin. **P** is unit distance from the origin. See Figure 8.1.

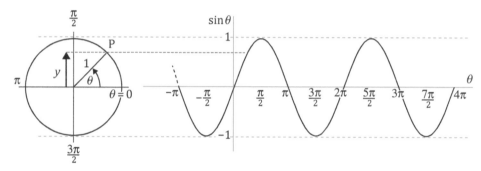

Fig 8.1

Note the following properties of the sin θ function:

- The maximum value of sin θ is +1 and minimum value is −1.
- We can go on rotating indefinitely, e.g. the lowest point of the circle could equally well be marked $\frac{7\pi}{2}, \frac{11\pi}{2}$ ....
- Negative values of θ correspond to clockwise rotations from the x axis, so we could also mark the lowest point $-\frac{\pi}{2}, -\frac{5\pi}{2}$ ....
- sin $(-\theta) = -\sin\theta$: we say that sin θ is an *odd function* of θ. [Another example of an odd function is x^3, because $(-x)^3 = -x^3$.]
- sin $(\theta + 2n\pi) = \sin\theta$, where n is an integer: ...−2, −1, 0, 1, 2, 3, ...

quickfire ▶ 8.1

Use the values in Table 5.1 on page 54 and Figure 8.1 to determine:

(a) $\sin\left(-\frac{\pi}{3}\right)$,

(b) $\sin\frac{13\pi}{6}$ [Hint: $\frac{13\pi}{6} = 2\pi + \frac{\pi}{6}$],

(c) $\sin\frac{15\pi}{4}$ [Hint: $\frac{15\pi}{4} = 4\pi - \frac{\pi}{4}$]

8.2.2 Graph of cos θ against θ

This is slightly less easy to visualise. We consider the x co-ordinate of the point **P** as it rotates. The form of the graph is the same, but the value of cos θ is 1 when $\theta = 0$. See Figure 8.2.

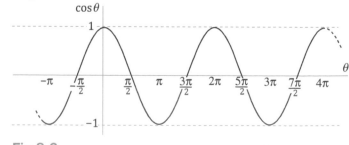

Fig 8.2

The properties of the $\cos\theta$ function are the same as those of the $\sin\theta$ function apart from:

- The cos graph is the sine graph shifted by $\frac{\pi}{2}$ in the θ direction, so $\cos\theta = \sin\left(\frac{\pi}{2}+\theta\right)$
- $\cos(-\theta) = \cos\theta$: $\cos\theta$ is called an *even function*.

The sine and cosine graphs are both referred to as *sinusoids*.

Example A: Show that $\sin(\pi - \alpha) = \sin\alpha$

From Section 5.8: $\sin(\theta + \phi) = \sin\theta\cos\phi + \cos\theta\sin\phi$

$\therefore \sin(\pi - \alpha) = \sin\pi\cos(-\alpha) + \cos\pi\sin(-\alpha)$. But, $\sin\pi = 0$; $\cos\pi = -1$ and $\sin(-\alpha) = -\sin\alpha$

So $\sin(\pi - \alpha) = 0 \times \cos(-\alpha) + (-1) \times (-\sin\alpha) = \sin\alpha$.   QED.

NB. Look at the $\sin\theta$ graph, Figure 8.1, and convince yourself that it agrees with this result.

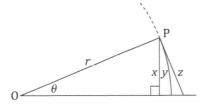

quickfire 8.2

Use values in Table 5.1 on page 54 and Figure 8.2 to determine

(a) $\cos\left(-\frac{\pi}{3}\right)$, (b) $\cos\frac{7\pi}{3}$, (c) $\cos\frac{5\pi}{3}$

8.2.3 Graph of $\tan\theta$ against θ

This is the most difficult of the three graphs to visualise. Remember that $\tan\theta = \frac{\sin\theta}{\cos\theta}$.
This leads to:

- $\tan\theta$ becomes infinite where $\cos\theta = 0$. This is when $\theta = (n + \frac{1}{2})\pi$, where n is an integer, ... $-2, -1, 0, 1, 2$ ... .
- $\tan\theta = 0$ when $\sin\theta = 0$. This is when $\theta = ... -\pi, 0, \pi, 2\pi$ ... .
- $\tan(-\theta) = -\tan\theta$, i.e $\tan\theta$ is an odd function.
- $\tan(\pi + \theta) = \tan\theta$.

You are less likely to need to use the graph of $\tan\theta$ in A-level Physics, than the sin or cos graphs. Knowledge of $\tan\theta$, for values of θ between $-\pi$ and π, arises in the solution of differential equations.

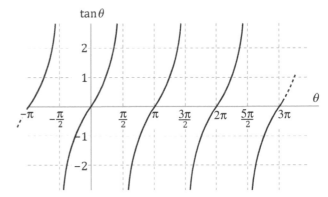

Fig 8.3

quickfire 8.3

Use values in Table 5.1 and Figure 8.3 to determine

(a) $\tan\left(-\frac{\pi}{4}\right)$, (b) $\tan\frac{5\pi}{4}$, (c) $\tan\frac{5\pi}{3}$.

8.2.4 Values of the $\sin\theta$ and $\tan\theta$ for small values of θ

Consider Figure 8.4. The distance y is the curved length of the arc centred on **O**, and z is the distance along the tangent to the arc at **P**.

From their definitions:

$$\sin\theta = \frac{x}{r}; \quad \theta = \frac{y}{r}\text{ [radians!]}; \quad \tan\theta = \frac{z}{r}$$

From the geometry, $x < y < z$, so we can write:

$$\sin\theta < \theta < \tan\theta.$$

Fig 8.4

If we make θ smaller and smaller, the three lengths will be increasingly indistinguishable so the values of $\sin\theta$, θ and $\tan\theta$ become closer and closer, until, when $\theta = 0$, they are indeed the same. So for small angles we can write: $\sin\theta \approx \theta \approx \tan\theta$, where the symbol $\approx$ means 'is approximately equal to'.

How good is the approximation?

Table 8.1 gives values of $\sin\theta$, θ and $\tan\theta$ as well as their ratios. Even for $\theta = 0.5$ rad [approx 30°], the values of $\sin\theta$ and θ are less than 5% apart; at 0.2 rad, the difference is less than 1%; at 0.1 rad it is less than 0.2%. For most purposes, for angles less than 0.2 radians [about 10°], we can consider the three to be the same and the ratios of $\frac{\sin\theta}{\theta}$ and $\frac{\tan\theta}{\theta} \approx 1$.

quickfire 8.4

A 50 m high church spire subtends an angle of 1° to the eye. By converting 1° to radians, estimate the distance of the church.

quickfire 8.5

An asteroid at a distance of 10 million km has an apparent size of 2×10^{-5} rad. What is its diameter?

Table 8.1

θ / rad	$\sin \theta$	$\tan \theta$	$\dfrac{\sin \theta}{\theta}$	$\dfrac{\tan \theta}{\theta}$
0.50	0.47943	0.54630	0.95885	1.09260
0.20	0.19867	0.20271	0.99335	1.01355
0.10	0.09983	0.10033	0.99833	1.00335
0.05	0.04998	0.05004	0.99958	1.00083
0.02	0.02000	0.02000	0.99993	1.00013
0.01	0.01000	0.01000	0.99998	1.00003

8.3 Oscillations

The equations $x = A \sin(\omega t + \varepsilon)$ or $y = A \cos(\omega t + \phi)$, for some variables x and y, often arise in the solution of physical problems. A few examples:

- Simple harmonic motion (shm), e.g. small angle oscillations of a pendulum. The variables will be x, v and a [position, velocity and acceleration].
- ac electrical circuits, in which the variables are V or I.
- Waves, in which the variables could be the x (position), p (pressure), E or B (electric or magnetic fields).

Not all of these are likely to occur in the physics specification you are following. We shall restrict ourselves here to shm and ac circuits.

8.3.1 The relationship between rotations and oscillations

Figure 8.5 shows a vector of magnitude A rotating about the origin. Such vectors are called *phasors*. In the position shown, the horizontal component of the phasor, x, is given by

$$x = A \cos \theta. \tag{1}$$

The angular velocity, ω, is defined as the change of angle per unit time. With this definition, the value of θ at time t is given by

$$\theta = \omega t + \varepsilon, \tag{2}$$

where ε is the value of θ when $t = 0$. NB. ε is always given in radians.

Substituting for θ in equation (1) gives $x = A \cos(\omega t + \varepsilon)$

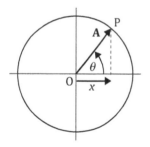

Fig 8.5

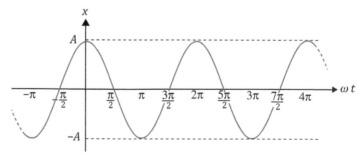

Fig 8.6a

If $\varepsilon = 0$ the graph of this function is the same as Figure 8.2 with ωt for θ on the horizontal axis and x as the vertical axis.

The period, T, is the time interval over which the oscillation repeats itself, i.e. when ωt increases by 2π.

Table 8.2

$$\omega = \frac{2\pi}{T}, \quad f = \frac{1}{T}, \quad \omega = 2\pi f$$

Hence $\omega T = 2\pi$ and so $\omega = \dfrac{2\pi}{T}$. ω is often called the *angular frequency* or the *pulsatance*. Table 8.2 summarises the relationships between the frequency, f, the period and angular frequency.

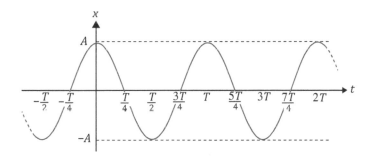

Fig 8.6b

Figure 8.6b shows the same function as in Figure 8.6a but plotted more conventionally against time, t rather than ωt. You should note the relationships between the scales.

The quantity A is referred to as the *amplitude* of the oscillation. It is the maximum deviation from the mean position.

The equation of the oscillation could equally well be written $x = A \sin(\omega t + \phi)$, with a different value of the *phase angle*. As an exercise, after looking at Example B, show that the equation in that case can be written $x = 0.085 \sin(224t + 0.45)$.

Example B:

Find the frequency, period and amplitude of the oscillation shown and write the equation of the oscillation in the form

$x = A \cos(\omega t + \varepsilon)$.

The graph crosses the axis in the same direction at 12 ms and 40 ms, so the period, T = 28 ms.

$$f = \frac{1}{T} = \frac{1}{0.028} = 35.7 \text{ Hz}. \quad \omega = 2\pi f = 224 \text{ s}^{-1}.$$

The extreme values of x are ± 8.5 cm, $\therefore A = 0.085$ m.

If ε were 0, the peak of the graph would be at $t = 0$. It is 5 ms late, which is $\frac{5}{28}$ of a period. One whole period corresponds to an angle of 2π, so $\varepsilon = -\frac{5}{28} \times 2\pi = -1.12$.

$\therefore$ The equation is $x = 0.085 \cos(224t - 1.12)$ [t in s and x in m].

Given a particular value for x we can solve the equation for t, i.e. we can ask at what times x has a certain value. Taking the equation $x = 0.085 \cos(224t - 1.12)$ as an example, we observe from the graph that the value of x when $t = 0$ is approximately 3.0 cm [0.030 m] and we ask when else it has this value.

The equation to be solved is $\qquad 0.030 = 0.085 \cos(224t - 1.12)$

Dividing by 0.085 we obtain: $\quad \cos(224t - 1.12) = 0.353$

$\therefore \qquad\qquad\qquad\qquad 224t - 1.12 = \cos^{-1} 0.353$

Making sure that the calculator is in radian mode, we obtain $\cos^{-1} 0.353 = 1.210$. We know that $\cos(-\theta) = \cos\theta$, so the solution to the equation is $224t - 1.12 = \pm 1.210$.

$\therefore \qquad\qquad\qquad t = \dfrac{1.12 \pm 1.210}{224} = -0.4$ ms or 10.4 ms.

[The estimated value of $t = 0$ for $x = 3.0$ cm was not quite right but we can really only read the graph to the nearest ms.] Because the cycle repeats every 28 ms we obtain as the general solution: $t = (-0.4 \text{ or } 10.4) + 28n$ ms [$n = \dots -1, 0, 1, 2 \dots$], to the nearest ms.

quickfire 8.6

Find the pulsatance, frequency, period and amplitude of the following oscillation:

$V = 339\cos(314t + 1.0)$ [V in V, t in s]

quickfire 8.7

What is the value of V in QF 8.6 at $t = 50$ ms?

quickfire 8.8

When is the first time after $t = 0$ when $V = 0$ in QF 8.6?

Pointer

If you notice, after doing a $\sin^{-1}$ or a $\cos^{-1}$ calculation, that you are in **degree** mode, multiply your answer by $\dfrac{\pi}{180}$ to convert to radians

8.3.2 Simple harmonic motion

In Chapter 11 we show that, if the resultant force, F, on a particle of mass m is related to its displacement, x, from a point by an equation of the form: $F = -kx$ the equation of motion is:

$$x = A \cos(\omega t + \varepsilon), \tag{1}$$

where $\omega = \sqrt{\dfrac{k}{m}}$ and A and ε are constants. This motion is referred to as *simple harmonic motion*. By differentiating this equation (see Chapter 10) we obtain the following relationships for velocity, v, and acceleration, a:

$$v = -A\omega \sin(\omega t + \varepsilon) \tag{2}$$

$$a = -A\omega^2 \cos(\omega t + \varepsilon) \tag{3}$$

Comparing equations (1) and (3) we see that $a = -\omega^2 x$, which is in agreement with $F = -kx$.

Remembering that the maximum value of a sine or cosine function is 1, the maximum values of v and a, from equations (1), (2) and (3) are:

$$v_{max} = A\omega \tag{4}$$

$$a_{max} = A\omega^2 \tag{5}$$

Equations (1)–(5) are summarised in the graphs in Figure 8.7 for $\varepsilon = 0$.

With this value of ε, equations (1)–(3) could be written:

$$x = A \cos \omega t \ ; \quad v = -A\omega \sin \omega t \ ; \quad a = -A\omega^2 \cos \omega t$$

Notice that each graph is out of step by $\frac{1}{4}$ of a cycle from the one above.

Another useful equation gives the velocity at any displacement. From equation (2) and using the relationship $\sin^2 \theta + \cos^2 \theta = 1$, we get:

$$v = \pm A\omega \sqrt{1 - \cos^2(\omega t + \varepsilon)}$$

$$= \pm \omega \sqrt{A^2 - A^2 \cos^2(\omega t + \varepsilon)}$$

i.e. $$v = \pm \omega \sqrt{A^2 - x^2} \tag{6}$$

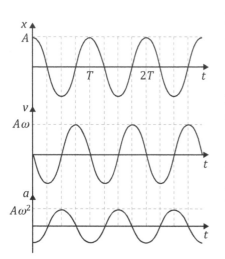

Fig 8.7

Pointer

v is the gradient of the x–t graph, so when x is maximum or minimum, $v = 0$. When the gradient of $x < 0$, so is v.

Pointer

Acceleration is the gradient of the v–t graph.

Example C:

A particle oscillates with displacement x (in m) given by the equation $x = 0.10 \cos 5t$, with t in s.

Calculate (a) the maximum values of the velocity and acceleration and (b) the first two times, $t > 0$, at which the velocity $v = 30 \text{ cm s}^{-1}$.

(a) $v_{max} = A\omega = 0.10 \times 5 = 0.5 \text{ m s}^{-1}$;
$a_{max} = A\omega^2 = 0.1 \times 5^2 = 2.5 \text{ m s}^{-2}$.

(b) $v = -A\omega \sin \omega t$, $\therefore 0.3 = -0.5 \sin 5t$
$\therefore 5t = \sin^{-1}(-0.6)$, for which the calculator gives -0.644 rad,
i.e. $t = -0.13$ s.
The period $T = \dfrac{2\pi}{\omega} = \dfrac{2\pi}{5} = 1.26$ s.

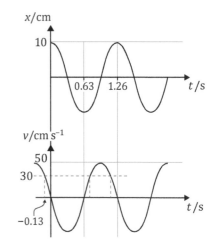

If we look at the sketch v–t graph we see that the first two positive times are:

- 0.63 s + 0.13 s = 0.76 s, and

- 1.26 s – 0.13 s = 1.13 s.

Hint: It often pays to draw a sketch graph to make sure that you have the correct times.

8.4 Alternating currents

Currents, I, and potential differences, V, in ac circuits vary in a sinusoidal way, i.e.
$I = I_0 \cos(\omega t + \varepsilon)$ and $V = V_0 \cos(\omega t + \phi)$.

The frequency of mains circuits in Europe, including the UK, is tightly controlled at 50 Hz, making $\omega = 2\pi \times 50 = 314$ Hz. In the USA the frequency is 60 Hz. The values of ε and ϕ in these expressions are not necessarily the same. Circuits containing motors have a significant phase difference between I and V. We look first at the power dissipated in circuits with purely resistive loads.

8.4.1 RMS and peak values – power in resistive circuits

Figure 8.8 shows a resistor of value R with a pd V across it which results in a current I. Note that the arrow representing the current does not imply a direct current – we are considering alternating currents. The initial phase angle is not significant here.

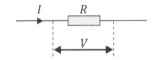

Fig 8.8

In a purely resistive circuit the current responds practically instantaneously to changes in voltage. The equation $V = IR$ relates the instantaneous values of I and V. Figure 8.9 illustrates this for a 5 Ω resistor connected across a sinusoidal pd supply with a *peak voltage* of 10 V. The peak current is 2 A and occurs at the same instant, t_2, as the peak voltage. Similarly, at t_1, $V = 5$ V and $I = 1$ A and at t_3, $V = -5$ V and $I = -1$ A.

The power dissipated at any instant is given by $P = VI$ and, at $t = 0$, t_1, t_2 and t_3, has the values 0, 5 W, 20 W, and 5 W respectively. What is the mean power dissipation, $\langle P \rangle$? We'll take the general case.

Consider a pd $V = V_0 \cos \omega t$ applied across a resistor, R.

Then $\qquad\qquad I = I_0 \cos \omega t$, where $I_0 = \dfrac{V_0}{R}$.

$\therefore \qquad\qquad P = V_0 I_0 \cos^2 \omega t.$

V_0 and I_0 are constants, so $\langle P \rangle = V_0 I_0 \langle \cos^2 \omega t \rangle$. What is the mean value of $\cos^2 \omega t$ over a cycle? The function oscillates between 0 and 1, so it is tempting to write $\cos^2 \omega t = \frac{1}{2}$. This can be proved as follows:

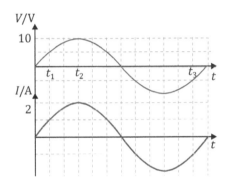

Fig 8.9

From Test Yourself 5.1, Q22 we know that $\cos 2\omega t = 2\cos^2 \omega t - 1$.

$\therefore \qquad\qquad \cos^2 \omega t = \dfrac{1 + \cos 2\omega t}{2}.$

$\cos 2\omega t$ varies between -1 and $+1$; $\langle \cos 2\omega t \rangle = 0$

$\therefore \qquad\qquad \langle \cos^2 \omega t \rangle = \dfrac{1 + 0}{2} = \dfrac{1}{2}.$

$\therefore \qquad\qquad \langle P \rangle = \frac{1}{2} V_0 I_0$

The graphs in Figure 8.10 show how V, I and P vary with time and the value of $\langle P \rangle$. The values on the time axis are only illustrative and are correct for a 50 Hz supply. Note that P is always positive: if V and I are both positive, VI is also positive; if V and I are both negative, VI is positive; because the two are in phase, they are either both positive or both negative at any time.

To avoid the inconvenient factor of $\frac{1}{2}$ the *root mean-squared*, or rms, values of V and I are introduced. V_{rms} is defined in a similar way to molecular rms speeds:

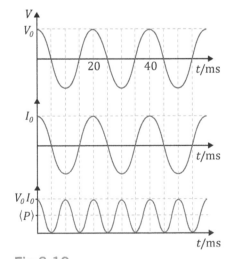

Fig 8.10

i.e. $V_{rms} = \sqrt{\langle V^2 \rangle}$. I_{rms} is defined similarly.

If $V = V_0 \cos \omega t$ then $V^2 = V_0^2 \cos^2 \omega t$.

quickfire 8.9

A square-wave voltage alternates between -5 V and $+5$ V with equal times at each value. What is the value of (a) the mean voltage, $\langle V \rangle$, (b) V_{rms}?

quickfire 8.10

Describe the current drawn by a 20 Ω resistor from the power supply in QF 8.9.

quickfire 8.11

Calculate the mean power dissipated by the resistor in QF 8.10.

quickfire 8.12

The rms mains voltage in the US is 120 V. What is the peak voltage?

Table 8.3

$$\langle P \rangle = \frac{1}{2}\frac{V_0^2}{R} = \frac{1}{2}I_0^2 R = \frac{1}{2}V_0 I_0$$

$$\langle P \rangle = \frac{V_{rms}^2}{R} = I_{rms}^2 R = V_{rms} I_{rms}$$

$$V_{rms} = \frac{V_0}{\sqrt{2}}; I_{rms} = \frac{I_0}{\sqrt{2}}$$

quickfire 8.13

A heater with a resistance 30 Ω is connected to the US mains. Calculate:
(a) the rms current, (b) the peak current, (c) the mean power, (d) the peak power.

quickfire 8.14

The frequency of the US mains is 60 Hz. With what frequency does the instantaneous power fluctuate?

$$\therefore \quad V_{rms} = V_0 \sqrt{\langle \cos^2 \omega t \rangle} = \frac{V_0}{\sqrt{2}}. \text{ Similarly } I_{rms} = \frac{I_0}{\sqrt{2}}$$

Hence $\langle P \rangle = V_{rms} I_{rms} = \frac{V_{rms}^2}{R} = I_{rms}^2 R$, which have the same form as the equivalent equation for dc circuits. We can use I_{rms} similarly. Table 8.3 summarises these relationships for sinusoidal currents and voltages.

In fact rms values are used universally and if a label reads 10 V ac it is understood that it is the rms value that is meant.

The equations $\langle P \rangle = \frac{V_{rms}^2}{R} = I_{rms}^2 R = V_{rms} I_{rms}$ are still valid even if the pd and current vary in a non-sinusoidal manner. The figure of $\frac{1}{\sqrt{2}}$ is specific to sinusoidal variations.

See Example D for the calculation of power in a non-sinusoidally varying case.

Example D:

A square wave voltage which oscillates between 0 and 10 V, with a mark-space ratio of 1 [i.e. equal times at 0 and 10 V] is applied across a 20 Ω resistor.

(a) Calculate the rms pd, V_{rms}.

(b) Show that the mean power dissipated is given by $\langle P \rangle = \frac{V_{rms}^2}{R}$ and calculate its value in this case.

(a) The value of V^2 oscillates between 0 and 100 V^2 with equal times at each value.
$\therefore$ The mean square voltage, $\langle V \rangle^2 = 50\ V^2$. $\therefore V_{rms} = \sqrt{50} = 7.071$ V

(b) The instantaneous power dissipated $= \frac{V^2}{R}$. $\therefore$ The power dissipated oscillated between 0 and $\frac{10^2}{20} = 5$ W with equal times at each value. $\therefore \langle P \rangle = 2.5$ W $= \frac{7.071^2}{20}$.

8.4.2 Current and power in capacitors and inductors

We show in Chapter 10 that, if a current $I = I_0 \cos \omega t$ is taken by an inductor, L, and a capacitor, C, the pd's across the components are given by:

$$V_L = I_0 \omega L \cos\left(\omega t + \frac{\pi}{2}\right) = -I_0 \omega L \sin \omega t$$

$$V_C = \frac{I_0}{\omega C} \cos\left(\omega t - \frac{\pi}{2}\right) = \frac{I_0}{\omega C} \sin \omega t$$

The graphs in Figure 8.11 illustrate the relative phases of I, V_L and V_C.

In both cases we observe two things:

1   The peak current is proportional to the peak voltage.

2   The voltages are $\frac{\pi}{2}$ out of phase with the current but in opposite directions. A useful mnemonic is CIVIL – 'in a capacitor, the current leads the voltage; the voltage leads the current in an inductor'.

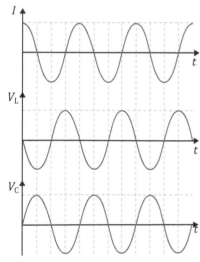

Fig 8.11

quickfire 8.15

A 1 kΩ resistor, a 1 μF capacitor and a 1 H inductor are connected separately to a power supply with a frequency of 100 Hz. Produce a table similar to Table 8.4 for these components.

The ratio $\frac{V}{I}$ for a component, where V and I are the peak or rms values, is generally called its *impedance*, Z.[!] If the current and voltage are in phase, this ratio is called the *resistance*. If they are $\frac{\pi}{2}$ out of phase, the ratio is called the *reactance*, X. Table 8.4 summarises the values for resistors, inductors and capacitors.

The instantaneous power dissipated, P, is given by $P = VI$.

For an inductor this gives: $P = -I_0^2 \omega L \cos \omega t \sin \omega t$.

Table 8.4

	R	X	Z
Resistor	R	0	R
Inductor	0	ωL	ωL
Capacitor	0	$\frac{1}{\omega C}$	$\frac{1}{\omega C}$

[!]   The rms voltage is directly proportional to the peak voltage. The rms and peak currents are also proportional so the ratios, $\frac{V_0}{I_0}$ and $\frac{V_{rms}}{I_{rms}}$ are the same.

In Section 5.8 we saw that $\sin(\theta + \phi) = \sin\theta\cos\phi + \cos\theta\sin\phi$.

Putting both θ and ϕ as ωt we get $\sin 2\omega t = 2\sin\omega t\cos\omega t$

$\therefore$ For the inductor: $P = -\dfrac{I_0^2\omega L}{2}\sin 2\omega t$, so $\langle P\rangle = -\dfrac{I_0^2\omega L}{2}\langle\sin 2\omega t\rangle = 0$.

The mean power taken by a pure inductor is zero because of the $\frac{\pi}{2}$ phase difference between the current and voltage. This is also true of a capacitor for the same mathematical reason. A physics reason: the components store energy in their magnetic or electric fields respectively; because of the alternating nature of the current, this energy is returned to the circuit twice each cycle.

8.5 Phasor analysis of ac circuits

As was stated in 8.3.1, the projection on to the *x*-axis of a phasor of magnitude *A*, which rotates with angular speed, ω, is given by $A\cos(\omega t + \varepsilon)$.

Thus an oscillation, e.g. of an electric current, a voltage or the displacement of a wave at a point, can be **regarded** as the rotation of such a vector, in which any instantaneous measurement of the current, voltage or displacement will always be the *x*-projection of the rotating vector.

Figure 8.12 shows the voltage and current in a purely resistive circuit at two times $\frac{1}{4}$ of a cycle apart. The phasors are coincident because they have the same phase – they rotate together. Both *V* and *I* are positive in the first diagram and negative in the second.

If all oscillations were in phase, there would be little point in phasors. We shall examine aspects of ac theory in which they are very useful.

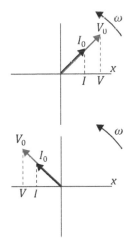

Fig 8.12

8.5.1 RC circuits

Figure 8.13 shows the current and voltage phasors for a capacitor – remember that the current in a capacitor is $\frac{\pi}{2}$ ahead of the voltage.

The instantaneous values *I* and *V* are shown on the *x*-axis. At the instant of the diagram, *I* is **decreasing** and *V* **increasing** because the phasors are rotating anticlockwise.

The usefulness of phasors becomes apparent if we consider a resistor and capacitor in series. Consider Figure 8.14.

The **instantaneous** voltages are related by

$$V = V_R + V_C$$

but because the voltages are not in phase, this equation does not apply to peak or rms voltages.

As for all components in series, the currents are the same. Consider the instant when the current phasor is along the *x*-axis.

The voltage phasor, V_C for the capacitor is $\frac{\pi}{2}$ behind, ie down the negative *y*-axis; V_R is along the *x*-axis. Figure 8.15 shows the three phasors at this instant. All future diagrams will have the current phasor in this direction and we'll separate it from the voltage phasors for clarity.

To find the total voltage *V* we find resultant of the V_C and V_R phasors. Using Pythagoras' theorem in Figure 8.16:

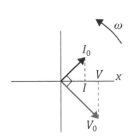

Fig 8.13

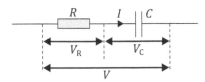

Fig 8.14

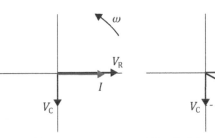

Fig 8.15   Fig 8.16

Pointer

In the formulae $V = \dfrac{I}{\omega C}$ and $V = I\omega L$, either the peak or rms values of current and voltage can be used – **but you can't mix them!** The formulae do **not** relate instantaneous values.

Pointer

The formula $V = IR$, relates peak, rms or instantaneous values.

quickfire 8.16

Calculate (a) the reactance of a 50 µF capacitor at 50 Hz, (b) the current if a 50 Hz pd of 10 V is applied across it?

quickfire 8.17

A current of rms value 2 A is taken by a 20 Ω resistor and a 1000 µF capacitor in series. What is the mean power dissipated? Explain your reasoning.

quickfire 8.18

Draw the phasors diagram for the oscillations in Figure 8.12:
(a) $\frac{1}{8}$ cycle and (b) $\frac{5}{8}$ cycle after the 2nd diagram.

quickfire 8.19

Redraw Figure 8.13 $\frac{1}{4}$ cycle later. What can you say about the voltage and current at this instant?

quickFire 8.20

A capacitor of reactance 1 kΩ is in series with a 1 kΩ resistor. What is the total impedance?

quickFire 8.21

If the frequency in QF 8.20 were doubled, what would be (a) the reactance, (b) the resistance and (c) the impedance of the combination?

$$V = \sqrt{V_R^2 + V_C^2}$$

Substituting $V_R = IR$ and $V_L = I\omega L$ gives

$$V = \sqrt{(IR)^2 + \left(\frac{I}{\omega C}\right)^2} = I\sqrt{R^2 + \frac{1}{\omega^2 C^2}}$$

The impedance Z_{RC}, which is defined as the ratio of the peak (or rms) voltage to the peak (rms) current, is given by:

$$Z_{RC} = \sqrt{R^2 + \frac{1}{\omega^2 C^2}} = \sqrt{R^2 + X_C^2}.$$

The phase angle, ε, by which the voltage lags the current is given by:

$$\varepsilon = \tan^{-1}\left(\frac{V_C}{V_R}\right) = \tan^{-1}\left(\frac{1}{R\omega C}\right) = \tan^{-1}\left(\frac{X_C}{R}\right).$$

Attention is drawn to Example F in Chapter 11. There the current and phase angle are derived using calculus techniques. The only difference between the two solutions is the minus sign in the solution for ε: here we just state that the voltage **lags** the current by ε (CIVIL – in a capacitor the current leads ...).

Example E:

A 390 Ω resistor and an 820 nF capacitor are connected in series across a 12 V (rms), 1 kHz power supply. Calculate (a) the current and (b) the phase angle between the voltage and the current (c) the mean power dissipated in the circuit.

(a) $X_C = \dfrac{1}{2\pi f C} = \dfrac{1}{2\pi \times 1000 \times 820 \times 10^{-9}} = 194\,\Omega. \therefore Z = \sqrt{R^2 + X^2} = \sqrt{390^2 + 194^2} = 436\,\Omega$

$$I = \frac{V}{Z} = \frac{12}{436} = 0.0275\,\text{A (rms)}$$

(b) The voltage lags by $\varepsilon = \tan^{-1}\left(\dfrac{X_C}{R}\right) = \tan^{-1}\left(\dfrac{194}{390}\right) = 0.46\,\text{rad}.$

(c) The capacitor doesn't dissipate power. $\therefore \langle P \rangle = I_{rms}^2 R = 0.028^2 \times 390 = 0.29\,\text{W}$

8.5.2 RL circuits

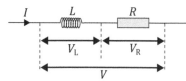

Fig 8.17

quickFire 8.22

A 100 Ω resistor is in series with an inductor of reactance 100 Ω. What is the total impedance?

quickFire 8.23

If the frequency in QF 8.22 were doubled, what would be (a) the resistance, (b) the reactance and (c) the impedance of the combination?

The current in an RL circuit can be found in the same way as that in an RC circuit. The only difference is that V_L leads the current, and hence is $\frac{\pi}{2}$ **ahead** of V_R.

Drawing the phasor diagram is left as an exercise. As for capacitors, the voltage phasors are at $\frac{\pi}{2}$, so:

$$V = \sqrt{V_R^2 + V_L^2}, \text{ which gives:}$$

$\therefore$ $V = \sqrt{(IR)^2 + (I\omega L)^2} = I\sqrt{R^2 + \omega^2 L^2}$ and the phase angle $\varepsilon = \tan^{-1}\left(\dfrac{V_L}{V_R}\right) = \tan^{-1}\left(\dfrac{\omega L}{R}\right)$

Generally, for both RC and RL circuits, $Z = \sqrt{R^2 + X^2}$ and $\varepsilon = \tan^{-1}\left(\dfrac{X}{R}\right).$

The **sign** of the phase angle, i.e. ±, needs careful consideration. A safe way is to consider ε to be positive and to insert the sign using CIVIL. For example, in an inductive circuit the voltage leads.

$\therefore$ If $I = I_0 \cos \omega t$, the voltage will be given by $V = V_0 \cos(\omega t + \varepsilon)$

In a capacitive circuit with the same current it would be $V = V_0 \cos(\omega t - \varepsilon)$ because the voltage lags behind the current.

8.5.3 RCL circuits

Figure 8.18 shows a series combination of a resistor, a capacitor and an inductor.

The phasor diagram is more complicated because there are three vectors to add, two of which, V_C and V_L, are in opposition.

Figure 8.19 shows the phasor diagram – as usual the I phasor is drawn along the x-axis. The V_L phasor is drawn longer than the V_C phasor: as we shall see, their relative lengths depend upon the frequency.

To find the resultant voltage phasor, we'll redraw Figure 8.19 slightly larger and without axes and I phasor, for clarity. Figure 8.20 shows that V is the resultant of phasors V_R and $V_L - V_C$ at right angles to phasor V_R.

So, using Pythagoras' theorem: $V = \sqrt{V_R^2 + (V_L - V_C)^2}$.

Applying the same substitutions and manipulation as in 8.5.1 and 8.5.2 we get

$$V = I\sqrt{R^2 + \left(\omega L - \frac{1}{\omega C}\right)^2},$$

which could also be written $V = I\sqrt{R^2 + (X_L - X_C)^2}$. So once again we see that the total impedance $Z = \sqrt{R^2 + X^2}$ where $X = X_L - X_C$. The resultant reactance is the difference of the reactances of the inductor and capacitor: this is because the voltages across the inductor and capacitor are in opposition.

The phase angle, ε, by which the voltage leads the current is given by: $\varepsilon = \tan^{-1}\left(\dfrac{X_L - X_C}{R}\right)$.

Once again we could always treat ε as positive and insert the sign into $V = V_0 \cos(\omega t \pm \varepsilon)$ by inspection. Alternatively, if $X_C > X_L$ the value of $X_L - X_C$ will be negative, so ε will also be negative.

8.5.4 Resonance in series RCL circuits

We saw in 8.5.3 that the current in an RCL circuit varies with voltage according to:

$$I = \frac{V}{\sqrt{R^2 + \left(\omega L - \dfrac{1}{\omega C}\right)^2}}$$

The term $\left(\omega L - \dfrac{1}{\omega C}\right)^2$ has a minimum value of 0 when $\omega L = \dfrac{1}{\omega C}$, i.e. when $\omega = \dfrac{1}{\sqrt{LC}}$.

For a voltage supply with a constant rms [or peak] voltage, the rms [or peak] current will have a **maximum** value at this value of pulsatance. The circuit is said to exhibit resonance; the graph of current against frequency is similar to those in mechanical resonance.

Figure 8.21 shows the resonance curve for a circuit with a 2.0 V supply containing a 1 kΩ resistor, a 1.1 H inductor and a 1.0 μF capacitor.

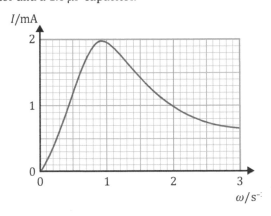

Fig 8.21

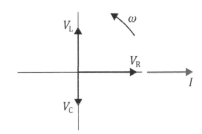

Fig 8.18

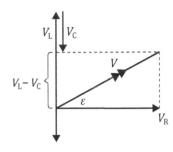

Fig 8.19

Fig 8.20

quickfire ▸ 8.24

A capacitor of reactance 1 kΩ is in series with a 1 kΩ resistor and an inductor of reactance 500 Ω. What is (a) the total reactance and (b) the total impedance?

quickfire ▸ 8.25

If the frequency in QF 8.24 were doubled, why would the answers stay the same?

quickfire ▸ 8.26

Show that the phase angle, ε, between the voltage and the current in QF 8.24 is 0.463 rad (26.6°) and state whether the voltage or the current leads.

8.5.5 Three last words on phasor diagrams

Data Exercise 8.1

Use a spreadsheet to reproduce the curve of Figure 8.21 and investigate the effect of varying the values of the components, especially the effect of R on the sharpness of the curve.

As an extension, use the equation $\varepsilon = \tan^{-1}\left(\dfrac{X_L - X_C}{R}\right)$ to investigate the variation of the phase angle with frequency. You should show that ε varies from $-\pi/2$ through 0 [at resonance] to $+\pi/2$.

1   In a series circuit, the current is the same in each component. The impedance of each component is the ratio of pd to current, so if we draw a voltage phasor diagram and then redraw dividing each voltage phasor by the current, the diagrams will look exactly the same – they will be similar figures.

We illustrate this by an example: Consider a series RCL circuit with a 0.2 A current, consisting of a 200 Ω resistor, a capacitor with a reactance of 150 Ω and an inductor with a reactance of 100 Ω.

The pds across the components are: 40 V, 30 V and 20 V respectively. Figure 8.22 shows the two phasor diagrams: (a) of the voltages and (b) of the impedances.

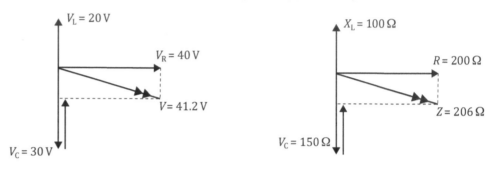

Fig 8.22

Adding the reactances and resistances in this way enables one to solve problems where the total pd is known and the current needs to be found.

2   When drawing a phasor diagram, it doesn't matter whether the phasor magnitudes are the rms values of voltage or the peak value of voltage [or indeed the resistance or reactances] as long as we do not mix up different sorts of value.

3   We haven't given any examples, but phasor diagrams can be used for components in parallel. In this case the voltage is the same for all the components – its phasor is normally drawn in the x direction. The current phasors add up to give the total current. CIVIL still applies: I_C will be in the $+y$ direction and I_L in the $-y$ direction with the rotation taken to be anticlockwise.

Test Yourself 8.1

❶   Find the value of the following functions when $\theta = 1.5$ rad
    (a) $\sin(\theta + 0.5)$ (b) $25\cos(2\theta + 0.5)$ (c) $5\tan\left(\tfrac{1}{2}\theta + 0.5\right)$

❷   Find the values of θ between -2π and $+2\pi$ for which
    (a) $\cos\theta = 0.7$ (b) $10\sin\theta = -8$ (c) $3\cos\left(\tfrac{1}{2}\theta + 0.5\right) = 1.5$

❸   The diameter of Mars is 6794 km. What angle does it subtend at the eye from a distance of 100 million km?

❹   The *parsec* is the distance from which the radius of the Earth's orbit, 149 500 000 km subtends an angle of 1″ of arc [$= \tfrac{1}{3600}°$]. Express the parsec in (a) km, (b) light years.

❺   To 2 s.f. what is the percentage difference between $\sin\theta$ and θ for $\theta = 0.03$ rad?

❻   A particle oscillates with an amplitude of 10 cm and a frequency of 1 Hz. Write down the relationship between x and t if:
    (a)   its displacement is 10 cm when t = 0,
    (b)   its displacement is −10 cm when t = 0
    (c)   its displacement is 10 cm when t = 0.25 s
    (d)   its speed is maximum and positive when $t = 0.9$ s.

7 For the particle in Q6, calculate:

(a) the maximum velocity and acceleration

(b) the times at which the maximum velocity and acceleration occur for each of parts (a)–(d).

Questions 8–13 relate to the following: An object of mass, $m = 0.5$ kg is suspended from a spring with a spring constant, $k = 25$ N m^{-1}. It is raised by from its equilibrium position by 12 cm and released at $t = 0$ after which its displacement, x, is given by $x = A \cos(\omega t + \varepsilon)$.

8 Calculate the pulsatance, frequency, period and amplitude of the oscillation.

9 Sketch the displacement–time, velocity–time and acceleration–time graphs between 0 and 2 s; label significant values. [Advice: 9 and 10 should be answered together.]

10 Write the equations for x, v and a with t, with the appropriate numbers.

11 Calculate the values of x, v and a when $t = 0.7$ s.

12 Find the values of t between 0 and 2 s for which $v = 60$ cm s^{-1}.

13 Find the kinetic energy and the energy stored in the spring at $t = 0.2$ s.

14 A particle of mass 2 kg oscillates with the displacement x, in metres, given by $x = 2.0 \sin 10t$.

(a) Find the velocity and kinetic energy of the particle at t = 0.

(b) Taking the potential energy of the particle to be zero in the equilibrium position, sketch the variation of the particle's kinetic energy, potential energy and total energy with time over two cycles of its oscillation.
$$\left[\text{Hint: } \cos^2 \theta = \frac{1 - \cos 2\theta}{2}\right]$$

15 A particle executes shm with its displacement, in m, given by $x = 0.2 \cos(10\pi t + 0.785)$. Find the times between $t = -0.2$ s and $t = +0.2$ s for which

(a) $x = 0.1$ m

(b) $v = -5$ m s^{-1}.

Questions 16–19 relate to a power supply with terminal pd, V, given by $V = 12 \cos 200\pi t$.

16 The power supply is connected across a 100 Ω resistor. The current varies as $I = I_0 \cos(\omega t + \varepsilon)$.

(a) Rewrite this equation inserting the appropriate values of I_0, ω, and ε.

(b) At time $t = 0.002$ s, calculate the value of (i) the pd, (ii) the current and (iii) the power dissipated.

(c) Calculate: (i) the rms pd, (ii) the rms current and (iii) the mean power dissipated.

17 The power supply is connected across a 10 µF capacitor.

(a) Calculate: (i) the reactance of the capacitor and (ii) the peak value of the current.

(b) Write an equation for the current in the form $I = I_0 \cos(\omega t + \varepsilon)$.

(c) Find the current at 0.002 s.

18 The power supply is connected across a 0.1 H inductor.

(a) Write an equation for the current in the form $I = I_0 \cos(\omega t + \varepsilon)$.

(b) Find the current at 0.002 s.

19 The power supply is connected across a 10 µF capacitor and a 100 Ω resistor in series.

(a) Calculate: (i) the impedance of the combination, (ii) the peak current, (iii) the peak pd across each component, V_R and V_C.

(b) Draw a phasor diagram for the voltages V_R, V_C and the applied voltage (i.e. the resultant voltage).

(c) Calculate the phase angle between the current and applied voltage.

Questions 20–22 refer to the voltage phasor diagram, which relates to a series combination of two components, X and Y. The pulsatance and the current phasor are also shown. Show your working.

20 (a) Identify the components X and Y.

(b) Determine the value of components X and Y.

(c) Determine the applied voltage and the angle between the voltage and current phasors.

21 The frequency of the power supply doubles and the value of I remains the same.

(a) Redraw the phasor diagram and insert appropriate values.

(b) Determine the applied voltage and the angle between the voltage and current phasors.

22 The pulsatance of the power supply is changed to $250\ s^{-1}$ and the applied voltage is the same as in Q20. Redraw the voltage phasor diagram, inserting appropriate values.

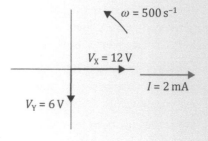

Questions 23–25 relate to the series RCL circuit shown.

23 The pulsatance of the supply is $500\ s^{-1}$ and the rms current is 0.1 A.

(a) Draw a phasor diagram of the rms pd's across each component.

(b) Determine rms magnitude of the applied voltage.

(c) Determine the mean power dissipated.

24 The frequency of the supply is 100 Hz and the rms voltage $V = 40$ V. By drawing a phasor diagram of the impedances, determine the total impedance and hence the current.

25 The frequency of the supply is adjusted so that the circuit is at resonance. The rms pd of the supply is 50 V. Showing your working, calculate:

(a) the frequency, (b) the current, (c) the pd across each component and (d) the mean power dissipated.

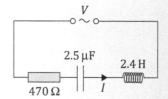

Chapter 9 · Fields

9.1 Introduction

A *field* in physics is a region of space in which each point has a quantity associated with it. Atmospheric pressure and atmospheric temperature are examples of *scalar fields* – the values of the pressure and temperature at any instant vary from place to place and influence the wind velocity, which is a *vector field*. These two fields are of interest to meteorologists.

The vector fields met in A-level Physics are gravitational, electric and magnetic fields. The vectors in these fields are defined in magnitude and direction by the effect of the field on particular objects. Gravitational and electric fields are mathematically very similar; magnetic fields are also vector fields but their properties are different and they are dealt with separately in Section 9.5

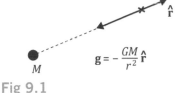

Fig 9.1

$$\mathbf{g} = -\frac{GM}{r^2}\hat{\mathbf{r}}$$

quickfire 9.1

Show that the units for g, $N\,kg^{-1}$ and $m\,s^{-2}$, are equivalent.

9.2 Gravitational and electric fields

9.2.1 Gravitational fields

The effect of a gravitational field is to exert a force, $\mathbf{F}$, on a test body, which is proportional to its mass, m. The *gravitational field strength*, $\mathbf{g}$, is defined by $\mathbf{g} = \dfrac{\mathbf{F}}{m}$.

From Newton's law of gravitation, the field strength produced by a point object of mass M at a point with position vector, $\mathbf{r}$, from the object is given by:

$$\mathbf{g} = -\frac{GM}{r^2}\hat{\mathbf{r}},$$

where $\hat{\mathbf{r}}$ is the unit vector in the direction of $\mathbf{r}$, and G is the universal constant of gravitation, $6.67 \times 10^{-11}\,N\,m^2\,kg^{-2}$. The field strength at a point produced by two or more bodies is the [vector] sum of the field strengths produced by each body separately. The field strength produced by a macroscopic body, e.g. the Earth, is the sum of the fields of all the individual particles of which the Earth is composed.

Example A:

A point, $\mathbf{P}$, is in the gravitational field of the Earth and Moon. Find the direction of the gravitational field at the point $\mathbf{P}$ (see diagram).

The field strength, $\mathbf{g}$, is the resultant of the field due to the Earth, $\mathbf{g}_E$, and that due to the Moon, $\mathbf{g}_M$.

The distance EP = 4.00×10^8 by Pythagoras' theorem.

$$\mathbf{g}_E = \frac{6.67 \times 10^{-11} \times 6 \times 10^{24}}{(4 \times 10^8)^2} = 2.50 \times 10^{-3}\,N\,kg^{-1} \text{ in the direction } \overrightarrow{PE}$$

$$\mathbf{g}_M = \frac{6.67 \times 10^{-11} \times 7.5 \times 10^{22}}{(2 \times 10^7)^2} = 1.25 \times 10^{-2}\,N\,kg^{-1} \text{ downwards.}$$

Horizontal component of $\mathbf{g}_E = 2.50 \times 10^{-3} \cos\theta = 2.50 \times 10^{-3}\,N\,kg^{-1}$.

Vertical component of $\mathbf{g}_E = 2.50 \times 10^{-3} \sin\theta = 1.25 \times 10^{-4}\,N\,kg^{-1}$. This is negligible compared to g_M.

From the vector diagram: $\phi = \tan^{-1}\left(\dfrac{2.5 \times 10^{-3}}{0.0125}\right) = 11.3°$. This gives the direction of $\mathbf{g}$.

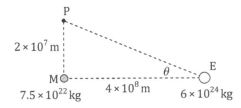

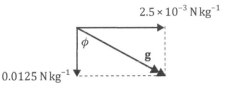

quickfire 9.2

Express the unit of G in terms of the base SI units.

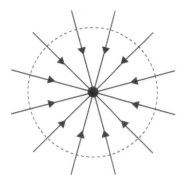

Fig 9.2

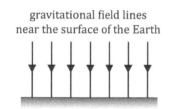

gravitational field lines
near the surface of the Earth

Fig 9.3

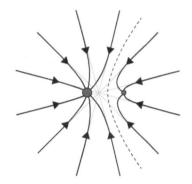

Fig 9.4

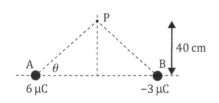

quickfire 9.3

Express the unit of ε_0 in terms of the base SI units, m, kg, s and A.

Vector fields can be represented by *field lines*, often called *lines of force*. They indicate the direction of the field vector at different points in the field. With care they can be used to give a semi-quantitative indication of the variation of the strength of the field. For a single point mass, the gravitational field lines are radial lines pointing inwards. The actual number of lines is unimportant.

Figure 9.2 is a 2D slice through a symmetrical 3D field. The dotted line represents a sphere. If the radius of the sphere halves, the number of field lines crossing it per unit area goes up by a factor of 4, in line with the inverse square nature of the field.

Because of the definition of **g**, the gravitational field lines always start at ∞ and end on the object whose mass produces the field. Field lines can never cross: if they did, the field would have two different directions at the point of intersection. The field from two bodies is the resultant of the individual fields and so will have a direction between the two.

For small displacements near the surface of the Earth, the field is almost uniform and downwards, so the field is as shown in Figure 9.3.

To see how field lines can be used in a quantitative way, look at Figure 9.4, a hand-drawn sketch of the gravitational field lines due to two masses, $2m$ (the larger one) and m. The number of field lines you draw is arbitrary but it is very useful to make the number of lines proportional to the mass – this makes the relative contributions of the two fields easier to picture. The body of mass m has 4 field lines, which are radial at points close to it; $2m$ has 8; the combination has 12 lines which are radial at large distances, lining up with the centre of mass of the two bodies. The faint lines show the field lines of a body of mass $3m$. The dotted lines show the separation between the effective regions of influence of each body.

9.2.2 Electric fields

The effect of an electric field is to exert a force, **F**, on any test charge, which is proportional to its charge, q. The *electric field strength*, **E**, is defined by $\mathbf{E} = \dfrac{\mathbf{F}}{q}$.

From Coulomb's law, the field strength produced by a point object of mass Q at a point with position vector, **r**, from the object is given by $\mathbf{E} = \dfrac{1}{4\pi\varepsilon_0}\dfrac{Q}{r^2}\hat{\mathbf{r}}$, where ε_0 is the *permittivity of free space*, 8.854×10^{-12} F m^{-1}.

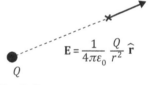

$$\mathbf{E} = \frac{1}{4\pi\varepsilon_0}\frac{Q}{r^2}\hat{\mathbf{r}}$$

Fig 9.5

The mathematics of the electric field is the same as that of the gravitational field apart from:

1   the sign of the of the force law is + instead of –,

2   there are positive and negative charges, and

3   the constant of proportionality is $\dfrac{1}{4\pi\varepsilon_0}$. ❶

Other practical differences are that, with electric fields, the distances tend to be small, possibly as small as nm and the charges tend to be small, either nC or μC.

Example B:

Find the resultant electric field, *E*, at P, which is on the line of symmetry between the two charges, which are separated by 60 cm. $\dfrac{1}{4\pi\varepsilon_0} = 9 \times 10^9$ F^{-1} m.

Using Pythagoras' theorem, AP = BP = 50 cm; $\sin\theta = 0.8$; $\cos\theta = 0.6$.

At P: $E_A = 9 \times 10^9 \dfrac{6 \times 10^{-6}}{0.5^2} = 216$ kV m^{-1};

Components: Horizontal = $216 \times 0.6 = 129.6$ kV m^{-1}; Vertical = $216 \times 0.8 = 172.8$ kV m^{-1}

---

❶ Examiners often use the very good approximation $\dfrac{1}{4\pi\varepsilon_0} = 9 \times 10^9$ F^{-1} m

$$E_B = 9 \times 10^9 \frac{3 \times 10^6}{0.5^2} = 108\,\text{kV m}^{-1};$$

Components: Horizontal = $108 \times 0.6 = 64.8\,\text{kV m}^{-1}$; Vertical = $-108 \times 0.8 = -86.4\,\text{kV m}^{-1}$

Resultant horizontal component = $129.6 + 64.8 = 194.4\,\text{kV m}^{-1}$.

Resultant vertical component = $172.8 - 86.4 = 86.4\,\text{kV m}^{-1}$.

$$\therefore \qquad E = \sqrt{194.4^2 + 86.4^2} = 214\,\text{kV m}^{-1}.$$

Direction, $\phi = \tan^{-1}\left(\dfrac{86.4}{194.4}\right) = 23.1°$ below the horizontal to the right.

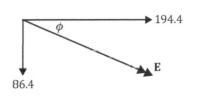

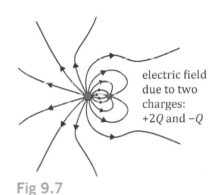

Because of the existence of + and − charges, the field lines begin on a + charge and end on a − charge. If there are unbalanced charges in a distribution, some field lines will extend to ∞. The sketch diagram shows the electric field due to two charges: $+2Q$ and $-Q$. The field lines are radial close to each charge and twice as many lines come from the $+2Q$ as end on the $-Q$. As with gravitational fields, the lines cannot cross and at a large distance there are eight lines radiating outwards as from a single $+Q$ charge.

9.2.3 Field due to a sphere

Newton's and Coulomb's laws refer to point masses and charges respectively, that is objects whose size is insignificant compared with the distance between them. We frequently need to work out the fields due to macroscopic bodies. The simplest shape is that of a sphere. We'll work in terms of an electric field but the maths of gravitational fields is the same.

We consider first a spherical shell and ask what the field strength is: (a) inside and (b) outside.

Inside a uniformly charged spherical shell

Consider a point **P** inside a spherical shell (Figure 9.8). Consider two very small areas A_1 and A_2 on the shell surface as shown. The two areas have the same shape and, from geometrical considerations:

$$\frac{A_1}{A_2} = \frac{r_1^2}{r_2^2}.$$

The charges on A_1 and A_2 are proportional to their areas so $\dfrac{Q_1}{Q_2} = \dfrac{r_1^2}{r_2^2}$, so $\dfrac{Q_1}{r_1^2} = \dfrac{Q_2}{r_2^2}$.

Because of the inverse square law the field strength at **P** due to Q_1 and Q_2 are equal and opposite, so the resultant field from these two areas is zero. We can repeat this process for the same point **P** covering the entire sphere with opposing areas, so the total field inside the shell is zero.

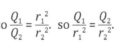

An alternative reasoning is based upon field lines: there can be no field lines inside the shell because the field line would have to end on a charge. If there are no charges inside the shell, no field lines can end there. Could a field line cross the void and emerge from the other side? No; from symmetry there would be an equally strong field line in the other direction and the two fields would cancel out.

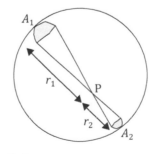

Fig 9.8

Fig 9.7

quicKfire 9.4

Find a value for $\dfrac{1}{4\pi\varepsilon_0}$ to 3 s.f. given that $\varepsilon_0 = 8.854 \times 10^{-12}\,\text{F m}^{-1}$.

quicKfire 9.5

Show that the units of electric field strength, V m^{-1} and N C^{-1}, are equivalent.

quicKfire 9.6

Find the resultant of two electric fields, $100\,\text{V cm}^{-1}$ and $160\,\text{V cm}^{-1}$ if they act: (a) in the same direction, (b) in opposite directions and (c) at right angles.

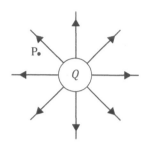

Fig 9.9

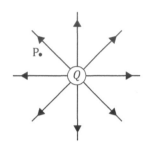

Fig 9.10

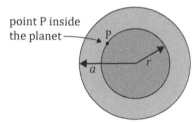

point P inside the planet

Fig 9.11

Outside a uniform spherical shell

Consider a point **P** outside a uniformly charged spherical shell. From above, all the field lines point outwards. Each starts on a + charge. Imagine shrinking the shell to, say, half the size. The only change to the diagram is that the field lines start closer to the centre – in other words, the field at **P** is unchanged.

We conclude that the field at **P** is independent of the radius of the sphere – even if we let the sphere shrink towards a 0 radius. So the field at **P**, outside the sphere, is the same as if all the charge were concentrated at a point in the centre.

Note that this interpretation of the field lines as an indication of the strength of the field is only possible in an inverse square field – see the text following Example A.

The gravitational field of a planet

Assuming that a planet is spherically symmetric, which is true to a good approximation, it can be considered to be made up of a large number of nested spherical shells. Thus the field **outside** the planet is given by:

$$\mathbf{g} = -\frac{GM}{r^2}\hat{\mathbf{r}},$$

as if all the mass were concentrated at the centre.

Figure 9.11 shows a point P at a distance r from the centre of a planet of radius a, with $r < a$. The field **inside** the planet depends upon the way the density varies with depth. The field at **P** is given by

$$\mathbf{g} = -\frac{Gm}{r^2}\hat{\mathbf{r}},$$

where m is the mass of the sphere of radius r. The mass at greater radii is not relevant because P is within the hollow shells for this mass (as shown above).

For a planet of **uniform density**, ρ, and radius, a

$$M = \tfrac{4}{3}\pi a^3 \rho \quad \text{and} \quad m = \tfrac{4}{3}\pi r^3 \rho = M\frac{r^3}{a^3}$$

$\therefore$ at P, $\mathbf{g} = -\dfrac{GMr}{a^3}\hat{\mathbf{r}}$ i.e. g is proportional to r and the graph of g against r rises from 0 at the centre to $\dfrac{GM}{a^2}$ at the surface and then drops off as $\dfrac{GM}{r^2}$ for $r > a$. See Figure 9.12.

Of course planets are not of uniform density: the Earth's mean density is $\sim 5500 \text{ kg m}^{-3}$, whereas the silicate rocks of the crust are about 2500 kg m^{-3}, which produces a maximum g below the surface. This is shown in by the dotted graph.

Because of the similar mathematics, the same would be true of a charged sphere: there is no electric field inside an empty spherical shell of charge and the field outside is as if the charge were concentrated at the centre. This latter would also be true of a sphere which was uniformly charged throughout its volume.

quickfire 9.7

If g at the Earth's surface is $\sim 10 \text{ N kg}^{-1}$, what is its value at double this distance from the centre of the Earth.

quickfire 9.8

Assuming uniform density, what value of g would there be halfway to the Earth's core.

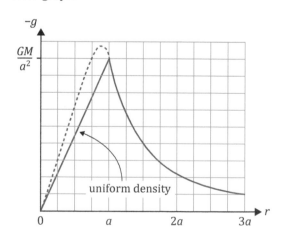

Fig 9.12

9.3 Electric and gravitational potential – scalar fields

If we move an object between two points in a gravitational field, the work we do against the field is independent of the route we take between the two points.[?] The same is true if we move a charge between two points in an electric field. This work we do is recoverable so it represents a change in potential energy.

We define the *potential* at a point in an electric field as 'the work done per unit charge against the field in moving a small charge from a place of zero potential'. For inverse square fields, it is normal to define ∞ as the place of zero potential, so the definition of potential can be stated as, 'the work done per unit charge against the field in moving a small charge from infinity to that point'.

We can relate the potential, V, to the electric field strength. Consider moving a small charge, q, from the point with potential V_1 to the point with potential V_2 against a uniform electric field of strength $\mathbf{E}$ as shown in Figure 9.14.

The force, $\mathbf{F}$, exerted by the field $= q\mathbf{E}$

So the work done against the field, $W = -q\mathbf{E}.\mathbf{x}$. $\therefore \Delta V = V_2 - V_1 = \dfrac{W}{q} = -\mathbf{E}.\mathbf{x}$

If $\mathbf{x}$ is at 90° to $\mathbf{E}$ then $W = 0$, therefore $\Delta V = 0$ and the two points are at the same potential. All points on a surface at right angles to an electric field are at the same potential and we call such surfaces *equipotentials*. The dotted line in Figure 9.14 is an equipotential.

In Test Yourself 10.2, Questions 13–17, we demonstrate that the electric potential, V_E, due to a point charge, Q, and the gravitational potential, V_G, due to a point mass, M, are, at a distance r:

$$V_E = \frac{Q}{4\pi\varepsilon_0 r} \quad \text{and} \quad V_G = -\frac{GM}{r}.$$

The results of Section 9.2.3 show that the same formulae are valid for a point outside spherical charges or masses.

Combining potentials

The electric field strength in a region of space due to two charges is the sum of the fields due to each charge seperately. The same holds for potentials: the potential at any point in the fields is the sum of the potentials due to each charge separately. However, electric field strength is a vector and potential is a scalar – electric **potential does not have a direction**, though it may be + or –. This makes it much easier to deal with. It is exactly the same with gravitational potential – it is a scalar.

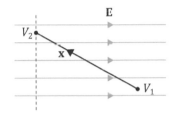

Fig 9.13

Fig 9.14

quickfire 9.9

A and B are 10 cm apart. V_A, the potential at A, is 500 V; $V_B = 650$ V. Calculate E.

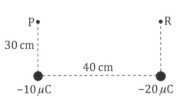

Example C:

Calculate (a) the potential at point **P** in the diagram and
(b) the work done in moving a charge of $-5\,\mu C$ from **P** to **R**.

(a) V_P = potential due to $-10\,\mu C$ + potential due to $-20\,\mu C$

$$= \frac{1}{4\pi\varepsilon_0}\frac{(-10\times10^{-6})}{0.3} + \frac{1}{4\pi\varepsilon_0}\frac{(-20\times10^{-6})}{0.5}$$

$$= -660\,\text{kV} \left[\text{using } \frac{1}{4\pi\varepsilon_0 r} = 9\times10^9\,\text{F}^{-1}\,\text{m}\right].$$

(b) $V_R = \dfrac{1}{4\pi\varepsilon_0}\dfrac{(-10\times10^{-6})}{0.5} + \dfrac{1}{4\pi\varepsilon_0}\dfrac{(-20\times10^{-6})}{0.3}$

$= -780\,\text{kV}. \therefore \Delta V = -120\,\text{kV}.$

$\therefore$ From the definition of potential, Work done $= Q\Delta V = -5\,\mu C \times (-120\,\text{kV}) = 0.6\,\text{J}.$

quickfire 9.10

Add the 500 V and 650 V equipotential lines to the diagram in QF9.9.

[?] The proof of this is beyond the scope of this book.

quickfire ▶ 9.11

A and B are 10 cm apart. Their potentials are as in QF 9.9.
The field is at 30° to BA.
(a) Calculate E
(b) Add the equipotentials as in QF 9.10

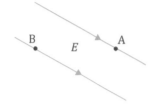

9.4 The flux of a field

The *flux, Φ,* of an electric field, **E**, through a surface of area, A, is defined by

$$\Phi = \mathbf{E}.\mathbf{A}$$

where **A** is a vector of magnitude A at right angles to the surface.

If the field is not uniform and/or the surface is not flat, then Φ is calculated by dividing up the surface into very small areas, working out the flux through each and then adding the fluxes together:[note]

$$\Phi = \mathbf{E}_1.\Delta\mathbf{A}_1 + \mathbf{E}_2.\Delta\mathbf{A}_2 + \mathbf{E}_3.\Delta\mathbf{A}_3 + \ldots$$

Pictorially, we can think of the flux as being the number of field lines which cross the surface. A large field crossing a small surface can have the same flux as a weak field crossing a large surface. A consequence of Coulomb's law is that, for any closed surface, e.g. the surface of a sphere, $\Phi = \dfrac{Q}{\varepsilon_0}$, where Q is the total charge enclosed by the surface. This is called **Gauss's law**.

This puts into mathematics the idea that the number of field lines emerging from a closed surface is proportional to the charge enclosed.

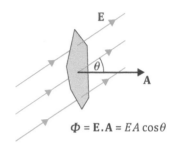

$$\Phi = \mathbf{E}.\mathbf{A} = EA\cos\theta$$

Fig 9.15

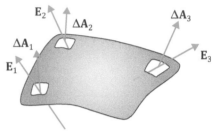

Fig 9.16

Example D:

Show that Gauss's law gives the correct answer for the electric field at the surface of a charged sphere.

Let the sphere have a charge Q and radius a. The field is radial so it is at right angles to the surface and it is also the same magnitude at all points on the surface.

$\therefore \quad \Phi = E \times 4\pi a^2$.   Gauss's law: $\Phi = \dfrac{Q}{\varepsilon_0}$.

Eliminating Φ gives: $E \times 4\pi a^2 = \dfrac{Q}{\varepsilon_0}$.

$\therefore E = \dfrac{Q}{4\pi\varepsilon_0 a^2}$, which is the correct answer from Coulomb's law.

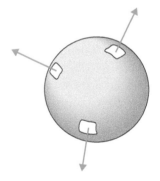

We can define the flux of any vector field in the same way. The change in flux of a magnetic field is important for electromagnetic induction – see Section 9.5.3.

The electric field inside a capacitor

Consider a parallel plate capacitor with an air gap. Assume that the gap, d, is small and the area, A, comparatively large so that edge effects can be ignored; hence the charges $+Q$ and $-Q$ will be spread uniformly over the inner surfaces of the plates.

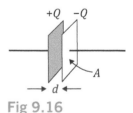

Fig 9.16

[note] We then reduce the size of the areas and take the limit of the sum as each of the $\Delta\mathbf{A}$s tend to zero – this process is called a surface integral. Surface integrals with non-uniform fields are beyond the scope of this book.

To calculate the field, **E**, between the plates we apply Gauss's law. Surround the positive plate with a closed surface as shown in Figure 9.17.

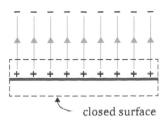

E is at right angles to the top face of the surface, so Φ, the flux through this area is $EA \cos 0° = EA$. Below the plate the field is 0. The flux through the sides surfaces is 0 because the field is parallel to these surfaces (above the plate) or 0 (below the plate).

closed surface

Fig 9.17

∴ The total flux through the closed surface, $\Phi = EA$.

From Gauss's law: $\Phi = \dfrac{Q}{\varepsilon_0}$. ∴ $E = \dfrac{Q}{\varepsilon_0 A}$. [see note ❹]

From this result, we can calculate the **capacitance of a parallel plate capacitor with an air gap:**

The electric field strength in between the plates, $E = \dfrac{Q}{\varepsilon_0 A}$.

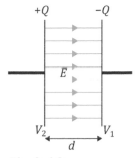

∴ The potential difference ❺ between the plates, $V = V_2 - V_1 = \dfrac{Q}{\varepsilon_0 A} d$

Capacitance is defined by $Q = CV$, so the last equation becomes

$$C = \frac{\varepsilon_0 A}{d}.$$

Fig 9.18

Example E:

A plane insulating sheet is charged with a surface charge density of -5 nC m^{-2}. Calculate the electric field, E, in the vicinity of the sheet.

Consider a cylinder at right angles to the sheet, with end area A. The total charge enclosed is $-\sigma A$.

Pointer

The surface density, σ, is the charge per unit area. Its unit is C m^{-2}.

∴ The flux emerging from the cylinder, $\Phi = \dfrac{-\sigma A}{\varepsilon_0}$.

The field **E** is at right angles to the sheet surfaces, of total area $2A$, and parallel to the side surfaces,

∴ $\qquad\qquad\qquad \Phi = 2AE.$

∴ $2AE = \dfrac{-\sigma A}{\varepsilon_0}$ $\qquad$ ∴ $E = -\dfrac{\sigma}{2\varepsilon_0} = -\dfrac{5 \times 10^{-9}}{2 \times 8.854 \times 10^{-12}} = -282\,\text{V m}^{-1}$.

9.5 Magnetic fields

These are more complicated than electric or gravitational fields.

1 They are produced and detected by moving charged particles. Velocity is a vector quantity, so the production and detection of magnetic fields involve vectors in a way which electric and gravitational fields do not.

2 Magnetic field lines are closed; they do not begin and end.

---

❹ The quantity $\dfrac{Q}{A}$ is called the surface charge density, σ.

❺ In electric fields, we normally write the potential difference as ΔV; in electric circuits it is usually written as V.

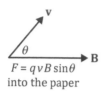

Fig 9.19

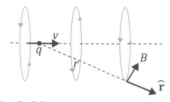

Fig 9.20

9.5.1 Definitions and basic formulae

The strength of a magnetic field is called the *magnetic flux density*, **B**. **B** is defined by the force, **F**, on a charge, q, moving with velocity, **v**. The force is the vector product of q**v** with **B**:

$$\mathbf{F} = q\mathbf{v} \times \mathbf{B}$$

i.e. $F = qvB \sin \theta$ at right angles to both **v** and **B**. The unit of **B** is the tesla, T.

From this equation we can derive the force on a length ℓ of wire, carrying a current, I, placed in a magnetic field.

The current, I, is given by $I = nAqv$ where A is the cross sectional area of the wire and n the number of charge carriers per unit volume.

The total number of charge carriers is $nA\ell$, so $F = nA\ell qvB \sin \theta = BI\ell \sin \theta$.

The direction of the force is the direction of $q\mathbf{v} \times \mathbf{B}$.

The flux density produced at a point **P**, with position vector **r** measured from q, by a charge q, moving with velocity **v** is also given by a vector product:

$$\mathbf{B} = \frac{\mu_0}{4\pi} \frac{q}{r^2} \mathbf{v} \times \hat{\mathbf{r}}, \text{ where } \hat{\mathbf{r}} \text{ is the unit vector from } q \text{ to } \mathbf{P}.$$

i.e. $\mathbf{B} = \frac{\mu_0}{4\pi} \frac{qv \sin \theta}{r^2}$ with the field lines being circles of direction clockwise around the direction of movement of the charge.[6] The constant μ_0 is the *permeability of free space*, $4\pi \times 10^{-7}$ H m^{-1}.

Example F:

Show that the torque, τ, on a rectangular coil, of area A, with N turns, whose axis of rotation is at right angles to a magnetic field, **B**, is given by

$$\tau = BANI \cos \theta.$$

Let WX = YZ = a and XY = ZW = b

The force on side WX, $F_{WX} = BIa$ vertically downwards; $F_{YZ} = BIa$ vertically upwards.

The forces on XY and ZW are equal and opposite in the plane of the coil and cancel out.

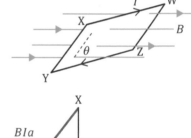

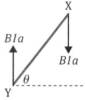

The diagram shows the edge view of the coil:

$$\tau = BIa \times XY \cos \theta = BabNI \cos \theta = BANI \cos \theta.$$

Note: This result is also true for coils other than rectangular.

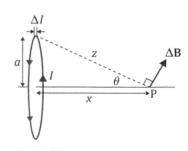

quickfire 9.12

Express the tesla in terms of the base SI units, m, kg, s and A.
[Hint: use the equation $\mathbf{F} = q\mathbf{v} \times \mathbf{B}$]

9.5.2 Magnetic field on the axis of a plane coil

Consider a point **P** on the axis of a plane coil, with a single turn, of radius a, carrying a current, I, at a distance x from the centre of the coil.

Using the usual symbols: $I = nAvq$.

Consider the contribution, $\Delta \mathbf{B}$, from the section of the coil, $\Delta \ell$, at the top. The dotted line is at right angles to the coil. The number of charge carriers in $\Delta \ell = nA\Delta \ell$,

Fig 9.21

---

[6] Direction of the field lines – note that q can be either + or –. If q is negative the field line direction will be opposite.

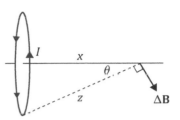

Fig 9.22

$$\therefore \quad \Delta \mathbf{B} = \frac{\mu_0}{4\pi}\frac{nAqv\Delta \ell}{z^2} = \frac{\mu_0}{4\pi}\frac{I\Delta\ell}{z^2} \quad \text{in the direction shown.}$$

Consider next, the contribution from the opposite section. The horizontal component of $\Delta\mathbf{B}$ is the same as for the top section – the vertical components are equal and opposite so they cancel out.

In fact, for all segments of the coil, the components of the $\Delta\mathbf{B}$ vectors at right angle to the axis cancel in pairs, whilst the components along the axis add. These are all $\Delta B \sin\theta$. If we add up all the $\Delta\ell$ to give $2\pi a$ and using $z^2 = a^2 + x^2$ we get

$$\therefore \quad \mathbf{B} = \frac{\mu_0}{4\pi}\frac{I 2\pi a \sin\theta}{(a^2 + x^2)}, \quad \text{i.e } \mathbf{B} = \frac{\mu_0 I a \sin\theta}{2(a^2 + x^2)} \text{ along the axis to the right.}$$

$$\sin\theta = \frac{a}{z} = \frac{a}{\sqrt{(a^2 + x^2)}}, \quad \text{so we can rewrite this: } B = \frac{\mu_0 I a^2}{2(a^2 + x^2)^{\frac{3}{2}}}$$

At the centre of the coil, $x = 0$ so we obtain the familiar formula $B = \frac{\mu_0 I}{2a}$.

With N turns on the coil these formulae become $B = \frac{\mu_0 N I a^2}{2(a^2 + x^2)^{\frac{3}{2}}}$ and $B = \frac{\mu_0 N I}{2a}$

Using the techniques of integral calculus, we can also derive the following formulae for flux density:

- at a distance r from a long straight wire: $B = \frac{\mu_0 I}{2\pi r}$, with field lines clockwise around the wire

- inside a long solenoid: $B = \mu_0 n I$, the direction given by the right-hand grip rule.

See Chapter 12 for the derivation of these formulae.

Example G:

Two long, straight, parallel wires, X and Y, 1 cm apart, carry a current of 10 A in the same direction. A third wire, Z, of length 1 m, carrying a current of 5 A is placed parallel to the others, as shown in the diagram.   XZ = YZ = 1 cm

Calculate the magnetic force on wire **Z**.

The field $\mathbf{B_X}$ due to X at Z $= \frac{4\pi \times 10^{-7} \times 10}{2\pi \times 0.01} = 2.0 \times 10^{-4}$ T: Direction, to the right at 30° below the horizontal.

The field due to Y at Z $= 2.0 \times 10^{-4}$ T to the right at 30° above the horizontal.

The resultant field $\mathbf{B} = 2 \times (2.0 \times 10^{-4}) \cos 30° = 3.46 \times 10^{-4}$ T, horizontal to the right.

The force, $\mathbf{F}$ on Z is given by: $\mathbf{F} = BI\ell$ downwards

$$F = 3.46 \times 10^{-4} \times 5 \times 1 = 1.73 \text{ mN.}$$

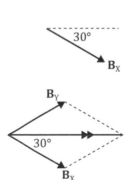

9.5.3 Magnetic flux – electromagnetic induction

The flux of a magnetic field through an area is defined in the same way as the flux of an electric field:

$$\Phi = \mathbf{B.A}$$

The unit of Φ is the weber, Wb.

Another useful quantity is *flux linkage*: if the magnetic field passes through a coil with N turns, the magnetic flux linkage is defined as $N\Phi$. Its unit is weber-turn, Wb-turn. Oddly, there is no symbol for flux linkage – it is always $N\Phi$!

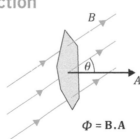

$\Phi = \mathbf{B.A}$

Fig 9.23

Faraday's law of electromagnetic induction states that an emf is induced if the flux linkage in a circuit changes. The induced emf, $\mathcal{E}_{in}$, is equal to the rate of change of flux linkage:

$$\mathcal{E}_{in} = \frac{\Delta(N\Phi)}{t} = \frac{d}{dt}(N\Phi) \quad \text{in the language of calculus.}$$

Whether the emf produces a current – the *induced current* – depends upon the nature of the circuit. We'll deal with a few examples. The direction of the induced emf is the subject of **Lenz's** law [pronounced *lentses*]: 'The direction of the induced emf is such as to tend to oppose the change producing it.' This rather opaque wording can be interpreted in several equivalent ways, which will be dealt with in the examples that follow.

Example H is a scenario beloved of examiners!

Example H:

A conducting bar slides over a pair of rails. A magnetic field of flux density 5 mT links the circuit at right angles as shown. If the circuit has a resistance of 0.2 Ω, calculate the induced current and state its direction.

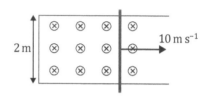

$\Phi = \mathbf{B}.\mathbf{A}$ and $\mathbf{A}$ is increasing at 2 m × 10 m s^{-1} = 20 m^2 s^{-1}.

So from Faraday's law $\mathcal{E}_{in} = \frac{\Delta(N\Phi)}{t} = 5 \times 10^{-3} \times 20 = 0.1$ V.

$$\therefore \qquad I_{in} = \frac{\mathcal{E}_{in}}{R} = \frac{0.1}{0.2} = 0.5 \text{ A}.$$

> Direction of I_{in}: **One** way of applying Lenz's law is to say that, because there is a current in the bar, it will experience a force which opposes the motion. Applying $\mathbf{F} = q\mathbf{v} \times \mathbf{B}$, with $\mathbf{F}$ to the left → $q\mathbf{v}$, i.e. I, is **upwards** in the bar.

Simple generator

Consider a coil, WXYZ, of area A rotating with angular speed ω in a magnetic field of flux density $\mathbf{B}$. Figure 9.25 shows the coil edge on, when it is at an angle θ to $\mathbf{B}$.

In this position: $N\Phi = BAN\sin\theta$ [see footnote ⑦]

If the coil rotates at ω, $\theta = \omega t + \varepsilon$

$$\therefore \qquad N\Phi = BAN\sin(\omega t + \varepsilon)$$

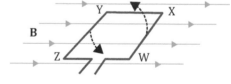

Fig 9.24

$\mathcal{E}_{in}$ is the rate of change of $N\Phi = \frac{d}{dt}(N\Phi) = BAN\omega\cos(\omega t + \varepsilon)$

If the resistance of the circuit is R, $I_{in} = \frac{BAN\omega}{R}\cos(\omega t + \varepsilon)$

To work out the direction of the induced emf (and current) we could use the same technique as in Example F. An alternative is to consider the change of flux in the coil. In the diagrams the flux is *increasing*, so the induced current will *oppose* the change, i.e. it will produce a field in the opposite direction, which requires the current direction to be $\overrightarrow{WXYZ}$ at that time.

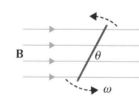

Fig 9.25

coil horizontal, WX moving up

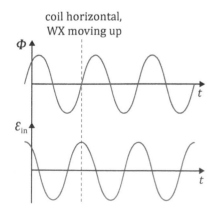

Fig 9.26

110

---

⑦ The angle between the normal to the plane coil and $\mathbf{B}$ is 90°− θ ; cos(90°− θ) = sin θ

Self-inductance – the inductance of a coil

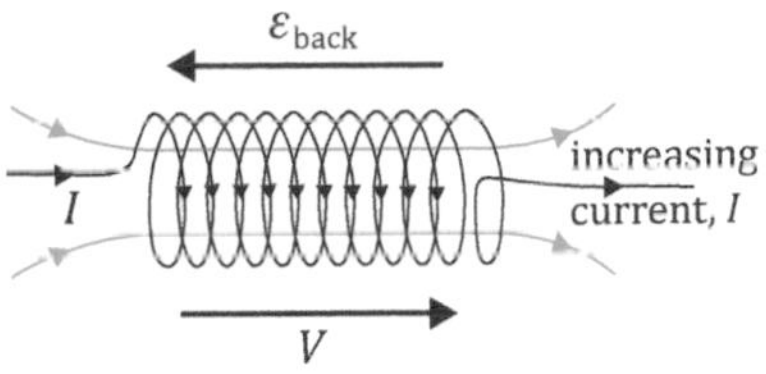

Consider a conducting coil with a current, I, in it. The current produces a magnetic field which links the coil. If a voltage, V, is applied, the current increases, causing an increase in the flux linkage producing an opposing emf – the *back emf*, $\mathcal{E}_{back}$.

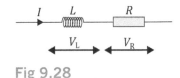

Fig 9.27

This emf is proportional to the rate of change of flux linkage and hence to the rate of change of current.

Assuming that the coil has negligible resistance, the electric field within the wire will be zero, so the back emf is equal and opposite to the applied voltage. [A practical coil with a non-negligible resistance can be treated as a zero-resistance coil in series with a non-inductive resistor – see Section 8.5.2 and below.]

Hence the equation $V = L\dfrac{dI}{dt}$ applies, where L is a constant called the *self-inductance* of the coil. The unit of L is the henry, H.

The flux density, **B**, inside a long solenoid with n turns per metre, is given by $B = \mu_0 nI$. If the solenoid has length ℓ and cross-sectional area A, the flux linkage is given by $N\Phi = \mu_0 n^2 \ell AI$, ignoring the short region at each end in which B is less.

$\therefore \qquad\qquad V = \mathcal{E}_{back} = \mu_0 n^2 \ell A \times$ rate of change of current.

$\therefore \qquad\qquad L = \mu_0 n^2 \ell A$

Example I:

A coil has a length of 50 cm, a cross-sectional area 5 cm² and 10 000 turns per metre.

Calculate (a) the self-inductance of the coil and (b) the rate of growth of current if a pd of 10 V is applied to the coil.

(a) $L = 4\pi \times 10^{-7} \times 10\,000^2 \times 0.5 \times 5 \times 10^{-4} = 31$ mH

(b) $\dfrac{dI}{dt} = \dfrac{V}{L} = \dfrac{10}{2.5 \times 10^{-3}} = 318$ A s^{-1}.

Unless it is superconducting, a solenoid possesses resistance as well as self-inductance. We can treat such a coil as a series combination of a pure inductor [i.e. a coil with no resistance] and a resistor; see Figure 9.28. What happens if we apply a potential difference, V, across it?

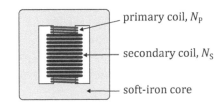

Fig 9.28

The total pd, $\quad V = V_L + V_R$

$\therefore \qquad\qquad V = L\dfrac{dI}{dt} + IR$

The solution is: $\;I = \dfrac{V}{R}(1 - e^{-kt})$, where $k = \dfrac{R}{L}$. [See footnote[8]]. The final current is $\dfrac{V}{R}$, as expected.

Transformers

The details of the physics of transformers, e.g. the purpose of the soft-iron core and the laminations, are beyond the scope of this book.

If a pd, V_P is applied to the primary coil it causes a current I, in the primary which in turn produces a flux, Φ, which links both coils.

The flux linkage in the secondary $= N_S \Phi$.

primary coil, N_P

secondary coil, N_S

soft-iron core

Fig 9.29

The pd across the secondary, V_S = the emf induced in the secondary $= N_S \dfrac{d\Phi}{dt}$.

The back-emf generated in the primary $= N_P \dfrac{d\Phi}{dt}$.

---

[8] See Chapter 11 for the treatment of differential equations of this type.

The primary coil has some resistance but in practice the back-emf is almost the same size, and opposite to the applied pd V_P. Using this approximation, this essentially means a 100% efficient transformer:

$$V_P = N_P \frac{d\Phi}{dt} \text{ and } V_S = N_S \frac{d\Phi}{dt} \text{ lead to the transformer equation: } \frac{V_S}{V_P} = \frac{N_S}{N_P}.$$

Test Yourself 9.1

Where appropriate, the following data should be used:

Mass of Earth = 6×10^{24} kg; Mass of Sun = 2×10^{30} kg; Mass of Moon = 7.5×10^{22} kg.

Radius of Earth's orbit = 150×10^6 km; Radius of Moon's orbit = 400×10^3 km

$G = 6.67 \times 10^{-11}$ N m^2 kg^{-2}; $\varepsilon_0 = 8.854 \times 10^{12}$ F m^{-1}; $\frac{1}{4\pi\varepsilon_0} = 9 \times 10^9$ F^{-1} m

$e = 1.60 \times 10^{-19}$ C; $m_e = 9.11 \times 10^{-31}$ kg; $m_p = 1.67 \times 10^{-27}$ kg

1. A $-1\,\mu$C charge experiences an upward force of 3 mN due to an electric field, **E**. Calculate **E**.

2. A body of mass 1 g carries a charge of $+10\,\mu$C. What strength and direction of electric field will support it against the Earth's gravity?

3. A freely-falling object has an acceleration of 6 m s^{-2} at a distance of 10 000 km from the centre of a planet. Calculate the mass of the planet.

4. The Earth and Moon are separated by 400 000 km. At what point do their gravitational fields balance?

5. Calculate the gravitational potential at a point 400 000 km from the centre of the Earth and 40 000 km from the centre of the moon.

6. Compare the accelerations of the moon due to the gravitational fields of the Earth and the Sun.

7. An electron, travelling at 1.0×10^6 m s^{-1} enters a uniform electric field of strength 100 V m^{-1} at right angles. Calculate its velocity 10 ns later.

8. Calculate the electric field, E, at the surface of a metal sphere of radius 10 cm which carries a charge of $5\,\mu$C.

9. Calculate the electric potential, V, at the surface of a metal sphere of radius 10 cm which carries a charge of $5\,\mu$C.

10. Use the answer to Q9 to calculate the capacitance of a 10 cm radius sphere.

11. Show that the capacitance of a conducting sphere, of radius a, is $4\pi\varepsilon_0 a$

12. A long metal wire lies along the axis of a long hollow metal cylinder. The wire carries a charge of $+3\,\mu$C per m of its length. Use Gauss's law to calculate the field strength 10 cm from the axis of the cylinder [internal radius of cylinder > 10 cm]. Show your working.

13. If the radius of the cylinder in Q12 is 20 cm, calculate the surface charge density on the inner surface of the cylinder.

Questions 14–19 relate to Figure 9.30. Two small insulating spheres, each of mass 0.1 g, are suspended from light threads as shown. They carry equal charges, Q, and repel each other so that their equilibrium separation is 10 cm.

14. Calculate Q.

15. Calculate (a) the electric field, E, due to each at point O and (b) the resultant field at O.

16. Calculate the electric potential at O.

17. Show that the electrical potential energy of the two charges is approximately 25 μJ.

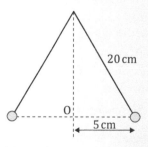

Fig 9.30

⑱ The charges are moved so that they are 5 cm apart and released. In the absence of frictional losses, calculate their speed when they pass through their equilibrium position. Show your working.

⑲ The charge on one of the spheres is changed to $-Q$. They are now separately suspended on 20 cm threads but their separation is still 10 cm. Calculate:

(a) the resultant field at O, the midpoint of the line joining them, and

(b) the electric potential at O.

The structure of the Earth can be approximated as a series of concentric spheres of uniform density as follows:

Inner core – radius 1000 km; density 13 000 kg m^{-3}

Outer core – outer radius 3500 km; density 11 000 kg m^{-3}

Mantle / Crust – outer radius 6370 km; density 4400 kg m^{-3}

Use these data to answer questions 20 and 21.

⑳ Calculate: (a) the total mass of the Earth and (b) the gravitational field strength at the surface and compare your answers with the accepted values for the Earth.

㉑ Calculate the gravitational field strength at the surface of the outer core and compare it to the figure for a uniform density planet.

㉒ An electron travels with a velocity of 1×10^5 m s^{-1} at right angles to a magnetic field of flux density 5×10^{-4} T. As a result it travels in a circle. Calculate:

(a) the acceleration of the electron, (b) the radius of the circle and (c) the gyrofrequency [i.e. the number of circulations per second].

㉓ Show that the gyrofrequency of a charged particle in a magnetic field is independent of the speed of the (non-relativistic) particle and calculate the proton gyrofrequency in a region of the Earth's magnetic field in with flux density 30 μT.

㉔ The rms current in an overhead conductor is 20 A. The frequency is 50 Hz. The wire is at 60° to the Earth's magnetic field. How does the force, F, on a 1 m length of wire vary with time? $B = 50$ μT

㉕ In Example G, the wire experiences a force due to the motor effect. Show that the work done per unit time against this force is equal to the electrical power dissipated in the circuit.

Chapter 10

Calculus

10.1 Introduction

Physics ideas are often expressed in terms of rates of change.

- Newton's second law of motion – the rate of change of momentum is directly proportional to the resultant force.
- Faraday's law – the induced emf is equal to the rate of change of flux linkage.
- the stiffness of an object is the change of tensile force per unit increase in length.

Note that 'rate' does not always mean 'per unit time' as the third example shows. As long as the rates of change are constant, little more than GCSE mathematics is required, such as the equations of motion for constant acceleration, $v = u + at$ etc. Varying rates of change are tackled by the branch of maths called **differential calculus**.

Other physics ideas involve the product of quantities; e.g. the work done is the product of the displacement and the component of the force in the direction of the displacement. Again, if the force is constant we can write this as $Fx \cos \theta$ but we often need to consider situations where the force varies with the distance; e.g. the increasing tension in a spring with increasing stretch. The calculation of such products in which the quantities vary is called **integral calculus**.

This chapter will explore both differential and integral calculus and find that they are closely related. In most A-level Physics specifications candidates are expected to be familiar with the results of calculus analysis, though the examinations themselves usually do not involve the application of calculus.

10.2 Differential calculus – the analysis of rates of change

10.2.1 An illustrative example

We'll illustrate the technique with a slightly contrived example. The momentum of an object varies with time according to the graph (Figure 10 1). We'll ask the simple question, 'What is the resultant force on the object at time $t = 1.0$ s?'

From the graph, the mean rate of change of momentum between 1 and 2 s is obtained from the gradient of the chord between 1 s and 2 s.

$$\text{Force} = \frac{\Delta p}{\Delta t} = \frac{50}{1} = 50 \text{ N}$$

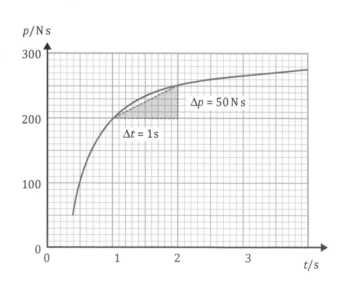

Fig 10.1

Δp? This is pronounced *delta p* and means the change in the value of p.

$\Delta p = p_2 - p_1 = 250 - 200 = 50$ N s. Similarly $\Delta t = 2 - 1 = 1$ s.

So, we can find the mean force between any two instants, but what about the force *at* an instant? Clearly we can't use the above method because our triangle would have sides of zero length and we'd have:

$$\text{Force} = \frac{\Delta p}{\Delta t} = \frac{0}{0} = \text{which we can't evaluate!}$$

The answer is to sneak up on the point. We start with a large triangle, find the gradient, then repeat with smaller and smaller triangles, but never quite getting to 0, and see what the gradient tends to.

To follow this, you need a calculator or a spreadsheet to hand. You also need to know that the equation of the graph above is $p = 300 - \dfrac{100}{t}$. In Table 10.1 t_1 is 1.0 s and p_1 is 200 N s.

Table 10.1

t_2 /s	p_2 / Ns	Δt / s	Δp / Ns	$\dfrac{\Delta p}{\Delta t}$ / N
2.0	250	1.0	50.0	50.0
1.5	233.333	0.5	33.333	66.7
1.1	209.091	0.1	9.091	90.9
1.05	204.762	0.05	4.726	94.5
1.01	200.9901	0.01	0.990	99.0
1.005	200.4975	0.005	0.4975	99.5

It looks as though the gradient is homing in on a value of 100 N. Can we be sure? If we look at a couple of negative values of Δt this confirms it. Check for yourself that

- With $t_2 = 0.99$ s, $\dfrac{\Delta p}{\Delta t} = 101.0$ N

- With $t_2 = 0.995$ s, $\dfrac{\Delta p}{\Delta t} = 100.5$ N

That seems to nail it.

In the next sections, we'll develop the technique to allow us to find the gradient of any graph at any point without going through the same laborious process every time.

Data Exercise 10.1

Use the above technique to show that the gradient of the graph of $y = 3x^2 + 2$ is 12 at the point $x = 2$, $y = 14$.

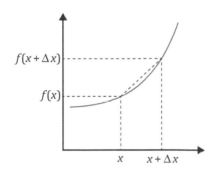

10.2.2   Differentiating any function and the result for x^n

In the work that follows it will be useful to write functions in the form $f(x)$. This is pronounced '*f of x*' and emphasises that the value of f depends upon the value of x. The following symbols are often used for functions f, g, u, v, w, y. [1] The (x) part of the function notation is omitted if there is no confusion. The independent variable, x, could equally well be t, I or any other familiar variable in physics, e.g. with this way of writing, the pd across a power supply equation could be written $V(I) = E - Ir$.

Look at the graph of the function $f(x)$ opposite (Figure 10.2). The gradient of the chord is given by

$$\text{Gradient} = \frac{f(x + \Delta x) - f(x)}{\Delta x}$$

If we make Δx smaller and smaller, the gradient of the chord will approach a limit which is the gradient of the tangent to the curve at $f(x)$.

Fig 10.2

---

[1]   When we are dealing with functions of time, x is also used, i.e. $x(t)$.

We write this gradient $\frac{df(x)}{dx}$ or we can leave out the bracket and write it $\frac{df}{dx}$, and we call it the *derivative of f with respect to x*. The process of finding the derivative is called *differentiating*.

So, by definition, $\frac{df(x)}{dx} = \lim_{\Delta x \to 0} \frac{f(x + \Delta x) - f(x)}{\Delta x}$. [$df$ by dx= *the limit as Δx tends to 0 of ...*]

Let's see how this works for the function $y(x) = x^n$.

From the definition, $\frac{dy}{dx} = \lim_{\Delta x \to 0} \frac{(x + \Delta x)^n - x^n}{\Delta x}$

We'll rewrite $(x + \Delta x)^n$ as $x^n \left(1 + \frac{\Delta x}{x}\right)^n$ and use the binomial expansion [see Section 3.4]:

$x^n \left(1 + \frac{\Delta x}{x}\right)^n = x^n \left(1 + n\frac{\Delta x}{x}\right) = x^n + nx^{n-1}\Delta x$, where we are ignoring $(\Delta x)^2$ and higher terms.

So $(x + \Delta x)^n - x^n = nx^{n-1}\Delta x +$ terms of order $(\Delta x)^2$ and higher

Dividing by Δx; $\frac{dy}{dx} = \lim_{\Delta x \to 0} nx^{n-1} +$ terms of order Δx and higher.

But as $\Delta x \to 0$, all terms except the first one become 0 and we are left with the following result:

If $y(x) = x^n$, $\frac{dy}{dx} = nx^{n-1}$.

You will often see this written as $\frac{d}{dx}(x^n) = nx^{n-1}$.

Example A: If $y = x^5$, what is the gradient when $x = 1.75$?

$\frac{dy}{dx} = 5x^4 = 5 \times 1.75^4 = 46.9$ [3 s.f.]

Example B: If $x = t^2$, what is the rate of change of x when $t = 10$?

$\frac{dx}{dt} = 2t^1 = 2t$, so the rate of change of $x = 20$ when $t = 10$.

Two special cases to remember

- If $y = x$, $\frac{dy}{dx} = 1$ [Remember that $x = x^1$]

- If $y = a$ [a constant], $\frac{dy}{dx} = 0$ [Remember that $1 = x^0$]

10.2.3   Differentiating transcendental functions

The functions $\sin x$, $\cos x$, e^x and $\ln x$ are among the most important in mathematical physics. This section gives the results of differentiating them. These results are obtained in a similar manner to that for x^n, the derivations being given in Chapter 12. It is worth working through the derivations to check that you understand the ideas.

The results are in Table 10.2:

Table 10.2

$\frac{d}{dx}(\sin x) = \cos x$	$\frac{d}{dx}(\cos x) = -\sin x$	$\frac{d}{dx}(e^x) = e^x$	$\frac{d}{dx}(\ln x) = \frac{1}{x}$

Pointer

$\frac{dy}{dx}$ is often written y', $\frac{df}{dx}$ is written f'.

$\frac{dx}{dt}$ is often written as $\dot{x}$

Pointer

Velocity, v, is the rate of change of displacement, x, i.e. $v = \frac{ds}{dt} = \dot{s}$.

Pointer

Acceleration, a, is the rate of change of velocity, v, i.e. $a = \frac{dv}{dt} = \dot{v}$.

quickfire 10.1

If $y = x^4$, what is $\frac{dy}{dx}$?

quickfire 10.2

If $y = \frac{1}{x}$, what is $\frac{dy}{dx}$? $\left[\text{Hint: } \frac{1}{x} = x^{-1}\right]$.

quickfire 10.3

If $y = \sqrt{x}$, what is the gradient when $x = 4$? $\left[\text{Hint: } \sqrt{x} = x^{\frac{1}{2}}\right]$

10.2.4 Differentiating combinations of functions

Most function in physics are combinations of functions, e.g.

- $s(t) = ut + \frac{1}{2}at^2$, which has a linear and a square term, both multiplied by a constant
- $\sin(\omega t + \varepsilon)$, sine is a function and so is $\omega t + \varepsilon$.

We need some rules for handling this sort of thing. Table 10.3 gives useful rules. As with the results in 10.2.3, the proofs are given in Chapter 12. For the work that follows, u and v are functions of x; u' and v' are shorthand for $\dfrac{du}{dx}$ and $\dfrac{dv}{dx}$ respectively.

Table 10.3

Function $f(x) =$	Notes	$\dfrac{df}{dx}$ [or f']
$f = \alpha u$	α is a constant	$\dfrac{df}{dx} = \alpha\dfrac{du}{dx}$ [or $\alpha u'$]
$f = \alpha u + \beta v$	α and β are constants	$\dfrac{df}{dx} = \alpha\dfrac{du}{dx} + \beta\dfrac{dv}{dx}$ [or $\alpha u' + \beta v'$]
$f = uv$	product of functions	$\dfrac{df}{dx} = u\dfrac{dv}{dx} + v\dfrac{du}{dx}$ [or $uv' + vu'$]
$f = \dfrac{u}{v}$	ratio of functions	$\dfrac{df}{dx} = \dfrac{1}{v^2}\left[v\dfrac{du}{dx} - u\dfrac{dv}{dx}\right]$ $\left[\text{or }\dfrac{vu' - uv'}{v^2}\right]$
$f = f(g(x))$	'function of a function'	$\dfrac{df}{dx} = \dfrac{df}{dg}\dfrac{dg}{dx}$ – the chain rule

The chain rule is probably the most difficult to understand. The most common examples in A-level Physics are in radioactive or capacitor decay and in simple harmonic motion.

- Decay equations: If $f(t) = f_0 e^{-kt}$, we can write this $f(t) = f_0 e^{g(t)}$, where $g(t) = -kt$.

$$\frac{dg}{dt} = -k \text{ and } \frac{df}{dg} = f_0 e^g$$

So $\quad \dfrac{df}{dt} = -kf_0 e^{-kt}$

- SHM: If $f(t) = A\sin(\omega t + \varepsilon)$, we can write this $f(t) = A\sin(g(t))$, where $g = \omega t + \varepsilon$.

$$\frac{dg}{dt} = \omega \text{ and } \frac{df}{dg} = A\cos g$$

So $\quad \dfrac{df}{dt} = A\omega\cos(\omega t + \varepsilon)$

Similarly, if $f(t) = A\cos(\omega t + \varepsilon)$, $\dfrac{df}{dt} = -A\omega\sin(\omega t + \varepsilon)$

10.2.5 Multiple differentiation – 2nd derivatives

As we have seen, if we differentiate y with respect to x, we write this $\dfrac{dy}{dx}$. Differentiating this again gives: $\dfrac{d}{dx}\left(\dfrac{dy}{dx}\right)$ which we write as $\dfrac{d^2y}{dx^2}$, pronounced *dee two y by dee x squared*.

Similarly: $\dfrac{d}{dt}\left(\dfrac{dx}{dt}\right) = \dfrac{d^2x}{dt^2}$.

Example C:

If $x = 5t^2 + 3t + 7$, $\dfrac{dx}{dt} = 10t + 3$ and $\dfrac{d^2y}{dx^2} = 10$

This will be important in Section 11.5.

Pointer

As before $\dfrac{d^2y}{dx^2}$ can be written y'' and $\dfrac{d^2}{dx^2}(f(x)) = f''$

quickfire ➤ 10.4

Find f'' [i.e. $\dfrac{d^2f}{dx^2}$], if $f(x) = 10e^{-5x}$.

quickfire ➤ 10.5

Find $\ddot{y}$, i.e. $\dfrac{d^2y}{dt^2}$, if $y = 10\ln 5t$.

Test Yourself 10.1

Use the result for $f = \alpha u$ in Table 10.3 to differentiate the functions in Questions 1–4 and calculate the gradient of the graph at the value given.

① $y = 25x^3$, when $x = 1.5$ **②** $x = 15 \sin t$, when $t = 3.142$

③ $N = 600e^t$, when $t = 0.5$ **④** $y = 6.0 \ln x$, when $x = 6.0$

Use the result for $f = \alpha u + \beta v$, in Table 10.3 to differentiate the functions in Questions 5–8 and calculate the gradient of the graph at the value given.

⑤ $y = 8t + 3t^2$ when $t = 2.5$,   **⑥** $x = 3 \cos t + 8 \sin t$ when $t = 1.571$

⑦ $y = 2x^3 + 3e^x$ when $t = 1.5$ **⑧** $x = 10 \ln t - 3\sqrt{t}$, when $t = 4.0$

Use the result for $f = uv$ in Table 10.3 to differentiate the functions in Questions 9–12.

⑨ $y = 2x^3(x^2 - 5)$: [Hint: put $u = 2x^3$ and $v = x^2 - 5$]   **⑩** $y = (x + 3)(x^2 - 5)$ **⑪** $y = x^2 e^x$ **⑫** $x = 3t^2 \sin t$

Use the result for $f = \dfrac{u}{v}$ in Table 10.3 to differentiate the functions in Questions 13–16.

⑬ $y = \dfrac{x+1}{x-1}$ [Hint: $u = x + 1$, $v = x - 1$]   **⑭** $y = \dfrac{x^2 + 3x + 1}{x - 2}$

⑮ $x = \dfrac{2t^4}{\cos t}$ **⑯** $y = \dfrac{\ln x}{x^2}$ [Check the result by using $f = uv$ and putting $v = x^{-2}$]

Use the chain rule to differentiate the functions in Questions 17–21.

⑰ $f = (x^2 + 2)^3$. Use the following steps:

    (a) Identify the functions: $g = x^2 + 2$ and $f = g^3$.

    (b) Differentiate f and g [i.e. find $\dfrac{df}{dg}$ and $\dfrac{dg}{dx}$]

    (c) Apply the chain rule: $\dfrac{df}{dx} = \dfrac{df}{dg}\dfrac{dg}{dx}$

[Check your answer by multiplying out $(x^2 + 2)^3$ and differentiating the resulting expression]

⑱ $x = 25 \sin 3t$ [Hint: $g = 3t$ and $x = 25 \sin g$]   **⑲** $v = 100 \cos (314t - \frac{\pi}{4})$

⑳ $N = (1.0 \times 10^{12})e^{-0.1t}$ [Hint $g = -0.1t$ and $A = (1.0 \times 10^{12})e^g$]   **㉑** $Q = 5e^{-t/25}$

㉒ The pd, V, across a power supply of emf E and internal resistance r, depends upon the value, R, of resistor connected across it according to the equation

$$V = \frac{ER}{R + r}.$$

    Differentiate this equation with respect to R and hence find the gradient of the V, R graph when $R = 0$.

㉓ The charge, Q, on a capacitor of capacitance C decays through a resistor of resistance R, according to the equation: $Q = Q_0 e^{-t/RC}$, where Q_0 is the initial charge stored.

    (a) Differentiate this equation.

    (b) Determine the value of $\dfrac{dQ}{dt}$ at $t = 10$ s, if $Q_0 = 0.25$ C, $R = 1$ kΩ and $C = 10$ mF.

    (c) What would be the reading on an ammeter in series with the resistor when $t = 10$ s?

㉔ The flux linkage, $N\Phi$, in a coil is given by $N\Phi = BAN \sin \omega t$. By differentiating this expression and using Faraday's law for the induced emf, $\mathcal{E}_{in} = \dfrac{d}{dt}(N\Phi)$, sketch a graph of the induced emf against time if $B = 0.05$ T, $A = 4 \times 10^{-3}$ m^2, $N = 1000$ turns and $\omega = 100\pi$ s^{-1}.

㉕ A particle undergoes simple harmonic motion. Its position, x, varies with time according to the equation $x = A \sin (\omega t + \frac{\pi}{4})$.

    (a) By differentiating this equation, find the relationship between v and t [Hint: $v = \dfrac{dx}{dt}$]

    (b) By differentiating again, find the relationship between a and t [Hint: $a = \dfrac{dv}{dx}$]

    (c) Sketch graphs of x, v and a against t if $A = 10$ cm and $\omega = 6$ s^{-1}.

    (d) If the mass of the particle is 100 g, find the maximum resultant force upon it.

10.3 Integral calculus

10.3.1 Approximate integration

Suppose we have a sample of gas which expands and does work against a piston. The variation of p with V is shown in Figure 10.3. How much work does the gas do in expanding from $1.0 \times 10^{-3} \, m^3$ to $5.0 \times 10^{-3} \, m^3$? It is the 'area' between the graph and the V axis. How to estimate this:

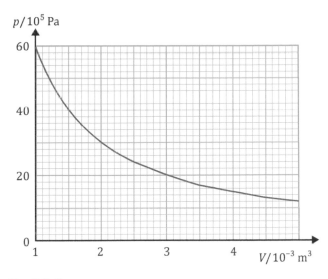

Fig 10.3

Method 1: Square counting

Identify the number of '1 cm' squares underneath the graph – the rule is $> \frac{1}{2}$ square = 1 square, $< \frac{1}{2}$ square = 0 squares. Tally = 19 squares.

The 'area' of each square = $0.5 \times 10^{-3} \times 10 \times 10^5$ i.e. 500 J

$\therefore$ Total 'area' = $19 \times 500 = 9500$ J

Method 2: Divide up into trapeziums

We approximate the graph by a series of straight lines, e.g. 4 lines : 1–2 , 2–3, 3–4, 4–5 $\times 10^{-3} \, m^3$. The pressures at the ends of these lines are 60, 30, 20, 15 and 12 $\times 10^5$ Pa, so the areas of the trapeziums are:

$$\tfrac{1}{2} \times 1 \times 10^{-3}[(60 + 30) + (30 + 20) + (20 + 15) + (15 + 12)] \times 10^5 = 10\,100 \text{ J}.$$

The approximation will be better if we use more sections: with $0.5 \times 10^{-3} \, m^3$ sections the result is 9770 J. This is a hint about the way to get an exact solution [see next section].

10.3.2 Working towards an exact answer – by approximating!

Consider the function $y = \sqrt{x}$ up to $x = 4$ [see graph]. What is the area, A, below the graph?

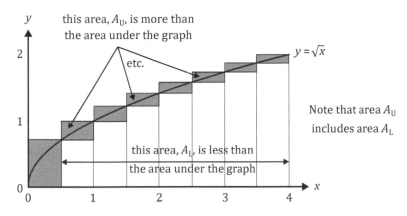

this area, A_U, is more than the area under the graph

etc.

$y = \sqrt{x}$

Note that area A_U includes area A_L

this area, A_L, is less than the area under the graph

Fig 10.4

Practice »»»»»»»»»»»»»»»

Show that dividing the graph into 8 trapeziums gives an 'area' of 9770 J.

Look at the white rectangles. The area, A, underneath the graph lies between the lower area, A_L and the upper area A_U: i.e.

$$A_L < A < A_U$$

Using a spreadsheet $A_L = 0 + 0.35355 + 0.50000 + 0.61237 + ...$ $= 4.7650$ [to 5.s.f.]

Similarly $A_U = 0.35355 + 0.50000 + 0.61237 + 0.70711 + ... = 5.7650$ [to 5 s.f.]

Now we'll creep up on it! It's time for you to do some work:

Data Exercise 10.2

For the function $y = \sqrt{x}$, divide up the x range between $x = 0$ and $x = 4$ into 40 strips of width 0.1 and use a spreadsheet to show that the values of A_L and A_U are as shown in the table to 4 s.f., then repeat this for 400 strips of width 0.01.

No. of strips	Lower area (A_L)	Upper area (A_U)
40	5.227	5.427
400	5.323	5.343

With 1000 strips of width 0.004, the values of A_L and A_U are 5.329, 5.337 respectively.

Data Exercise 10.3

Using the same process as in this section, integrate the function $y = 3x^2$ up to a value of $x = 2$. Check that the areas tend towards 8.000 which is the value of 2^3. Why should this be the case?

As the number of strips gets larger, the upper and lower values of A get closer and closer to a limiting value which in this case is 5.3333...

Now for the payoff: Calculate the value of $y = \frac{2}{3}x^{\frac{3}{2}}$, when $x = 4$. Answer= 5.3333

If we differentiate the function $y = \frac{2}{3}x^{\frac{3}{2}}$, we get $\frac{dy}{dx} = x^{\frac{1}{2}}$, i.e. $\sqrt{x}$. From this it seems that this process, called **integrating is the inverse process to differentiating**. This is not the whole story. We'll explore a refinement in the next section.

10.3.3   Definite and indefinite integration

(a) Definite integration

The process in 10.3.2 can be summed up as follows:

1   Divide up the x axis into equal width strips. Width = Δx

2   Find the minimum [or maximum] value of y in each strip

3   Calculate the 'area' of each strip, $\Delta A = y\Delta x$

4   Add up all the areas between $x = 0$ and $x = 4$: $A = \sum_{x=0}^{4} y\Delta x$ [see footnote[2]]

5   Find the limiting value of A as the width of the strips approaches 0.

We indicate this limiting value by $A = \int_{0}^{4} \sqrt{x}\, dx$ and read this out as 'A is the integral of root x, dx, between $x = 0$ and $x = 4$'.

We have seen that $A = \int_{0}^{4} \sqrt{x}\, dx$ = the value of $\frac{2}{3}x^{\frac{3}{2}}$, when $x = 4$ which is 5.333...

Clearly the area up to $x = 2$ is $\int_{0}^{2} \sqrt{x}\, dx$ = the value of $\frac{2}{3}x^{\frac{3}{2}}$, when $x = 2$ which is 1.8856...

If we want to find the area between $x = 2$ and $x = 4$:

$$A = \int_{2}^{4} \sqrt{x}\, dx = \int_{0}^{4} \sqrt{x}\, dx - \int_{0}^{2} \sqrt{x}\, dx$$

This is written as follows:

$$\int_{2}^{4} \sqrt{x}\, dx = \left[\frac{2}{3}x^{\frac{3}{2}}\right]_{x=2}^{x=4}$$

The symbol $\left[\frac{2}{3}x^{\frac{3}{2}}\right]_{x=2}^{x=4}$ means 'the value of $\frac{2}{3}x^{\frac{3}{2}}$ when $x = 4$, **minus** the value when $x = 2$. This process is called **definite integration**.

quickfire ▶ 10.6

Find c if $y = 2x^3 + x + c$ and $y(0) = 5$.

quickfire ▶ 10.7

Find c if $y = \ln 2t + c$ and $y(10) = 0$.

---

[2]   The Σ symbol indicates 'sum', i.e. add the $y\Delta x$ values. The figures above and below the Σ indicate that we are doing this between $x = 0$ and $x = 4$.

Example D:

The p, V graph in 10.3.1 has the equation $p = \dfrac{6.00 \times 10^3}{V}$, so the work done is given by

$W = \displaystyle\int_{V_1}^{V_2} p\, dV$, where V_1 and V_2 are the beginning and end volumes.

Putting in the numbers:

$$W = \int_{1 \times 10^{-3}}^{5 \times 10^{-3}} \frac{6.00 \times 10^3}{V}\, dV$$

To solve this we need to know what function differentiates to give $\dfrac{1}{V}$. In 10.2.3 we saw that:

$$\frac{d}{dV}(\ln V) = \frac{1}{V}$$

So

$$W = \int_{1 \times 10^{-3}}^{5 \times 10^{-3}} \frac{6.00 \times 10^3}{V}\, dV = \left[6.00 \times 10^3 \ln V\right]_{V = 1 \times 10^{-3}}^{V = 5 \times 10^{-3}}$$

So

$$= 6 \times 10^3 \ln (5 \times 10^{-3}) - 6 \times 10^3 \ln (1 \times 10^{-3})$$

$$= 9657\,J$$

quickfire 10.8

Find c if $y = 10\cos\omega t + c$ and $y(0) = 5$.

(b) Indefinite integration

Integration is the inverse process to differentiation. Now x^4 differentiates to give $4x^3$, but so do $x^4 - 10$, $x^4 + 10$, $x^4 - 10^6$.... This means that, if we don't know what values of x we are integrating between [aka the limits of integration], we cannot say definitely what the answer is.

So, $\dfrac{dy}{dx} = 4x^3$, then all we can say is $y(x) = \displaystyle\int 4x^3 dx = x^4 + c$ where c is an unknown constant.

How do we find c? We need to know the value of y for a particular value of x. For example, if we know that $y = 25$ when $x = 2$, then we can substitute these values in to find c:

In that case $25 = 2^4 + c$, so $c = 9$.

quickfire 10.9

By differentiating $\dfrac{1}{n+1}x^{n+1}$, show that the integral of x^n in Table 10.4 is correct.

Example E:

Suppose $y(t) = 10e^{-0.1t} + c$ and $y(\infty) = 10$. Remember that $e^{-\infty} = 0$. Substituting we get: $10 = 0 + c$.

$\therefore y(t) = 10e^{-0.1t} + 10 = 10(e^{-0.1t} + 1)$

(c) Standard integrals

Table 10.4 gives integrals that you should know. The constant of integration [i.e. '$+ c$'] needs to be added in cases of indefinite integration.

Table 10.4

$f(x)$	$\int f(x)dx$	$f(x)$	$\int f(x)dx$
x^n	$\dfrac{1}{n+1}x^{n+1}$ [Unless $n = -1$]	$\sin kx$	$-\dfrac{1}{k}\cos kx$
x^{-1}	$\ln x$	$\cos kx$	$\dfrac{1}{k}\sin kx$
e^{kx}	$\dfrac{1}{k}e^{kx}$		

As with differentiation, $\displaystyle\int (\alpha f(x) + \beta g(x))dx = \alpha \int f(x)\, dx + \beta \int g(x)\, dx$

10.4 Calculus relationships in A-level Physics

The following is a summary of the different quantities you are likely to meet which are related by differentiation and integration:

- Velocity, v and displacement, s: $\qquad v = \dfrac{ds}{dt} \qquad \Delta s = \int v\,dt$

- Acceleration, a and velocity, v: $\qquad a = \dfrac{dv}{dt} \qquad \Delta v = \int a\,dt$

- Force. F, and momentum, p: $\qquad F = \dfrac{dp}{dt} \qquad \Delta p = \int F\,dt$

- Charge on a capacitor, Q, and discharge current, I: $\qquad I = -\dfrac{dQ}{dt} \qquad \Delta Q = -\int I\,dt$

- Pd and current in an inductor: $\qquad V = L\dfrac{dI}{dt} \qquad \Delta I = \int \dfrac{V}{L}\,dt$

- Induced emf $\mathcal{E}_{in}$ and flux linkage, $N\Phi$: $\qquad E_{in} = -\dfrac{d}{dt}(N\Phi)$

- Power, P and work / energy transfer, W: $\qquad P = \dfrac{dW}{dt}$

- Work, W, force, F and displacement, s: $\qquad W = \int F\,ds$

- Work, W, pressure, p and volume, V: $\qquad W = \int p\,dV$

- Activity, A, and number of radioactive nuclei, N: $\qquad A = -\dfrac{dN}{dt}$

Test Yourself 10.2

Find the function f in Questions 1–5:

1 $f(x) = \int 25x^5\,dx;\ f(0) = 0.$

2 $f(x) = \int \dfrac{12}{x^3}\,dx\ ;\ f(1) = 2$

3 $f(t) = \int (4t + 1)\,dt\ ;\ f(-1) = 5$

4 $f(t) = \int 2.5e^{-0.005t}\,dt\ ;\ f(\infty) = 0$

5 $f(t) = \int (5.0\sin 2.5t + 10\cos 1.25t)\,dt\ ;\ f(0) = -2$

Evaluate the definite integrals in Questions 6–10:

6 $\int_2^4 6x^2\,dx$

7 $\int_0^{0.5} 5e^{-2t}\,dt$

8 $\int_1^5 \dfrac{10}{x}\,dx$

9 $\int_0^2 (2\cos\pi t + 2)\,dt$

10 $\int_1^\infty \dfrac{3}{x^4}\,dx$

11 A sample of gas has a pressure of 500 kPa and a volume of 10×10^{-3} m³. It expands at constant temperature to a volume of 30×10^{-3} m. Calculate the work done by the gas.

[Hint: pV = constant. Calculate the value of the constant then proceed as in Example D]

12 The sample of gas in Q11 is allowed to expand rapidly from its initial state. The relationship between p and V is $PV^{1.4} = k$, where k is a different constant from the one in Q11. Calculate the work it does in expanding.

Questions 14–17 derive the formulae for the potential in a gravitational field and an electric field. Q13 prepares the way!

13 A satellite weighs 5000 N on the surface of the Earth. How much work is needed to lift it from the surface of the Earth [radius 6400 km] to a height of 12000 km? The relationship between the weight [i.e. the gravitational force] and the radius from the Earth's centre, r, is:

$$F = \dfrac{k}{r^2}$$

[Ignore kinetic energy] Hint: first find k.

⑭ The gravitational force, F_G, between the two bodies is given by $F_G = -\dfrac{GMm}{x^2}$. The force,

F, needed to move the body of mass m away from M is thus given by $F = +\dfrac{GMm}{x^2}$.

The work done, W, in moving m is given by $W = \int F\,dx$. Determine the work done in moving m from $x = r_1$ to $x = r_2$.

⑮ Use the result of Q14 to deduce the work done by F in moving m from an infinite distance away to a point a distance a from the centre of M.

⑯ The potential at a point P in a gravitational field is defined as the work done, *per unit mass*, in moving a small test mass from infinity to P. Use the result of Q15 to deduce the formula of the gravitational potential at a distance a from the centre of a spherical object of mass M.

⑰ The electrostatic potential at a point in an electric field is defined as the work done, *per unit charge*, in moving a small test charge from infinity to P. The electric force exerted by a charge Q on another charge

q at a distance x is given by: $F_E = \dfrac{1}{4\pi\varepsilon_0}\dfrac{Qq}{x^2}$.

Deduce the formula for the electric potential at a distance a from the centre of a spherical charge Q.

⑱ The diagram shows a fixed electric dipole [equal and opposite charges, ±Q separated by a distance d] and a small particle, of charge q and mass m, which is free to move. The F on q is given by :

$$F = -\frac{2Qqd}{4\pi\varepsilon_0 x^3} \quad \text{if } x \gg d.$$

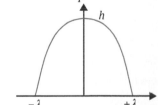

Using the concepts from Questions 13–17 and the formula for kinetic energy, $E_k = \frac{1}{2}mv^2$, to calculate the speed the particle acquires in falling from a large distance [∞] to $x = a$.

⑲ The activity, A, of a radioactive sample, i.e. the number of decays per unit time is given by $A = A_0 e^{-\lambda t}$. A_0 is the initial activity and λ the decay constant.

(a) By integrating A between 0 and ∞, find an expression for the initial number of radioactive nuclei, N_0.

(b) Evaluate N_0 if $A_0 = 3.5 \times 10^{10}$ Bq and $\lambda = 2 \times 10^{-6}$ s^{-1}.

⑳ A capacitor of capacitance, C, decays through a resistor of resistance, R, with a current, I, given by $I = I_0 e^{-t/RC}$.

(a) By integrating I find an expression for the charge, Q, remaining on the capacitor after time, t, given that $Q = 0$ when $t = \infty$.

(b) Find and expression for Q_0 in terms of I_0, R and C.

(c) If $I_0 = 5$ mA and $RC = 100$ s, find the charge on the capacitor at $t = 200$ s.

㉑ The force-time variation for a golf-club striking a golf ball can be approximated to by the function $F = a - bt^2$. This is the graph of the function.

(a) By substituting the points $(\lambda, 0)$ and $(0, h)$ into $F = a - bt^2$, show that this can be rewritten:

$$F = h\left(1 - \frac{t^2}{\lambda^2}\right).$$

(b) By integrating this function between $t = -\lambda$ and $+\lambda$, find an expression for the total impulse [i.e. the change in momentum] of the golf ball.

(c) Estimate the maximum force, h given that $\lambda = 0.5$ ms, the mass of the golf ball is 4.5×10^{-2} kg and the speed of the golf ball after being struck is 85 m s^{-1}.

㉒ The velocity of an object moving through water is given, in m s^{-1}, by $v = v_0 e^{-0.02t}$, where t is the time in seconds. The initial velocity, $v_0 = 25$ m s^{-1}.

  (a) By integrating v with respect to time, find the distance travelled by the object in time t. [Hint: indefinite integration with $x(0) = 0$.]

  (b) Use your answer to (a) to find the total distance D travelled by the object before coming to rest.

  (c) Write v as a function of x for $x < D$.

The rotational kinetic energy of an object can be written as $E = \frac{1}{2} I \omega^2$, where ω is the angular speed of the object and I is called the moment of inertia – it plays the same role in rotational as m does in translational motion. Questions 23–25 concern these concepts.

㉓ Calculate the rotational kinetic energy and hence the moment of inertia of a uniform rod of length l and mass M which is rotating about one end with angular speed ω. See diagram.

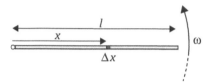

Method: Consider the small section of the rod of position, x and width Δx.

  (a) Write its mass in terms of M, l and Δx.

  (b) Show that the kinetic energy, ΔE of this section is: $\Delta E = \frac{1}{2} \frac{M\omega^2}{l} x^2 \Delta x$

  (c) By integrating this expression between $x = 0$ and l, show that the total kinetic energy, E, is:

$$\Delta E = \frac{1}{2}\left(\frac{1}{3} M l^2\right)\omega^2 \qquad \text{[Hint: } E = \int_{x=0}^{x=l} \frac{1}{2}\frac{M\omega^2}{l} x^2\, dx - \text{ the } \Delta x \text{ has become the } dx]$$

  (d) Hence write down an expression for I for the rod.

㉔ Derive an expression for the moment of inertia of the same rod as in Q23, when it is pivoted at its centre. [Hint: integrate from $x = -l/2$ to $+l/2$]

㉕ The diagram shows a uniform disc of mass M and radius a.

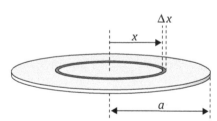

  (a) Show that the mass of the thin ring of radius, x, and width Δx is $\frac{2x\Delta x}{a^2} M$.

  [Hint: area of circle = πr^2, circumference = $2\pi r$]

  (b) If the angular speed of the disc is ω, write down the kinetic energy of the thin ring.

  (c) By integrating the answer to (b) from $x = 0$ to a find the kinetic energy of the disc and hence derive an expression for the moment of inertia of the disc.

[NB In fact you can forget about the $\frac{1}{2}\omega^2$ term and jump straight from (a) to (c)]

Chapter 11

Differential Equations

11.1 Introduction

As we have seen, many physics relationships are written in terms of differentiated functions. Chapter 10 dealt with how to handle these equations if they are of the following kind:

$$\frac{df}{dt} = g(t).$$

In this case we know that $f(t) = \int g(t)\, dt$ and as long as we also know the value of f at one particular time we can find an answer, **always assuming we can integrate g!**

Consider the following equations:

$$\frac{dx}{dt} + \lambda t = 0 \qquad \frac{dv}{dt} + \lambda v = F(t) \qquad \text{First order equations}$$

$$\frac{d^2x}{dt^2} + \omega^2 x = 0 \qquad \frac{d^2x}{dt^2} + k\frac{dx}{dt} + \omega^2 x = F(t) \qquad \text{Second order equations}$$

These are called *differential equations*. These particular differential equations arise in A-level Physics   and we shall now investigate their solutions. To prepare the ground we'll remind ourselves of two results:

1 If $x = Ae^{-kt}$, differentiating gives $\frac{dx}{dt} = -kAe^{-kt} = -kx$

2 If $x = A\cos(\omega t + \phi)$, differentiating gives $\frac{dx}{dt} = -A\omega \sin(\omega t + \phi)$

   Differentiating again gives $\frac{d^2x}{dt^2} = -A\omega^2 \cos(\omega t + \phi) = -\omega^2 x$. If you try $x = B\sin(\omega t + \phi)$ and $x = C\sin \omega t + D\cos \omega t$, you'll find that these functions also give $\frac{d^2x}{dt^2} + \omega^2 x = 0$.

We'll come back to these results.

They are called *linear differential equations with constant coefficients*. The function $F(t)$ is called the *forcing function*.

Pointer

The independent variable could also be x, e.g. $\frac{dy}{dx} + \lambda y = 0$.

quickfire 11.1

What is $\frac{d}{dx}(5e^{-3x})$?

quickfire 11.2

What is $\frac{d^2}{dt^2}(-5\cos(3t + \pi))$?

11.2 Decay [or growth] equations

Consider a pure sample of a radioactive nuclide. The probability of any given nucleus decaying in unit time is constant so, with a very large number of nuclei, the number of decays per second, i.e. the **rate of decrease** in the number of radioactive nuclei is directly proportional to the number of nuclei in the sample. In mathematical terms, if N is the number of radioactive nuclei present:

$$\frac{dN}{dt} = -\lambda N,$$

where λ is a positive constant, called the *decay constant*. Thus, as N decreases, the rate of decay also decreases, so we obtain the familiar half-life decay curve. There are many similar examples in physics, e.g. if a capacitor is discharging through a resistor, the rate of decrease in the charge, Q, on the capacitor is proportional to the voltage across the capacitor and resistor, which is proportional to the charge Q.

There are other situations in which a function **grows** at a rate that is proportional to its size, at least for a short period of time. A physics example is a runaway nuclear explosion – in biology, the unconstrained growth of bacterial colonies obeys the same mathematics.

11.2.1 The homogeneous equation

If $\frac{dx}{dt} = -kx$, then we can rewrite this as $\frac{dx}{dt} + kx = 0$. This kind of differential equation, with a 0 on the right hand side, is referred to as a *homogeneous* equation and it turns out that we know the solution already! The equation says, if we differentiate the function $x(t)$, we get the same function as before but multiplied by $-k$. Looking back to Section 11.1 we see that the answer is Ae^{-kt}. A is called an *arbitrary constant*, because without extra information, it can take any value. If we know the *initial value* of x, i.e. its value at $t = 0$, we can find a value for A.

Let $x(0) = x_0$. Substituting into $x = Ae^{-kt}$ we get: $x_0 = Ae^0$.

But $e^0 = 1$, so $A = x_0$, ie the solution of $\frac{dx}{dt} + kx = 0$ is $x = x_0e^{-kt}$.

We can also find A given the value of x at some other time – see Quickfire 11.4.

11.2.2 The inhomogeneous equation

The equation $\frac{dx}{dt} + \lambda x = F(t)$ is called an inhomogeneous equation. It arises when the quantity x is not allowed to decay on its own but is subject to outside influence. Examples:

- Radioactive decay in which the radioactive nucleus is part of a decay chain so the nuclei are constantly being replenished by the decay of other nuclei.

- A capacitor connected to an electrical supply (dc or ac).

The procedure for the solution of the equation builds on the result for the homogenous equation. The solution is two parts added together:

1 The function, called the *complementary function* (CF), which satisfies the homogeneous equation – this provides the arbitrary constant needed to match the solution to the initial conditions.

2 Any other function, called the *particular integral* (PI), which fits the inhomogeneous equation.

The procedure is:

Stage 1: Find the CF – but leave the arbitrary constant as unknown for the moment.

Stage 2: Find any PI which satisfies the inhomogeneous equation.

Stage 3: Add the CF and PI and apply the initial conditions to find the arbitrary constant.

In the inhomogeneous equation, F is called the *forcing function*. The forcing functions which commonly arise in A-level Physics are:

- F is a constant, e.g. a constant voltage power supply connected across a capacitor.

- F is a sinusoid, such as $F = P\cos \Omega t$, e.g. an ac power supply across a capacitor.

- F is an exponential decay, $F = Pe^{-mt}$, e.g. a radioactive nucleus in a decay chain.

Example A deals with an example where $F = $ constant.

Example A:

Solve the equation $\frac{dx}{dt} + 0.1x = 1.2$ with the initial condition $x(0) = 0$.

Step 1: The CF, i.e. the solution of $\frac{dx}{dt} + 0.1x = 0$, is $x = Ae^{-0.1t}$.

Step 2: The constant function $x = 12$ obviously satisfies the equation, so choose $x = 12$ as the PI.

Step 3: Add the two solutions CF + PI $\rightarrow x = Ae^{-0.1t} + 12$ and apply the initial condition:

If $x(0) = 0$, then $0 = Ae^0 + 12$, so $A = -12$ and the full solution is $x = 12(1 - e^{-0.1t})$.

The voltage across a capacitor, being charged by a power supply, would satisfy this form of equation.

quickfire 11.3

Write the solution of $\frac{dx}{dt} + 3x = 0$.

quickfire 11.4

The solution of a differential equation is $x = Ae^{-0.1t}$. Find the value of A if:
(a) $x(0) = 25$
(b) $x(10) = 37$

quickfire 11.5

(a) Write the solution of
$\frac{dx}{dt} + 0.1x = 0$, if $x_0 = 1000$.

(b) Find the value of x when $t = 100$.

quickfire 11.6

If $\tan \alpha = 0.5$, use Pythagoras' theorem to find $\cos \alpha$ and $\sin \alpha$, given that $0 < \alpha < \frac{\pi}{2}$

quickfire 11.7

Repeat QF 11.6 for $\pi < \alpha < \frac{3\pi}{2}$

quickfire 11.8

$\tan \beta = \frac{y}{x}$. Find $\cos \beta$ and $\sin \beta$.

Example B illustrates the method of finding the particular integral if the forcing function is an exponential decay.

Example B:

A radioactive nuclide has a decay constant λ. It is part of a decay series and new nuclei of this nuclide are being produced at a rate of $ke^{-\beta t}$. If the number of nuclei, N, is initially 0, find N as a function of time.

$$\frac{dN}{dt} + \lambda N = ke^{-\beta t}$$

Step 1: The CF is: $N = Ae^{-\lambda t}$.

Step 2: For the PI, look for a function of the form $N = Be^{-\beta t}$. We need to find the value of B.

Substitute $N = Be^{-\beta t}$ into the differential equation: $\frac{d}{dt}\left(Be^{-\beta t}\right) + \lambda Be^{-\beta t} = ke^{-\beta t}$.

Differentiating and cancelling by the common term of $e^{\beta t}$ gives $-B\beta + \lambda B = k$

So $B = \frac{k}{\lambda - \beta}$ and the full solution, CF + PI, is $N = Ae^{-\lambda t} + \frac{k}{\lambda - \beta}e^{-\beta t}$

Step 3: Applying the initial condition, $N(0) = 0$, gives $0 = A + \frac{k}{\lambda - \beta}$, so $A = -\frac{k}{\lambda - \beta}$ and so the full solution is $N = \frac{k}{\lambda - \beta}\left(e^{-\beta t} - e^{-\lambda t}\right)$

We'll look at the PI for a sinusoidal forcing function in conjunction with the second order equations.

11.3 Simple harmonic motion – unforced oscillations with no damping

Consider the equation $\frac{d^2x}{dt^2} = -\omega^2 x$. This is the defining equation for simple harmonic motion: the acceleration, $\frac{d^2x}{dt^2}$, is proportional to the distance, x, from a fixed point and directed towards the point [the minus sign].

If we rearrange the equation, we get $\frac{d^2x}{dt^2} + \omega^2 x = 0$.

Referring back to Section 11.1, we see that any of the sinusoids, $x = A\cos(\omega t + \phi)$, $x = B\sin(\omega t + \varepsilon)$ and $x = C\sin\omega t + D\cos\omega t$ satisfy this equation, where A, ϕ, B, ε, C and D are arbitrary constants. All these solutions are interchangeable: they are just different ways of writing the same solution, e.g. $\sin\omega t + \cos\omega t = \sqrt{2}\sin\left(\omega t + \frac{\pi}{4}\right) = \sqrt{2}\cos\left(\omega t - \frac{\pi}{4}\right)$.

Notice that there are two arbitrary constants in these solutions. This is true of all second order equations and we therefore need two pieces of information, e.g. x_0 and v_0 (the displacement and velocity at $t = 0$), to solve the equations completely.

quickfire ➤ 11.9

$A = A_0 e^{-0.002t}$. $A(0) = 1 \times 10^{12}$.
What is A_0?

quickfire ➤ 11.10

In QF 11.9, If $A(1000) = 1 \times 10^{12}$, what is A_0?

Example C:

An object of mass 250 g is attached to a spring which exerts a force of $F = -16x$ on it, where x is the displacement from the equilibrium position. If $x_0 = 0$ and $v_0 = 2$ m s^{-1} find the displacement as a function of time. [F is expressed in N and x in m]

Newton's 2nd law: $0.25\frac{d^2x}{dt^2} + 16x = 0$.

Dividing by 0.25: $\frac{d^2x}{dt^2} + 64x = 0$, which is of the form $\frac{d^2x}{dt^2} + \omega^2 x = 0$, with $\omega = 8$.

The form of the solution to choose is a matter of convenience. We'll explore all the forms!

- If $x = C \sin 8t + D \cos 8t$, applying $x_0 = 0$ at $t = 0$ we get: $0 = 0 + D$ ∴ $D = 0$

  Differentiating $x = C \sin 8t$, gives $v = 8C \cos 8t$ and applying $v_0 = 2 \text{ m s}^{-1}$ gives: $2 = 8C$

  ∴ $C = 0.25$ m, i.e. the solution is $x = 0.25 \sin 8t$

- If $x = A \sin(8t + \varepsilon)$, applying $x_0 = 0$ gives: $0 = A \sin \varepsilon$. Assuming $A \neq 0$, then $\sin \varepsilon = 0$, so $\varepsilon = 0$.

  Then proceed as above, giving the same solution.

- If $x = A \cos(8t + \phi)$, applying $x_0 = 0$, $0 = A \cos \phi$.

  Assuming $A \neq 0$, $\cos \phi = 0$, so $\phi = \pm \frac{\pi}{2}$.

  Differentiating $x = A \cos\left(8t \pm \frac{\pi}{2}\right)$ gives $v = -8A \sin\left(8t \pm \frac{\pi}{2}\right)$.

  Applying $v_0 = 2$, at $t = 0$ we get: $2 = -8A \sin\left(\pm \frac{\pi}{2}\right)$

  We'll choose the $-$ sign so that $\sin\left(\pm \frac{\pi}{2}\right)$ is < 0 and so $A > 0$. In that case applying $v_0 = 2 \text{ m s}^{-1}$

  gives $2 = -8A \times \left(-1\right)$, so A is 0.25 and the solution is $x = 0.25 \cos\left(8t - \frac{\pi}{2}\right)$, which is the same

  as $x = 0.25 \sin 8t$.

NB. You only need to apply one of these solutions – recognising the easiest one requires insight!

11.4 Unforced oscillations with damping

Oscillatory systems normally experience some sort of resistive force. If the resistance to motion is proportional to the speed, i.e. the rate of change of position [or rate of flow of charge in the case of an electrical circuit], the equation becomes

$$\frac{d^2x}{dt^2} + k\frac{dx}{dt} + \omega^2 x = 0.$$

The $k\dfrac{dx}{dt}$ term is reminiscent of the first order decay equation and the $\dfrac{d^2x}{dt^2} + \omega^2 x = 0$ part reminds us of the oscillatory motion in Section 8.3. The solution of this equation really calls for higher mathematics in the form of complex numbers. However if we restrict ourselves to a lightly damped system, defined by $\frac{1}{2}k < \omega$ [k and ω both > 0], the solution is a combination of the decay and oscillatory equations already met:

$$x = Ae^{-\frac{1}{2}kt} \cos(pt + \alpha)$$

where $p = \sqrt{\omega^2 - \frac{1}{4}k^2}$, and A and α are arbitrary constants. We shall now proceed to verify that this is indeed a solution. **You should work through all the steps – it's pencil and paper time.**

Starting with $\qquad\qquad x = Ae^{-\frac{1}{2}kt} \cos(pt + \alpha)$

Differentiating: $\qquad \dfrac{dx}{dt} = Ae^{-\frac{1}{2}kt}\left[-\frac{1}{2}k\cos(pt + \alpha) - p\sin(pt + \alpha)\right]$

Again: $\qquad\qquad \dfrac{d^2x}{dt^2} = Ae^{-\frac{1}{2}kt}\left[\frac{1}{4}k^2\cos(pt + \alpha) + kp\sin(pt + \alpha) - p^2\cos(pt + \alpha)\right]$

So $\qquad \dfrac{d^2x}{dt^2} + k\dfrac{dx}{dt} + \omega^2 x = Ae^{-\frac{1}{2}kt}\left[-\frac{1}{4}k^2\cos(pt + \alpha) - p^2\cos(pt + \alpha) + \omega^2\cos(pt + \alpha)\right]$

 **11.11**

Calculate $25e^{-0.5} \cos 0.6$.

You need to work quite hard to check that step!

$$= Ae^{-\frac{1}{2}kt}\left[-\frac{1}{4}k^2 - p^2 + \omega^2\right]\cos(pt + \alpha)$$

$$= 0 \text{ if } p^2 = \omega^2 - \frac{1}{4}k^2.$$

So the given function $x = Ae^{-\frac{1}{2}kt}\cos(pt + \alpha)$ is a solution of the differential equation and it contains two arbitrary constants to allow it to meet the initial conditions.

Example D:

Solve the differential equation $\frac{d^2x}{dt^2} + 14\frac{dx}{dt} + 625x = 0$ with initial conditions, $x_0 = 0.5$ m and $v_0 = 0$.

$k = 14$ and $\omega = 25$, $\therefore p = \sqrt{625 - \frac{1}{4} \times 196} = 24$ and the solution is: $x = Ae^{-7t}\cos(24t + \alpha)$.

Because $v_0 = 0$, the oscillation is clearly a maximum at $t = 0$, so $\alpha = 0$ and $A = 0.5$ m.

So the complete solution is $x = 0.5e^{-7t}\cos 24t$.

From the solution of Example D we see that the oscillation angular frequency is slightly lower than that of undamped oscillations [$24\,\text{s}^{-1}$ rather than $25\,\text{s}^{-1}$] and that there is an exponential decrease in amplitude. The degree of damping in the example is quite large – in one oscillation, ~ 0.26 s, the amplitude drops by 84%!

11.5 Forced oscillations – resonance

We'll now look at the equation $\frac{d^2x}{dt^2} + k\frac{dx}{dt} + \omega^2 x = F(t)$. In most cases of interest, the forcing function, F, is a sinusoid. As with the unforced equation we'll restrict our area of interest. The complete solution consists of a complementary function and a particular integral as with the forced decay equation. In this case the CF represents a temporary part of the answer and its contribution decays according to $e^{-\frac{1}{2}kt}$ which will tend to zero and we'll be left with the particular integral, a steady state solution which we'll examine.

If the forcing function is $B\cos\psi t$, we will look for a PI of the form $x = P\cos(\psi t - \varepsilon)$.

Substituting this into the differential equation:

$$-P\psi^2\cos(\psi t - \varepsilon) - Pk\psi\sin(\psi t - \varepsilon) + \omega^2 P\cos(\psi t - \varepsilon) = B\cos\psi t$$

Rearranging slightly: $\frac{B}{P}\cos\psi t = -k\psi\sin(\psi t - \varepsilon) + (\omega^2 - \psi^2)\cos(\psi t - \varepsilon)$

This equation has to be true at all values of time. We'll put in $\psi t = 0$ and $\psi t = \frac{\pi}{2}$:

$\psi t = 0$: $\qquad \frac{B}{P} = k\psi\sin\varepsilon + (\omega^2 - \psi^2)\cos\varepsilon$ $\qquad$ (1) See footnote[2]

$\psi t = \frac{\pi}{2}$: $\qquad 0 = -k\psi\cos\varepsilon + (\omega^2 - \psi^2)\sin\varepsilon$ $\qquad$ (2) See footnote[3]

From (2) and using $\frac{\sin\varepsilon}{\cos\varepsilon} = \tan\varepsilon$, we have $\tan\varepsilon = \frac{k\psi}{\omega^2 - \psi^2}$

From the triangle in Figure 11.1, we see that, using Pythagoras' theorem

$$\sin\varepsilon = \frac{k\psi}{\sqrt{(\omega^2 - \psi^2)^2 + k^2\psi^2}} \text{ and } \cos\varepsilon = \frac{(\omega^2 - \psi^2)}{\sqrt{(\omega^2 - \psi^2)^2 + k^2\psi^2}}$$

Substituting these in (1) gives: $\frac{B}{P} = \frac{k^2\psi^2}{\sqrt{(\omega^2 - \psi^2)^2 + k^2\psi^2}} + \frac{(\omega^2 - \psi^2)^2}{\sqrt{(\omega^2 - \psi^2)^2 + k^2\psi^2}}$,

which on simplification and rearranging gives $P = \frac{B}{\sqrt{(\psi^2 - \omega^2)^2 + k^2\psi^2}}$

The solution is thus: $x = \frac{B}{\sqrt{(\omega^2 - \psi^2)^2 + k^2\psi^2}}\cos(\psi t - \varepsilon)$, where $\varepsilon = \cos^{-1}\left[\frac{(\omega^2 - \psi^2)}{\sqrt{(\omega^2 - \psi^2)^2 + k^2\psi^2}}\right]$

Remember that this is the steady state solution, i.e. after the initial oscillations represented by the CF have died away.

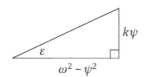

Fig 11.1

quickfire 11.12

$x = Ae^{-0.4t}\cos 2t$.
If $x(1) = -6.0$, calculate A.

quickfire 11.13

$\cos\alpha = 3\sin\alpha$.
Calculate α given that $0 < \alpha < \frac{\pi}{2}$
[Hint: $\cos\alpha = \sqrt{1 - \sin^2\alpha}$]

Data Exercise 11.1

Use a spreadsheet to plot the function $x = 2.5e^{-0.2t}\cos 3t$ for the period 0–8 s. You will need to experiment with different time steps.

---

[2] Here we have used the fact that $\sin(-\varepsilon) = -\sin\varepsilon$ and $\cos(-\varepsilon) = \cos\varepsilon$
[3] Because $\sin(\pi/2 - \varepsilon) = \cos\varepsilon$ and $\cos(\pi/2 - \varepsilon) = \sin\varepsilon$

With forced oscillations, it is usually the amplitude of the oscillations that is of interest. The graphs in Figure 11.2 show how the amplitude varies with frequency for various levels of damping. The resonance peak is clearly to be seen.

Data Exercise 11.2

Use a spreadsheet to investigate the variation of amplitude, P, with frequency, ψ. It is suggested that the numerical values of B and ω are set at 1 and the damping coefficient, k, allowed to take values between 0 and 1. [The values of k used in Figure 11.2 were: 0, 0.3, 0.5 and 0.8.]

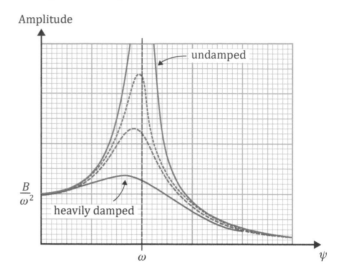

Fig 11.2

Note that, as the degree of damping increases, the peak frequency decreases slightly.

Data Exercise 11.3

Use a spreadsheet to investigate the variation of ε with frequency.

The phase angle, ε, also varies with frequency as shown in Figure 11.3. For all degrees of damping, ε is $\pi/2$ when $\psi = \omega$; ε tends to 0 as $\psi \to 0$ and tends to π as $\psi \to \infty$.

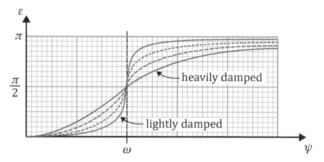

Fig 11.3

Example E:

A body of mass 2 kg is mounted on a spring system which exerts a force of $-32x$ when it is displaced by x. It is subject to a damping force of $6v$ and an oscillating force of $50 \cos 5t$. The forces are in newton and the displacement in m.

(a) Write down the differential equation which covers this situation.

(b) Find the steady state equation of motion of the body.

(c) Calculate the maximum velocity and acceleration of the body.

(a) From Newton's 2nd law: $2a = -32x - 6v + 50 \cos 5t$

$$\therefore \frac{d^2x}{dt^2} + 3\frac{dx}{dt} + 16x = 25 \cos 5t$$

(b) For the complementary function try $x = A \cos(5t - \varepsilon)$

Differentiating and substituting in the differential equation:

$$-25A \cos(5t - \varepsilon) - 15A \sin(5t - \varepsilon) + 16A \cos(5t - \varepsilon) = 25 \cos 5t$$

$$\therefore -9A \cos(5t - \varepsilon) - 15A \sin(5t - \varepsilon) = 25 \cos 5t$$

This identity must be correct at all instants.

At $t = 0$: $-9A \cos \varepsilon + 15A \sin \varepsilon = 25$ (1)   Because $\cos(-\varepsilon) = \cos \varepsilon$ and $\sin(-\varepsilon) = -\sin \varepsilon$

At $5t = \frac{\pi}{2}$: $-9A \cos\left(\frac{\pi}{2} - \varepsilon\right) - 15A \sin\left(\frac{\pi}{2} - \varepsilon\right) = 25 \cos \frac{\pi}{2}$

$\therefore \quad -9A \sin \varepsilon - 15A \cos \varepsilon = 0$ (2)   Because $\cos\left(\frac{\pi}{2} - \varepsilon\right) = \sin \varepsilon$, etc.

Rearranging (2), $\tan \varepsilon = \frac{15}{-9}$. $\therefore \varepsilon = 2.11$ rad.

And, using the diagram, $\cos \varepsilon = -0.5145$ and $\sin \varepsilon = 0.8575$

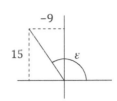

Substituting these values into equation (1)
and solving gives $A = 1.43$.

So the solution is $x = 1.43 \cos(5t - 2.11)$

(c) $v_{max} = A\omega = 1.43 \times 5 = 7.15$ m s^{-1}; $a_{max} = A\omega^2 = 35.75$ m s^{-1}.

NB. Not all systems with forced oscillations exhibit resonance. Second order equations with light damping do. Example F is of an electrical circuit with forced oscillations. The differential equation is a first order one. The problem can also be solved using phasors – see Chapter 8.

Example F:

Find how the steady current, I, varies with time in the circuit shown.

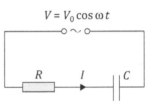

V_C the pd across the capacitor $= \frac{Q}{C}$

V_R the pd across the resistor $= IR$.

$\therefore IR + \frac{Q}{C} = V_0 \cos \omega t$. Differentiating and applying $I = \frac{dQ}{dt}$: $R\frac{dI}{dt} + \frac{I}{C} = -V_0\omega \sin \omega t$

Dividing by R gives: $\frac{dI}{dt} + \frac{I}{RC} = -\frac{V_0\omega}{R} \cos \omega t$

As in Example E, the complementary function is an exponential decay which tends towards zero with a characteristic time of $\sqrt{RC}$. To find the solution at times much larger than this we'll just find the particular integral.

Look for a solution of the form $I = I_0 \cos(\omega t - \varepsilon)$

Differentiating and substituting gives: $- I_0 \sin(\omega t - \varepsilon) + \frac{I_0}{RC} \cos(\omega t - \varepsilon) = -\frac{V_0\omega}{R} \sin \omega t$

The identity must be valid at $t = 0$ and $\omega t = \frac{\pi}{2}$. Multiplying by RC we get:

At $t = 0$: $I_0\omega RC \sin \varepsilon + I_0 \cos \varepsilon = 0$ (1)

At $\omega t = \frac{\pi}{2}$: $-I_0\omega RC \cos \varepsilon + I_0 \sin \varepsilon = -V_0\omega C$ (2)

From (1) $\tan \varepsilon = -\frac{1}{\omega RC}$

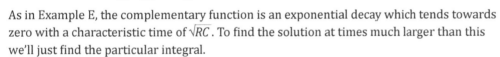

Using the triangle opposite, $\cos \varepsilon = \frac{\omega RC}{\sqrt{1 + (\omega RC)^2}}$ and $\sin \varepsilon = -\frac{1}{\sqrt{1 + (\omega RC)^2}}$.

Substituting these in equation (2) gives: $-I_0\frac{(\omega RC)^2}{\sqrt{1 + (\omega RC)^2}} - I_0\frac{1}{\sqrt{1 + (\omega RC)^2}} = -V_0\omega C$

Rearranging and simplifying gives: $I_0 = \dfrac{V_0}{\sqrt{\dfrac{1}{\omega^2 C^2} + R^2}}$

So $I = I_0 \cos(\omega t - \varepsilon)$, where $I_0 = \dfrac{V_0}{\sqrt{\dfrac{1}{\omega^2 C^2} + R^2}}$ and $\varepsilon = -\tan^{-1}\left[\dfrac{1}{\omega RC}\right]$

Test Yourself 11.1

In Questions 1–10, solve the homogeneous differential equation with the given initial conditions. Initial conditions: x_0 indicates the value of x when $t = 0$, etc.

1 $\dfrac{dv}{dt} + 5v = 0$; $v_0 = 10$

2 $\dfrac{dN}{dt} = -0.001N$; $N_0 = 1 \times 10^6$

3 $\dfrac{dI}{dt} + \dfrac{1}{RC}I = 0$; $I_0 = 6\,\mu A$; $RC = 5$ s

4 $\dfrac{d^2x}{dt^2} + 64x = 0$; $x_0 = 0$, $v_0 = 40$, where $v = \dfrac{dx}{dt}$.

5 $0.2\dfrac{d^2x}{dt^2} + 5x = 0$; $x_0 = 0.1$; $v_0 = 0$

6 $\dfrac{dh}{dt} + 0.02h = 0$; $\dot{h}_0 = -1$ $\left[\text{Remember } \dot{h} = \dfrac{dh}{dt}\right]$

7 $\dfrac{dV}{dt} + \dfrac{V}{RC} = 0$; $R = 4.7 \times 10^3\,\Omega$; $C = 2.2 \times 10^{-3}$ F; $V_0 = 9.0$ V

8 $\dfrac{d^2y}{dt^2} + 100y = 0$; $y_0 = 0.1$ and $\dot{y}_0 = 2$. $\left[\text{Hint: } \dfrac{\sin\theta}{\cos\theta} = \tan\theta\right]$

9 $\dfrac{d^2Q}{dt^2} + 2.5 \times 10^5 Q = 0$; $Q_0 = 0$, $I_0 = 0.1$ mA

10 $L\dfrac{d^2Q}{dt^2} + \dfrac{Q}{C} = 0$; $I_0 = 0$; $Q_0 = 47$ mC. If $C = 1000\,\mu F$ and $L = 100$ mH, find also the period of oscillation.

In Questions 11–18, solve the inhomogeneous differential equation with the given initial conditions.

11 $\dfrac{dv}{dt} + 0.1v = 5$; $v_0 = 20$

12 $\dfrac{dN}{dt} + \lambda N = R$; $N_0 = 0$

13 $\dfrac{dV}{dt} + 0.3V = 7.2$; $V_0 = 40$

14 $\dfrac{d^2I}{dt^2} + 169I = 30\sin 12t$; $I_0 = 0$; $\dot{I}_0 = 7.94$

15 $\dfrac{d^2x}{dt^2} + 100x = 20$; $x_0 = 0$; $v_0 = 0$

16 $\dfrac{dv}{dt} + 0.4v = 2t$; $v_0 = 0$

17 $\dfrac{dv}{dt} + 12v = 6\sin 2\pi t$; $v_0 = 0$

18 $\dfrac{dN}{dt} + 0.1N = Pe^{-0.2t}$; $P = 2 \times 10^6$; $N(0) = 0$

19 A pure radioactive sample, A, initially has 3×10^{15} nuclei. It decays with a decay constant of 0.125 day^{-1} into a second radioactive nuclide, B, which has a decay constant of 0.05 day^{-1}. If the initial number of nuclei of B [N_B] is zero, what is the value of N_B after 20 days?

[Hint – find N_A as a function of time, then set up the differential equation for N_B – it should look rather like the equation in Q18.]

20 A cylindrical buoy of mass 1600 kg floats upright as shown. A force of 1000 N is applied causing the buoy to rise $x = 10$ cm out of the water. The buoy is released. Find the equation of the subsequent oscillations.

[Assume that the force is proportional to the displacement and also that damping is negligible.]

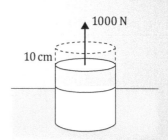

21 A particle undergoes damped harmonic motion with the equation: $\dfrac{d^2x}{dt^2} + 4\dfrac{dx}{dt} + 100x = 0$.

Find the solution of this equation with the initial conditions, $x_0 = 2.0$, $v_0 = 0$ [i.e. the particle is released at time $t = 0$, from $x = 2$ and zero velocity].

22 A flat load of mass 200 g is suspended from a spring with a spring constant, i.e. the force per unit extension, of 1.8 N m^{-1}. It is pulled down a distance of 15 cm [i.e. $x = -0.15$ m] and released. The air resistance on the load is $-0.8v$, where v is the velocity of the particle.

(a) Use the data to derive the differential equation, and

(b) find the solution.

㉓ A particle is observed to undergo damped harmonic motion and the following measurements are made: successive maximum positive values of x occur at 0.5 s, 2.5 s, 4.5 s etc; $x(0.5) = 0.6$ m and $x(20.5) = 0.221$ m [i.e. $0.6 \times e^{-1}$].

(a) Use the data to find the values of k, p and ω [see Section 11.4] and hence write the differential equation.

(b) Give the solution of the differential equation.

(c) Find change in the period of the oscillations caused by the damping.

㉔ A series combination of a resistor, R, and inductor, L, are connected across a power supply with voltage $V = V_0 \cos \omega t$. The pd, V_L, across an inductor is given by $V_L = L\dfrac{dI}{dt}$.

(a) Write a first order differential equation relating V, I, L, R and t.

(b) Find the phase difference between the voltage and current.

(c) Find the relationship between the peak voltage and current.

[Hint see Example F]

㉕ The current, I, in an LCR circuit with a pd, $V = V_0 \cos \psi t$ is given by the differential equation

$$L\frac{dI}{dt} + IR + \frac{Q}{C} = V_0 \cos \psi t$$

(a) By differentiating, form a second order equation and solve it to show that the peak steady state current is given by: $V_0 = I_0\sqrt{R^2 + \left(\psi L - \dfrac{1}{\psi C}\right)^2}$.

(b) Show that the frequency of resonance, f_R, of the circuit is given by $f_R = \dfrac{1}{2\pi\sqrt{LC}}$.

Chapter 12

Miscellaneous Proofs and Derivations

12.1 Introduction

The aim of this chapter is to present two types of mathematical derivations:

1. Certain reasonably formal demonstrations of calculus relationships that would have been out of place in the main body of the book; these are within the scope of A-level Mathematics courses and underpin the mathematical working of A-level Physics courses;

2. Certain physics derivations which are often omitted from A-level Physics textbooks and teaching because they are considered to be overly mathematical, e.g. the derivation of the pressure in an ideal gas.

There are no Quickfires, Pointers or Test Yourself exercises in this chapter but some examples are included to clarify the subject matter.

12.2 Differentiating transcendental functions

12.2.1 $\sin x$

$$\frac{d}{dx}(\sin x) = \lim_{\Delta x \to 0} \frac{\sin(x + \Delta x) - \sin x}{\Delta x}$$

We recall that

$$\sin(A + B) = \sin A \cos B + \cos A \sin B \text{ and } \lim_{\theta \to 0} \frac{\sin \theta}{\theta} = 1$$

Applying these:

$$\frac{d}{dx}(\sin x) = \lim_{\Delta x \to 0} \frac{\sin x \cos \Delta x + \cos x \sin \Delta x - \sin x}{\Delta x}$$

Looking at the numerator of the fraction: $\lim_{\Delta x \to 0} \cos \Delta x = 1 \therefore \lim_{\Delta x \to 0} \sin x \cos \Delta x = \sin x$

$$\therefore \qquad \frac{d}{dx}(\sin x) = \lim_{\Delta x \to 0} \frac{\cos x \sin \Delta x}{\Delta x} = \cos x \lim_{\Delta x \to 0} \frac{\sin \Delta x}{\Delta x} = \cos x$$

Corollary: We demonstrate in 12.4 that integration is the inverse process of differentiation.

$\therefore$ we can write $\int \cos x \, dx = \sin x$, not forgetting the constant of integration for an indefinite integral.

12.2.2 $\cos x$

$$\frac{d}{dx}(\cos x) = \lim_{\Delta x \to 0} \frac{\cos(x + \Delta x) - \cos x}{\Delta x}$$

Applying

$$\cos(A + B) = \cos A \cos B - \sin A \sin B$$

$$\frac{d}{dx}(\cos x) = \lim_{\Delta x \to 0} \frac{\cos x \cos \Delta x - \sin x \sin \Delta x - \cos x}{\Delta x}$$

$$\lim_{\Delta x \to 0} \cos \Delta x = 1 \quad \therefore \lim_{\Delta x \to 0} \cos x \cos \Delta x = \cos x$$

$$\therefore \qquad \frac{d}{dx}(\cos x) = \lim_{\Delta x \to 0} \frac{-\sin x \sin \Delta x}{\Delta x} = -\sin x \lim_{\Delta x \to 0} \frac{\sin \Delta x}{x} = -\sin x$$

Corollary: $\int \sin x \, dx = -\cos x$, not forgetting the constant of integration.

12.2.3 The exponential function

We start by defining exp(x) by requiring that:

- $\dfrac{d}{dx}\exp(x) = \exp(x)$, and
- $\exp(0) = 1$

We look for a power series definition of exp(x) of the form

$$\exp(x) = a_0 + a_1 x + a_2 x^2 + \dots + a_n x^n + \dots$$

$$\exp(0) = 1, \quad \therefore a_0 = 1$$

Because $\dfrac{d}{dx}\exp(x) = \exp(x)$, then $\dfrac{d}{dx}\exp(x)$, $\dfrac{d^2}{dx^2}\exp(x)$, ... $\dfrac{d^n}{dx^n}\exp(x)$ .... will all have the value 1 when $x = 0$.

Differentiating:
$$\frac{d}{dx}\exp(x) = a_1 + 2a_2 x + 3a_3 x^2 + \dots + na_n x^{n-1} + \dots$$

Putting $x = 0$ gives $a_1 = 1$

Differentiating a 2nd time:
$$\frac{d^2}{dx^2}\exp(x) = 2a_2 + (3 \times 2)a_3 x + \dots + n(n-1)a_n x^{n-2} + \dots$$

Putting $x = 0$ gives $2a_2 = 1 \therefore a_2 = \dfrac{1}{2}$

Repeated differentiation gives
$$a_3 = \frac{1}{3 \times 2} = \frac{1}{3!}, \dots a_n = \frac{1}{n(n-1)\dots(2)} = \frac{1}{n!}$$

$$\therefore \qquad \exp(x) = 1 + x + \frac{x^2}{2!} + \frac{x^3}{3!} + \dots$$

In Chapter 4 we showed that e^x and exp(x) are the same functions. $\therefore \dfrac{d}{dx}e^x = e^x$.

Corollary: $\int e^x \, dx = e^x$, not forgetting the constant of integration.

12.2.4 ln x

If $y = \ln x$, then $x = e^y$ because the ln function is the inverse function of e^x.

Differentiating $x = e^y$ with respect to y:

$$\frac{dx}{dy} = e^y, \quad \text{i.e } \frac{dx}{dy} = x$$

But
$$\frac{dy}{dx} = \frac{1}{\dfrac{dx}{dy}} \quad \therefore \frac{dy}{dx} = \frac{1}{x}, \quad \text{i.e. } \frac{d}{dx}(\ln x) = \frac{1}{x}.$$

Corollary: $\int \dfrac{1}{x} \, dx = \ln x$, not forgetting the constant of integration.

12.3 Differentiating combinations of functions

12.3.1 Linear combinations of functions

Let $y(x) = \alpha f(x) + \beta g(x)$, where α and β are constants.

Using the y' notation for $\dfrac{dy}{dx}$:

$$y' = \lim_{\Delta x \to 0} \frac{y(x + \Delta x) - y(x)}{\Delta x} = \lim_{\Delta x \to 0} \frac{(\alpha f(x + \Delta x) + \beta g(x + \Delta x)) - (\alpha f(x) + \beta g(x))}{\Delta x}$$

$$= \lim_{\Delta x \to 0} \frac{\alpha(f(x + \Delta x) - f(x)) + \beta(g(x + \Delta x) - g(x))}{\Delta x}$$

$$= \alpha \lim_{\Delta x \to 0} \frac{f(x + \Delta x) - f(x)}{\Delta x} + \beta \lim_{\Delta x \to 0} \frac{g(x + \Delta x) - g(x)}{\Delta x}$$

$$= \alpha f'(x) + \beta g'(x)$$

12.3.2 Function of a function – the chain rule

Let $\qquad y(x) = f(g(x))$.

Then $\qquad y' = \lim_{\Delta x \to 0} \dfrac{f(g(x + \Delta x)) - f(g(x))}{\Delta x}$

What is $f(g(x + \Delta x))$?

Recall that $\quad g'(x) = \lim_{\Delta x \to 0} \dfrac{g(x + \Delta x) - g(x)}{\Delta x}$

$\therefore$ as $\Delta x \to 0$, $g(x + \Delta x) \to g(x) + g'(x)\Delta x$. As we are going to let $\Delta x \to 0$, we shall write:

$$g(x + \Delta x) = g(x) + g'(x)\Delta x$$

$\therefore \qquad f(g(x + \Delta x)) = f(g(x) + g'(x)\Delta x),$

So, by the same reasoning, we can write

$$f(g(x + \Delta x)) = f(g(x)) + \frac{df}{dg}\frac{dg}{dx}\Delta x$$

Note , we have dropped the g' notation because of the possible confusion with differentiating with respect to two different variables.

$\therefore \qquad \dfrac{dy}{dx} = \lim_{\Delta x \to 0} \dfrac{f(g(x)) + \frac{df}{dg}\frac{dg}{dx}\Delta x - f(g(x))}{\Delta x}$

$$= \frac{df}{dg}\frac{dg}{dx}$$

12.3.3 Product of functions

Let $f(x) = u(x)v(x)$

Then $\qquad \dfrac{df}{dx} = \lim_{\Delta x \to 0} \dfrac{u(x + \Delta x)v(x + \Delta x) - u(x)v(x)}{\Delta x}$

As we showed in 12.3.2: $u(x + \Delta x) = u(x) + u'\Delta x$ and $v(x + \Delta x) = v(x) + v'\Delta x$.

$\therefore \qquad \dfrac{df}{dx} = \lim_{\Delta x \to 0} \dfrac{(u + u'\Delta x)(v + v'\Delta x) - uv}{\Delta x} = \lim_{\Delta x \to 0} \dfrac{uv'\Delta x + vu'\Delta x + u'v'(\Delta x)^2}{\Delta x}$

$\therefore \qquad \dfrac{d}{dx}(uv) = u\dfrac{dv}{dx} + v\dfrac{du}{dx}$

12.3.4 Quotient of functions

Let $f(x) = \dfrac{u(x)}{v(x)}$. We can write f as $f = uv^{-1}$

Applying the product rule from 12.3.3: $\quad \dfrac{df}{dx} = u\dfrac{d}{dx}(v^{-1}) + v^{-1}\dfrac{du}{dx}$

Applying the chain rule from 12.3.2: $\quad \dfrac{d}{dx}(v^{-1}) = -v^{-2}\dfrac{dv}{dx}$

$\therefore \qquad \dfrac{df}{dx} = -uv^{-2}\dfrac{dv}{dx} + v^{-1}\dfrac{du}{dx}$

Taking out a factor of $\dfrac{1}{v^2}$ and re-arranging slightly we get: $\dfrac{d}{dx}\left(\dfrac{u}{v}\right) = \dfrac{1}{v^2}\left(v\dfrac{du}{dx} - u\dfrac{dv}{dx}\right)$.

Example A:

The power output, P, of a power supply of emf E and internal resistance r, into a variable external resistance R is given by $P = \dfrac{E^2 R}{(R + r)^2}$. Show that the maximum power output occurs when $R = r$.

The function $P(R)$ is always positive, is zero when $R = 0$, tends to 0 as $R \rightarrow \infty$ and has a single maximum. The maximum occurs when $\dfrac{dP}{dR} = 0$, because the graph must be horizontal at a maximum.

This example illustrates the results of Sections 12.3.1, 12.3.2 and 12.3.4.

$\dfrac{dP}{dR} = \dfrac{d}{dR}\left(\dfrac{E^2 R}{(R + r)^2}\right)$, which is of the form $\dfrac{d}{dR}\left(\dfrac{u}{v}\right)$, where $u(R) = E^2 R$ and $v(R) = (R + r)^2$.

From 12.3.1, $\dfrac{du}{dR} = E^2 \dfrac{dR}{dR} = E^2$. From 12.3.2: $v(R) = f(g(R))$, where $f = g^2$ and $g = R + r$.

$$\therefore \qquad \dfrac{dv}{dR} = \dfrac{df}{dg} \times \dfrac{dg}{dR} = 2g \times 1 = 2(R + r)$$

Applying the result of 12.3.4: $\dfrac{dP}{dR} = \dfrac{(R + r)^2 E^2 - E^2 R \times 2(R + r)}{(R + r)^4}$.

Now $\dfrac{dP}{dR} = 0$ when the top line of the fraction is zero, i.e. when $(R + r)^2 E^2 - E^2 R \times 2(R + r) = 0$

Dividing by $E^2 (R + r)$ gives $R + r - 2R = 0$, which leads to $R = r$.

NB. This result is called the **maximum power theorem**. It is of great applicability in the design of electronic systems, e.g. maximum power is gained from speakers the impedance of which matches the internal impedance of the output stage of the amplifier.

12.4 Relationship between differentiation and integration

In Chapter 10 we noted that integration and differentiation are inverse processes. We shall now demonstrate this more formally.

Let
$$g(x) = \int_a^x f(y)\,dy$$

The first thing to note is that the expression on the right is a function of x and not y. The variable y is referred to as a *dummy variable*. The function $f(y)$ is integrated between $y = a$ and $y = x$. If x varies, so will the outcome of the integration, $g(x)$. In principle, g is also a function of a but we shall treat a as a constant. We shall now differentiate g.

By definition,
$$g' = \lim_{\Delta x \to 0} \frac{g(x + \Delta x) - g(x)}{\Delta x}.$$

$\therefore$ in this case
$$g' = \lim_{\Delta x \to 0} \frac{\int_a^{x + \Delta x} f(y)\,dy - \int_a^x f(y)\,dy}{\Delta x}$$

But
$$\int_a^{x + \Delta x} f(y)\,dy = \int_a^x f(y)\,dy + \int_x^{x + \Delta x} f(y)\,dy$$

$\therefore$
$$g' = \lim_{\Delta x \to 0} \frac{\int_x^{x + \Delta x} f(y)\,dy}{\Delta x}$$

Remembering that we are considering the limit as $\Delta x \to 0$ and looking back at the definition of integration in 10.3.2 and 10.3.3, as Δx approaches 0, the integral approaches the value $f(x)\,\Delta x$.

$$g' = \lim_{\Delta x \to 0} \frac{f(x)\Delta x}{\Delta x}, \text{ i.e. } g'(x) = f(x)$$

So, to be absolutely clear, $\frac{d}{dx}\left(\int_a^x f(y)dy\right) = f(x)$.

In the language of **indefinite integration** we would write this $\frac{d}{dx}\left(\int f(x)dx\right) = f(x)$ and clearly the corollary is $\int \frac{d}{dx}f(x)dx = f(x) + c$, where c is the constant of integration.

12.5 Waves

12.5.1 Diffraction at a single slit

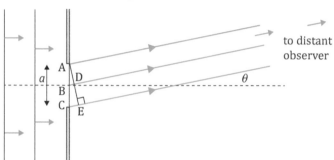

If monochromatic light of wavelength λ passes through a parallel-sided slit of width a, the light spreads out with most being concentrated within an angle $\sin^{-1}\frac{\lambda}{a}$ of the forward direction and increasingly small amounts in fringes with successive zeros at $\sin^{-1}\frac{2\lambda}{a}$, $\sin^{-1}\frac{3\lambda}{a}$, etc.

Usually, $a \gg \lambda$, so the angles can be written $\frac{\lambda}{a}, \frac{2\lambda}{a}, \frac{3\lambda}{a}$, etc.

The full treatment is beyond this book but the general shape of the diffraction curve and the position of its zeros can be demonstrated using Huygens's method. This treatment considers each point in a wavefront to be a source of secondary wavelets, with the resultant wave being the superposition of all the secondary wavelets.

The diagram shows a series of plane wavefronts incident at right angles upon a slit of width a, where $a \gg \lambda$. The arrows emerging from the slit are to be understood as directions of propagation of the secondary wavelets from points A, B and C on the wavefront in the slit[1]. These wavefront combine at the observer, who is so distant that these arrows are effectively parallel.

Consider first $\theta = 0$. In this case all the paths to the observer are the same length so the wavelets add up in phase and a large amplitude resultant is formed.

Consider next $\theta = \frac{\lambda}{a}$.

In the triangle ABD, BD = AB $\sin\theta$.

But, for $a \gg \lambda$, $\sin\theta = \theta = \frac{\lambda}{a}$. Also AB $= \frac{a}{2}$

$\therefore$ $$BD = \frac{a}{2} \times \frac{\lambda}{a} = \frac{\lambda}{2}.$$

In this direction, the wavelets from A and B will arrive at the observer with a path difference of $\frac{\lambda}{2}$ and will therefore negatively superpose, with zero resultant. The same will be true for any pair of points the same distance below A and B. The whole slit is entirely composed of such pairs of points, so there will be zero resultant in this direction.

Consider next $\theta = \frac{3\lambda}{2a}$.

---

[1] These secondary wavelets are spherical wavelets. They radiate in all directions. In the diagram the wavelets are not shown and we just concentrate on a few special directions. This idea was developed by Huygens.

In this case the wavelet from A will exactly cancel a wavelet from a point $\frac{1}{3}$ down. In the same way wavelets from all pairs of points covering the top $\frac{2}{3}$ of the slit will cancel – leaving the bottom third for which no complete cancellation can occur. This means that weak light will be observed in this direction.

If $\theta = \frac{2\lambda}{a}, \frac{3\lambda}{a} \dots$, you should be able to show that complete cancellation will occur; at the intervening directions, some light will emerge.

12.5.2 Young slits

S_1 and S_2 are two coherent monochromatic light sources, e.g. two slits illuminated by the same small light source. Assume that S_1 and S_2 are in phase.^[2]

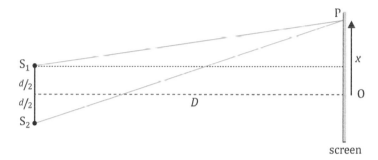

Fig 12.1

O is a point on the screen which is on the perpendicular bisector of the line $S_1 S_2$, a distance D from the midpoint of $S_1 S_2$. The point P is a distance x from O as shown.

Let the wavelength of the light sources be λ. Typically, $D \sim 1\text{--}2$ m; $d \sim 0.5$ mm, $x \sim 0\text{--}5$ mm.

Using Pythagoras' theorem, $S_1 P = \sqrt{D^2 + \left(x - \frac{d}{2}\right)^2}$. We'll write this as $D\left(1 + \frac{\left(x - \frac{d}{2}\right)^2}{D^2}\right)^{\frac{1}{2}}$.

Similarly $\qquad\qquad\qquad S_2 P = D\left(1 + \frac{\left(x + \frac{d}{2}\right)^2}{D^2}\right)^{\frac{1}{2}}$ [Note the + sign]

For small δ, $(1 + \delta)^n = 1 + n\delta$. D is at least $100x$, so $D^2 \sim 10^4 x^2$ or more

So $\qquad\qquad \left(1 + \frac{\left(x \pm \frac{d}{2}\right)^2}{D^2}\right)^{\frac{1}{2}} = 1 + \frac{1}{2}\frac{\left(x \pm \frac{d}{2}\right)^2}{D^2}$ very accurately.

Light from S_1 and S_2 reinforces at P if $S_2 P - S_1 P = n\lambda$, where n is an integer, $\dots$ $-2, -1, 0, 1, 2, 3 \dots$

$\therefore \quad S_2 P - S_1 P = D\left[\left(1 + \frac{1}{2}\frac{\left(x + \frac{d}{2}\right)^2}{D^2}\right) - \left(1 + \frac{1}{2}\frac{\left(x - \frac{d}{2}\right)^2}{D^2}\right)\right]$. Cancel the 1s and multiply in by the D.

Simplifying: $\therefore \qquad S_2 P - S_1 P = \dfrac{\left(x + \frac{d}{2}\right)^2 - \left(x - \frac{d}{2}\right)^2}{2D} = \dfrac{\left(x^2 + xd + \frac{d^2}{4}\right) - \left(x^2 - xd + \frac{d^2}{4}\right)}{2D}$

The x^2 and $d^2/4$ terms disappear, leaving $S_2 P - S_1 P = \dfrac{2xd}{2D} = \dfrac{xd}{D}$.

The point P is a bright fringe if $S_2 P - S_1 P = n\lambda$, ie. for a bright fringe: $n\lambda = \dfrac{xd}{D}$.

[After so much algebra, we'd better pause for a dimensions check:

The left-hand side of $n\lambda = \dfrac{xd}{D}$ has dimension L; the right-hand side has dimension $\dfrac{\text{L} \times \text{L}}{\text{L}} = \text{L}$ ✓]

So $x = \dfrac{n\lambda D}{d}$ and the separation of adjacent fringes is $\dfrac{\lambda D}{d}$.

---

^[2] If S_1 and S_2 are not exactly in phase but have a constant phase difference, the positions of the fringes will be different but their separation will be unchanged.

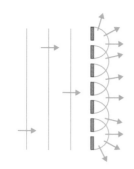

Fig 12.2

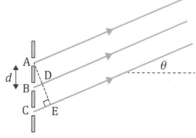

Fig 12.3

12.5.3 Diffraction grating

A transmission diffraction grating consists of a plane opaque plate crossed by a very large number of narrow parallel regularly spaced regions, known as slits, which are transparent.[3] A typical grating for school use has a width of 2 or 3 cm and has several thousand slits.

Figure 12.2 shows a series of plane wavefronts approaching a small region of such a grating. The waves diffract as they pass through the narrow slits. The width, w, of the slits is such that the angle to the first minimum of the diffracted waves is large, typically $> \frac{\pi}{3}$ rad [see Section 12.5.1]. The diagram shows some of the diffracted wavefronts.

We observe the transmitted light at a large distance from the diffraction grating. The diffracted waves add by superposition; we calculate the angles at which significant reinforcement occurs. Figure 12.3 shows thee adjacent slits, A, B and C and light propagation at an angle θ to the forward direction.

Let λ = wavelength of the waves

   d = the separation of adjacent slits

The line AE is perpendicular to the considered direction.

The diffracted waves at A, B and C are in phase. When they arrive at an observer, O, who is a long way off to the right, the path difference BO − AO = BD.

Let BD = $n\lambda$.   BD = AB sin$B\hat{A}D = d \sin \theta$

   $\therefore$ $n\lambda = d \sin \theta$

If n is an integer, i.e. −2, −1, 0, 1, 2, 3....., the path difference is a whole number of wavelengths so the waves from A and B will reinforce at ∞. The waves from C will also be a whole number of wavelengths out of step so they will also reinforce.... and so on across the whole grating.

What if θ is slightly different from $\sin^{-1}\left(\frac{n\lambda}{d}\right)$, where n is an integer? Let us suppose that BD is not $n\lambda$ but $(n + 0.1)\lambda$. The waves from A and B will arrive just one tenth of a cycle out of step so will reinforce quite well. However, the waves from five slits below A will have a path difference of $(n + 0.5)\lambda$ so will cancel the waves from A. The waves from B will be similarly cancelled by those from five slits below it. The result is no light in this direction. Similarly, if $(n + 0.01)\lambda$, the waves from any two slits a distance $50d$ apart will cancel. And if we have several thousand slits, even a path difference of $(n + 0.01)\lambda$, between adjacent slits will produce almost complete cancellation. We conclude that, from a monochromatic source, we observe a series of single sharp lines at angles θ such that:

$$\theta_0 = 0, \theta_1 = \pm \sin^{-1}\frac{\lambda}{d}, \theta_2 = \pm \sin^{-1}\frac{2\lambda}{d} \dots .$$

If the light source is polychromatic we observe the so-called zero-, first-, second-, ... order spectra

Example B shows how sharp a typical line is and gives a clue as to how the width of the line depends upon the total number of lines in the diffraction grating.

Example B:

A diffraction grating has 1000 lines. From a particular monochromatic (or 'line') source, a first order spectral line is at 0.5 rad [~30°] to the forward direction. Estimate the width of this spectral line.

$$\sin \theta = \frac{n\lambda}{d} \text{ for } \theta = 0.5 \text{ rad and } n = 1.$$

If the diffraction grating has 1000 lines, almost complete cancellation will occur for an additional path difference from neighbouring slits of 0.001λ. We calculate the additional value, $\Delta\theta$ which will produce this path difference.

$$\Delta(\sin \theta) = \Delta\theta \times \frac{d}{d\theta}(\sin \theta) = \Delta\theta \cos \theta$$

---

[3]   In practice, the opaque plate is not 100% absorbent and the slits are not 100% transparent.

Also
$$\Delta(\sin\theta) = \frac{(1 + 0.001)\lambda}{d} - \frac{\lambda}{d} = \frac{0.001\lambda}{d} = 0.001\sin\theta$$

$\therefore$
$$\Delta\theta\cos\theta = 0.001\sin\theta$$

$\therefore$
$$\Delta\theta = 0.001\tan\theta = 0.001\tan(0.5\text{ rad}) = 5.5\times10^{-4}\text{ rad }[\sim0.03°]$$

12.5.4 Snell's law

Figure 12.4 shows a series of snapshots of a plane wavefront crossing a boundary from material 1, in which its speed is c_1, into material 2 with speed c_2. The wavefront is, as always, perpendicular to the direction of propagation of the waves. Consider the interval, τ, between the times when the wavefront is at AB and CD.

Figure 12.5 is a magnification of this region.

Then $\tau = \dfrac{BD}{c_1}$ and $\tau = \dfrac{AC}{c_2}$, so $\quad \dfrac{BD}{c_1} = \dfrac{AC}{c_2}$ 　　　　(1)

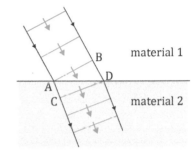

Fig 12.4

The angle of incidence $= \theta_1$.

$$\hat{BDA} = 90° - \theta_1, \quad \therefore\ \hat{BAD} = \theta_1 \quad \therefore\ BD = AD\sin\theta_1 \quad (2)$$

Similarly
$$AC = AD\sin\theta_2 \quad (3)$$

Substituting for BD and AC in equation (1) from (2) and (3) gives:

$$\frac{AD\sin\theta_1}{c_1} = \frac{AD\sin\theta_2}{c_2}, \text{ so, dividing by AD we get: } \frac{\sin\theta_1}{c_1} = \frac{\sin\theta_2}{c_2}. \quad (4)$$

$\therefore$
$$\frac{\sin\theta_1}{\sin\theta_2} = \frac{c_1}{c_2} = \text{constant, which is Snell's law.}$$

The *refractive index*, *n*, of a material is defined as the ratio of the speed of light in a vacuum to the speed of light in the material.

$\therefore$ for material 1, $n_1 = \dfrac{c}{c_1}$ and for material 2, $n_2 = \dfrac{c}{c_2}$.

Substituting in (4) for c_1 and c_2 gives the usual refraction formula: $n_1\sin\theta_1 = n_2\sin\theta_2$. This equation can also be written in the form $n\sin\theta = $ constant, which can be applied to situations in which the refractive varies continuously with position.

12.6 Momentum concepts

12.6.1 Pressure exerted by a light beam

Individual photons possess a momentum $p = \dfrac{h}{\lambda}$.

Using $c = \lambda f$ and $E = hf$, we can rewrite this as $p = \dfrac{hf}{c} = \dfrac{E}{c}$.

It is one of the peculiarities of wave-particle duality, that we can use a wave description of light, i.e. wavelength or frequency, to calculate the momentum of a particle.

Consider a beam of (monochromatic) radiation incident upon a non-reflecting surface at right angles, as shown. If N photons hit the surface per unit time:

The momentum change of the photons in time $\Delta t : \Delta p_{ph} = -N\dfrac{E}{c}\Delta t$

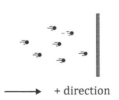

$\longrightarrow$ + direction

The minus sign is because the incident photons have a positive momentum which is destroyed as they are absorbed.

$\therefore$ The momentum change of the photons per unit time $= -\dfrac{NE}{c}$

By Newton's second law of motion, the force, F_w, exerted on the photons by the wall as it stops them is equal to their rate of change of momentum;

i.e. $F_W = -\dfrac{NE}{c}$. $\therefore$ By Newton's third law of motion, the force, F_{ph}, exerted by the photons on the wall is given by $F_{ph} = \dfrac{NE}{c}$.

NE is the total energy delivered to the wall per unit time, i.e the power, P, of the beam, so the force exerted on the wall by the beam is given by $F_{ph} = \dfrac{P}{c}$.

If the beam of photons is incident over an area, A, the pressure exerted $= \dfrac{P}{Ac}$. The fraction $\dfrac{P}{A}$ is the power per unit area of the beam, i.e. its intensity, I.

$\therefore$ The pressure, p, exerted by the light beam is given by $p = \dfrac{I}{c}$.

Notes:

1. It is unfortunate that the symbols for momentum and pressure are both p. We just have to live with it. This problem also arises in the kinetic theory of gases.

2. The pressure exerted by a beam of intensity I is independent of the wavelength of the photons in the beam. $\therefore$ The equation $p = \dfrac{I}{c}$ is valid for a non-monochromatic beam also.

3. If the surface is a 100% reflective surface, the momentum change of the photons is doubled; the pressure is also doubled to $p = \dfrac{2I}{c}$. For a reflective surface at a different angle to the incident beam, the vector change in momentum of the photons will need to be found to calculate the pressure.

Example C:

The intensity of solar radiation is approximately $1.36\,\mathrm{kW\,m^{-2}}$ at the Earth. What pressure would it exert on a non-reflecting surface?

$$p = \frac{I}{c} = \frac{1.36 \times 10^3\,\mathrm{W}}{3 \times 10^8\,\mathrm{m\,s^{-1}}} = 4.5\,\mathrm{\mu Pa}$$

12.6.2 Energy transfer on collision – fission reactor moderators

The role of the moderator in a nuclear reactor is to reduce the kinetic energy of the fission neutrons so that they can induce further fissions and also to extract the energy in order to generate electricity. How much energy is transferred on collision?

Consider a particle of mass m and velocity u in an elastic collision with a stationary particle of mass M. We consider the simple case of a head on collision.

before | after

Applying conservation of momentum and energy we can show that:

$$v = \frac{m - M}{m + M}u \quad \text{and} \quad V = \frac{2m}{m + M}u.$$

This is left as an exercise for the reader. [Hint: change to the centre of mass frame of reference – see Chapter 7]. Note that if $M > m$ then $v < 0$, i.e. the motion of m is reversed.

The initial kinetic energy is $\frac{1}{2}mu^2$. The E_k acquired by M is

$$\frac{1}{2}M\left(\frac{2m}{m+M}u\right)^2 = \frac{2m^2M}{(m+M)^2}u^2.$$

What value of M will give the maximum energy transfer? If we look at the expression we see that it is of the same form as the power output of an electrical supply, $P = \frac{E^2R}{(R+r)^2}$, in that the variable parts are $\frac{M}{(m+M)^2}$ and $\frac{R}{(R+r)^2}$ [see Example A] so the answer is the same: the maximum transfer occurs when $M = m$. In this case you should be able to show that the E_k acquired by M becomes $\frac{1}{2}mu^2$, i.e. it gets the lot! For oblique collisions, the result is similar, i.e most energy transfer occurs when M and m are the same.

What does this mean for moderators? They work most effectively if the target nucleus is not too much heavier than the neutron. Water has been used [hydrogen nuclei have almost same mass as neutrons] as has heavy water [deuterium nuclei have ~2 × neutron mass]. Carbon is also used with a mass 12 × that of the neutron. This is quite light and in the solid state, which is also a consideration.

12.6.3 Energy partition in α-decay

Consider a radioactive nucleus which decays into a daughter nucleus with mass M and an α-particle, with mass m_α. What fraction of the decay energy does each particle acquire?

Assuming the parent nucleus is stationary before decay, the initial momentum is zero, so the total momentum after decay is also zero [we are already in the centre of mass frame of reference!].

Let the momentum of the two particles be $+p$ and $-p$.

The kinetic energy acquired by the nucleus is $\frac{p^2}{2M}$.

[This can be derived by eliminating v from KE $= \frac{1}{2}Mv^2$ and $p = Mv$].

The kinetic energy acquired by the α-particle is $\frac{p^2}{2m_\alpha}$.

So the energy is divided in the ratio: $\frac{\text{Energy of }\alpha\text{-particle}}{\text{Energy of nucleus}} = \frac{\text{Mass of nucleus}}{\text{Mass of }\alpha\text{-particle}}$;

the energy ratio is the inverse of the mass ratio – the α-particle gets most.

And the fraction of the total decay energy carried away by the α-particle $= \frac{M}{m_\alpha + M}$.

Thus for a decay with a well-defined energy release, the alpha particles are mono-energetic – they all have the same energy. This is not the case in β-decay because a neutrino is released alongside the β-particle and shares the available energy: the energy spectrum of the β-particles was the initial evidence for the existence of the neutrino.

12.6.4 Conservation of momentum in different inertial frames of reference

An inertial frame of reference is one which is not accelerated. We show that, if the momentum of a system of particles is conserved in one inertial frame of reference, it is conserved in all inertial frames of reference.

Consider a system of N particles with masses, m_i and velocities $\mathbf{u}_i$ in a certain frame of reference, where i = 1, 2, ... N. At some later time let their velocities be $\mathbf{v}_i$ in the same reference frame.

In the absence of externally applied forces, momentum is conserved, i.e $\sum_{i=1}^{N} m_i\mathbf{u}_i = \sum_{i=1}^{N} m_i\mathbf{v}_i$.

If the particles were observed from a frame of reference moving with velocity $\mathbf{w}$ with respect to the first frame, the velocities would be $\mathbf{u}_i - \mathbf{w}$ and $\mathbf{v}_i - \mathbf{w}$ respectively.

Then the final momentum $= \sum_{i=1}^{N} m_i(\mathbf{v}_i - \mathbf{w}) = \sum_{i=1}^{N} m_i\mathbf{v}_i - \sum_{i=1}^{N} m_i\mathbf{w}$

$$= \sum_{i=1}^{N} m_i\mathbf{u}_i - \sum_{i=1}^{N} m_i\mathbf{w} = \sum_{i=1}^{N} m_i(\mathbf{u}_i - \mathbf{w}) = \text{the initial momentum.}$$

12.6.5 Kinetic energy change in different inertial frames of reference

We show that, if the momentum of a system of particles is conserved, the change of the total kinetic energy is the same in all inertial fames of reference.

Consider the same system of particles and frames of reference as above in 12.6.4. In the first frame of reference, the initial and final kinetic energies, E_1 and E_2 are given by:

$$E_1 = \sum_{i=1}^{N} \tfrac{1}{2} m_i u_i^2 \quad \text{and} \quad E_2 = \sum_{i=1}^{N} \tfrac{1}{2} m_i v_i^2$$

$\therefore$ The change of kinetic energy $\Delta E = \sum_{i=1}^{N} \left(\tfrac{1}{2} m_i v_i^2 - \tfrac{1}{2} m_i u_i^2 \right)$

In the second frame of reference, the energy change $= \Delta E' = \sum_{i=1}^{N} \left(\tfrac{1}{2} m_i (\mathbf{v}_i - \mathbf{w})^2 - \tfrac{1}{2} m_i (\mathbf{u}_i - \mathbf{w})^2 \right)$

Now: $(\mathbf{v}_i - \mathbf{w})^2 = v_i^2 - 2\mathbf{v}_i.\mathbf{w} + w^2$ and similarly for $(\mathbf{u}_i - \mathbf{w})^2$.

$$\therefore \qquad \Delta E' = \sum_{i=1}^{N} \tfrac{1}{2} m_i \left((v_i^2 - 2\mathbf{v}_i.\mathbf{w} + w^2) - (u_i^2 - 2\mathbf{u}_i.\mathbf{w} + w^2) \right)$$

$$= \sum_{i=1}^{N} \tfrac{1}{2} m_i (v_i^2 - u_i^2) + \left[\sum_{i=1}^{N} m_i (\mathbf{u}_i - \mathbf{v}_i) \right].\mathbf{w}$$

The first term is ΔE. The second term is the dot product with $\mathbf{w}$ of the sum of all the momentum changes of the particles, which is zero.

$$\therefore \qquad \Delta E' = \Delta E$$

Note that the **change** of kinetic energy is the same in all frames but the fractional change is not the same. For example, if two particles with total kinetic energy of 100 J in one frame, lose 40 J on collision they will lose 40 J in all frames; but they won't lose 40% of their kinetic energy in all frames. See the next example.

Example D:

An object of mass 4 kg and speed 20 m s^{-1} collides head on with a stationary object of mass 12 kg. If 20% of the kinetic energy is lost, find their velocities after collision.

Initial $E_k = \tfrac{1}{2} \times 4 \times 20^2 = 800$ J.

The total kinetic energy loss is 160 J.

The velocity of the CoM $= \dfrac{\text{total momentum}}{\text{total mass}} = \dfrac{80 \text{ N s}}{16 \text{ kg}} = 5$ m s^{-1}.

Now we'll change to CoM system: In the CoM the initial velocity of 4 kg = 20 − 5 = 15 m s^{-1} to the right.

Initial velocity of the 12 kg = 5 m s^{-1} to the left.

Total E_k in the CoM frame $= \left(\tfrac{1}{2} \times 4 \times 15^2 \right) + \left(\tfrac{1}{2} \times 12 \times 5^2 \right) = 600$ J

$\therefore$ After collision the E_k = 600 − 160 J = 440 J.

In this frame, if the 12 kg mass rebounds with a velocity v, the 4 kg rebounds with a velocity of $-3v$ because the total momentum in the CoM frame is 0.

$\therefore$ The total energy $= \left(\tfrac{1}{2} \times 4 \times 9v^2 \right) + \left(\tfrac{1}{2} \times 12 \times v^2 \right) = 24v^2 \therefore 440 = 24v^2. \therefore v = 4.3$ m s^{-1} [2s.f.]

$\therefore$ Changing back to the laboratory frame: the velocities are

4 kg:	$-12.9 + 5 = -7.9$ m s^{-1} [i.e. 7.9 m s^{-1} to the left]
12 kg:	$4.3 + 5 = 9.3$ m s^{-1} to the right.

12.6.6 Calculation of pressure and internal energy of ideal gas

Different A-level books derive the formula $pV = \frac{1}{3}Nm\langle c^2\rangle$ in different ways. We consider the number of impacts per unit time on an area of container wall of gas molecules with a velocity close to (u, v, w) [i.e. velocity = $u\mathbf{i} + v\mathbf{j} + w\mathbf{k}$]. Let the number of molecules, of mass m, within the gas be N and the number with a velocity close to this be N_{uvw}[a].

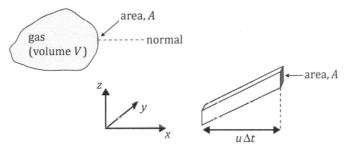

Consider a small patch A, area A, in the wall, perpendicular to the x direction, as shown.

The molecules in our group of molecules with velocity (u, v, w), travelling towards A which will hit A in a time Δt will be contained in an oblique prism of height $u\Delta t$. Each of the molecules has an x-component of momentum mu.

$\therefore$ The x-momentum of these molecules hitting A in Δt = $N_{uvw} \times \dfrac{\text{prism volume}}{\text{container volume}} \times mu$

$$= N_{uvw} \times \frac{Au\Delta t}{V} \times mu$$

$$= \frac{A\Delta t}{V}mN_{uvw}u^2$$

So the total x-momentum, p_x, brought to A in time Δt by **all** the molecules approaching A will be given by:

$$p_x = \sum_{u>0} \frac{A\Delta t}{V}mN_{uvw}u^2$$

where we are summing over all the molecules for which $u > 0$.

If the 50% of molecules for which $u < 0$ are included, the sum becomes

$$p_x = \frac{1}{2}\sum_{u} \frac{A\Delta t}{V}mN_{uvw}u^2 \quad \text{i.e. } \frac{1}{2}\frac{A\Delta t}{V}m\{u_1^2 + u_2^2 + \dots + u_N^2\}$$

Assuming that the collision with the wall is elastic, the rebound x-momentum is $-p_x$

So the x-momentum change $\quad \Delta p_x = -\dfrac{A\Delta t}{V}m\{u_1^2 + u_2^2 + \dots + u_N^2\}$.

The sum, $u_1^2 + u_2^2 + \dots + u_N^2 = N\langle u^2\rangle$, where $\langle u^2\rangle$ is the mean of u^2.

For any molecule: $u^2 + v^2 + w^2 = c^2$. So, for all the molecules, $\langle u^2\rangle + \langle v^2\rangle + \langle w^2\rangle = \langle c^2\rangle$. We shall assume that there is no preferred direction in the gas, so that $\langle u^2\rangle = \langle v^2\rangle = \langle w^2\rangle$.

$\therefore 3\langle u^2\rangle = \langle c^2\rangle$ and we can write $\quad \Delta p_x = -\dfrac{1}{3}\dfrac{A\Delta t}{V}Nm\langle c^2\rangle$.

This is the change of momentum of the molecules in Δt at the wall. So the force exerted by the wall on the molecules, $\dfrac{\Delta p_x}{\Delta t}$ is given by $-\dfrac{1}{3}\dfrac{A}{V}Nm\langle c^2\rangle$.

So, by Newton's 3rd law of motion, the force, F, exerted by the molecules on A is given by:

$$F = \frac{1}{3}\frac{A}{V}Nm\langle c^2\rangle$$

So the pressure, p, on the wall is given by $p = \dfrac{1}{3}\dfrac{Nm\langle c^2\rangle}{V}$, which we normally write as

$$pV = \tfrac{1}{3}Nm\langle c^2\rangle.$$

---

[a] It doesn't really matter exactly **how** close, as long as each molecule is eventually counted once only.

The **internal energy**, U, of a gas is the total energy of its molecules. A gas approximates to ideal behaviour if the intermolecular forces are negligible between collisions, i.e. the potential energy of the gas molecules is negligible. Hence the internal energy is just the total kinetic energy of the molecules. Monatomic gases possess negligible rotational kinetic energy for reasons which are beyond the scope of this book. Hence, for monatomic gases:

$$U = \sum_{i=1}^{N} \tfrac{1}{2}mc_i^2 = \tfrac{1}{2}Nm\langle c^2 \rangle$$

By comparison with the equation for p, we can write $U = \tfrac{3}{2}pV$.

And by comparison with the ideal gas equation, $pV = nRT$, we can write $U = \tfrac{3}{2}nRT$ and the molar heat capacity of an ideal gas [at constant pressure] $C_V = \tfrac{3}{2}R$.

12.7 Magnetic flux density calculations

12.7.1 Biot-Savat law

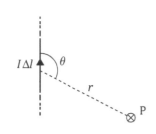

The flux density, **B**, produced by a charge q moving with velocity **v** at a point with position vector **r** with respect to the charge is given by $\mathbf{B} = \dfrac{\mu_0}{4\pi}\dfrac{q\mathbf{v} \times \hat{\mathbf{r}}}{r^2}$. In non-vector notation this equation can be written $B = \dfrac{\mu_0}{4\pi}\dfrac{qv\sin\theta}{r^2}$, where θ is the angle between the direction of the velocity and the direction of B is given by the right-hand grip rule [thumb in direction of velocity, fingers in direction of the field]. From this we can derive a method of working out the magnetic field due to electric currents.

Consider a short length, $\Delta\ell$, of wire, carrying a current I. The product $I\Delta\ell$ is called the current element. What is the flux at the point **P**? All the moving charges which carry the current are moving in the same direction (upwards if they are +) and produce a flux at 90° into the paper at **P**.

Because all the contributions are in the same direction, we can drop the vector notation.

The current I in the element is given by $I = nAqv$, where n is the charge density and A the cross-sectional area of the section of wire.

Multiplying by $\Delta\ell$: $I\Delta\ell = nA\Delta\ell qv$

The product $nA\Delta\ell$ is the total number of moving charges, N, which constitute the current.

The field, B, due to N charges moving at v is given by $B = \dfrac{\mu_0}{4\pi}\dfrac{Nqv\sin\theta}{r^2}$, which we can now rewrite as $B = \dfrac{\mu_0}{4\pi}\dfrac{I\Delta\ell\sin\theta}{r^2}$. This is the Biot–Savat law, which we write in vector notation:

$\mathbf{B} = \dfrac{\mu_0}{4\pi}\dfrac{I\Delta\mathbf{l} \times \hat{\mathbf{r}}}{r^2}$, where $\Delta\mathbf{l}$ is a vector of magnitude $\Delta\ell$ in the direction of the current. Historically, the Biot-Savat law was developed first. Now it is seen as a consequence of the magnetic fields due to all the moving charges which constitute an electric current.

12.7.2 Magnetic field close to a long straight wire

Consider the point **P** a distance a from a long straight wire [we'll assume it's infinitely long!] which carries a current I.

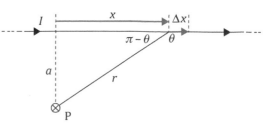

The flux density, ΔB, due to the current element $I\Delta x$ is given by $\Delta B = \dfrac{\mu_0}{4\pi}\dfrac{I\Delta x\sin\theta}{r^2}$, from 12.7.1.

So the flux density, B from the whole wire is given by $B = \dfrac{\mu_0 I}{4\pi}\displaystyle\int_{-\infty}^{+\infty}\dfrac{\sin\theta}{r^2}\,\mathrm{d}x$.

Unfortunately we have three variables in the integration: x, θ and r! To evaluate this we need to work in just 1. We'll use θ.

$$\frac{a}{r} = \sin(\pi - \theta) = \sin\theta \qquad \therefore \frac{1}{r^2} = \frac{\sin^2\theta}{a^2}.$$

$$\frac{a}{x} = \tan(\pi - \theta) = -\tan\theta \qquad \therefore x = -\frac{a}{\tan\theta} = -a\frac{\cos\theta}{\sin\theta}.$$

Using the rule for differentiating a ratio $\dfrac{dx}{d\theta} = \dfrac{a}{\sin^2\theta}$ [You should check this for yourself.]

$\therefore$ Instead of dx in the integration we write $dx = \dfrac{a}{\sin^2\theta}d\theta$

Finally, the limits of integration: when $x = -\infty$, $\theta = 0$. When $x = +\infty$, $\theta = \pi$

So the integration becomes

$$B = \frac{\mu_0 I}{4\pi}\int_0^\pi \sin\theta \times \frac{\sin^2\theta}{a^2} \times \frac{a\,d\theta}{\sin^2\theta}$$

$$= \frac{\mu_0 I}{4\pi a}\int_0^\pi \sin\theta\,d\theta$$

$$= \frac{\mu_0 I}{4\pi a}\left[-\cos\theta\right]_0^\pi$$

$$= \frac{\mu_0 I}{4\pi a}(1 - (-1)) = \frac{\mu_0 I}{2\pi a}$$

12.7.3 Magnetic field inside a long solenoid

Consider a point **P** on the axis of a long solenoid, with n turns per unit length carrying a current I.

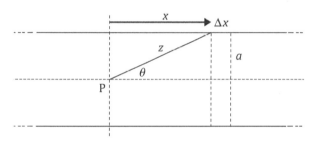

The contribution to the flux density, ΔB from the short section Δx indicated is given by:

$$\Delta B = \frac{\mu_0 I \sin\theta}{2z^2}n\Delta x \text{ along the axis of the solenoid.}$$

$\therefore$ the total flux density, $\qquad B = \dfrac{\mu_0 n I a}{2}\displaystyle\int_{-\infty}^{\infty} \frac{\sin\theta}{z^2}dx$

The function to be integrated is exactly the same as in the long straight wire derivation, with r replaced by z. The integration proceeds in the same manner by replacing the variables z and x with θ.

$$\frac{a}{z} = \sin\theta \quad \therefore \frac{1}{z^2} = \frac{\sin^2\theta}{a}$$

$$x = a\frac{\cos\theta}{\sin\theta} \text{ leading to } dx = -\frac{a}{\sin^2\theta}d\theta$$

Limits of integration: when $x = -\infty$, $\theta = -\pi$; when $x = +\infty$, $\theta = 0$.

$\therefore \qquad B = \dfrac{\mu_0 n I a}{2}\displaystyle\int_{-\pi}^{0} \frac{\sin^2\theta}{a^2}\sin\theta\frac{-a\,d\theta}{\sin^2\theta}$

$$= \frac{\mu_0 n I a}{2}\int_{-\pi}^{0} \frac{-\sin\theta}{a}d\theta$$

$$= \frac{\mu_0 n I}{2}\left[\cos\theta\right]_{-\pi}^{0}$$

$$= \frac{\mu_0 n I}{2} \times 2 = \mu_0 n I$$

Notes:

1   Because the magnetic field lines in the solenoid are parallel, the result holds for points off the axis too.

2   The axial flux density at the ends of the solenoid is half this value, i.e. $\frac{1}{2}\mu_0 nI$.

12.7.4   Helmholz coils

Helmholz coils are two plane coils of the same radius, a, with the same number of turns, N, on the same axis, separated by a, connected in series so that the currents in the two coils are in the same direction. This produces a magnetic field in the space between the coils, which is very nearly uniform. The arrangement allows for access to the volume between the coils. It is used, for example, in deflection tubes. We demonstrate that the flux density is reasonably constant along the axis between the coils.

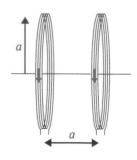

The flux density, B, on the axis of a single coil, a distance x from the plane of the coil is given by:

$$B = \frac{\mu_0}{2}\frac{NIa^2}{\left(a^2 + x^2\right)^{\frac{3}{2}}} \quad \text{(see Section 9.5.2)}$$

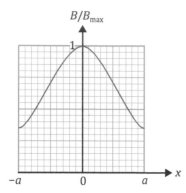

B/B_{max}

The graph shows this function for $-a < x < a$. The vertical scale gives the value of B as a fraction of the maximum value,

$$B_{max} = \frac{\mu_0 NI}{2a}, \text{ the value at the centre of the coil.}$$

The second coil is placed so that, at the midpoint of the coils, the value of B from one coil decreases at the same rate the value from the other coil increases – in other words we are looking for a cross-over point at the steepest part of the graphs. This point, the so-called point of inflexion in the graphs, appears to be when $x = \pm\frac{1}{2}a$. We demonstrate this as follows.

The gradient of the graph, $\dfrac{dB}{dx} = \dfrac{\mu_0 NIa^2}{2}\dfrac{d}{dx}\left(a^2 + x^2\right)^{-\frac{3}{2}} = \dfrac{\mu_0 NIa^2}{2}\left(-\dfrac{3}{2}\right)2x\left(a^2 + x^2\right)^{-\frac{5}{2}}$ – chain rule.

Tidying this up: $\dfrac{dB}{dx} = -\dfrac{3\mu_0 NIa^2}{2}\dfrac{x}{\left(a^2 + x^2\right)^{\frac{5}{2}}}.$

$\dfrac{dB}{dx}$ is maximum (or minimum) when its derivative is zero, i.e. when $\dfrac{d^2B}{dx^2} = 0$. Differentiating again, using the u/v rule (see 12.3.4) we get:

$$\frac{d^2B}{dx^2} = \frac{3\mu_0 NIa^2}{2}\frac{\left(a^2 + x^2\right)^{\frac{5}{2}} - 5x^2\left(a^2 + x^2\right)^{\frac{3}{2}}}{\left(a^2 + x^2\right)^{\frac{5}{2}}}.$$

This is left as an exercise for the reader.

For $\dfrac{d^2B}{dx^2}$ to be 0, the top line of the fraction must be zero.

Putting the top line to zero and dividing by $\left(a^2 + x^2\right)^{\frac{3}{2}}$ we get $(a^2 + x^2) - 5x^2 = 0$. This rearranges to give $x^2 = \frac{1}{4}a^2$, i.e. $x = \pm\frac{1}{2}a$, which was the result we were looking for. For the coils to be arranged so that the midpoint is $\frac{1}{2}a$ from each, the separation is a. The graph shows B due to each coil [the dotted lines] and the resultant flux density. The bands show the positions of the coils.

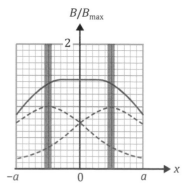

B/B_{max}

Data Exercise 12.1

(a) Use a spreadsheet to plot the variation of the axial flux density, B, with distance, x, from the centre of a plane coil of radius a. Use the equation:
$B = \dfrac{\mu_0}{2}\dfrac{NIa^2}{(a^2 + x^2)^{\frac{3}{2}}}.$

[Hint: put $\dfrac{\mu_0 NI}{2} = 1$, $a = 0.1$ and take a range of x between -0.1 and $+0.1$].

(b) Use the result of (a) to plot the variation of B with position of 2 similar coils placed a distance a apart.

Extension: Investigate the effect of varying the separation of the coils.

12.7.5 Induced charge in a circuit – search coil

A magnetic field links a circuit at right angles.

If the flux changes from Φ_1 to Φ_2, an emf, $\mathcal{E}_{in}$, is induced in the circuit for the time t in which the flux is changing.

$$\mathcal{E}_{in} = N\frac{d\Phi}{dt},$$

where N is the number of turns in the circuit.

The induced current, I_{in}, is thus given by $I_{in} = \frac{N}{R}\frac{d\Phi}{dt}$, where R is the resistance of the circuit.

The charge, Q_{in}, which passes each point in the circuit is given by: $Q_{in} = \int_{t_1}^{t_2} I_{in}\, dt$, where the change happens between t_1 and t_2.

Thus: $Q_{in} = \int_{t_1}^{t_2} \frac{N}{R}\frac{d\Phi}{dt}\, dt$, which, as we saw in Section 11.3 is the same as: $Q_{in} = \int_{\Phi_1}^{\Phi_2} \frac{N}{R}\, d\Phi$.

But N and R are constants, so $Q_{in} = \frac{N}{R}\int_{\Phi_1}^{\Phi_2} d\Phi = \frac{N}{R}(\Phi_2 - \Phi_1)$.

So the total charge passing through a charge meter, say, in the circuit can be used to determine the change of flux. If the area, A, of the coil is known, the induced charge can be used to determine the change of flux density:

$Q_{in} = \frac{NA}{R}(B_2 - B_1)$. This is the principle of the search coil.

12.8 Some miscellaneous results

12.8.1 Gravitational potential energy

The potential energy of a pair of particles with masses, M_1 and M_2, separated by a distance a is found as follows:

1   Imagine one of the particles, with mass M_1, in position in isolation.

2   Calculate the work done against the gravitational field of particle 1 in bringing particle 2, with mass M_2, from a position of defined 0 of potential energy to a distance a from the first particle.

We saw in Chapter 9 that the path doesn't matter, so we'll choose to bring the second particle along a radial line.

It is convenient to define the 0 of potential energy to be when the particles are an infinite distance apart. The gravitational force, $\mathbf{F}_G$ on particle 2 is given by $\mathbf{F}_G = -\frac{GM_1M_2}{r^2}\hat{\mathbf{r}}$, where $\hat{\mathbf{r}}$ is the unit vector in the direction from particle 1 to particle 2.

$\therefore$ The force, $\mathbf{F}$, we must apply to particle 2 is $\mathbf{F} = \frac{GM_1M_2}{r^2}\hat{\mathbf{r}}$

The work, ΔW, that we do in moving particle 2 by $\Delta\mathbf{r}$ is given by $\Delta W = \frac{GM_1M_2}{r^2}\hat{\mathbf{r}}.\Delta\mathbf{r}$.

As we are moving only along a radial line, $\hat{\mathbf{r}}.\Delta\mathbf{r} = \Delta r$, so $\Delta W = \frac{GM_1M_2}{r^2}\Delta r$

$\therefore$ The work done, W, in moving **from** ∞ **to** a is given by:

$$W = \int_{\infty}^{a} \frac{GM_1M_2}{r^2}\, dr = \left[-\frac{GM_1M_2}{r}\right]_{\infty}^{a} = -\frac{GM_1M_2}{a} = E_p,$$ where E_p is the gravitational potential energy.

Why is this expression for work the same as the potential energy? Because, unlike doing work against a dissipative force such as friction, the work done against the gravitational field is recoverable: if you do 100 J of work against the field and then let go, the field can do that same work back.

We now relate this expression to $\Delta E_p = mg\Delta h$.

Consider raising an object of mass m from a to $a + \Delta h$ in the gravitational field of a planet of mass M.

Then
$$\Delta E_p = -\frac{GMm}{a + \Delta h} - \left[-\frac{GMm}{a}\right] = GMm\left[\frac{1}{a} - \frac{1}{a + \Delta h}\right] = \frac{GMm}{a}\left[1 - \frac{1}{\left(1 + \frac{\Delta h}{a}\right)}\right]$$

From the binomial theorem, if $\Delta h \ll a$, then $\left(1 + \frac{\Delta h}{a}\right)^{-1} = 1 - \frac{\Delta h}{a}$ very closely.

Also, the gravitational force on m, $mg = \frac{GMm}{a^2}$.

$$\therefore \qquad \Delta E_p = -\frac{GMm}{a}\left[1 - \left(1 - \frac{\Delta h}{a}\right)\right] = \frac{GMm\Delta h}{a^2} = mg\Delta h$$

So the formula $\Delta E_p = mg\Delta h$ is consistent with $E_p = -\frac{GM_1M_2}{a}$ as long as $\Delta h \ll a$.

12.8.2 Potassium–argon radiometric dating

Potassium-40 decays with a half-life of 1.248×10^9 years. 89.1% of decays are β^- decays to calcium-40. The remaining 10.9% are β^+ decays or electron capture leading to argon-40. Molten lava or magma outgases, so the quantity of argon-40 in an igneous rock is a measure of the age of the rock, assuming that the Ar-40 atoms remain trapped within the lattice.

Specifically the ratio $\frac{N_{Ar}}{N_K}$ can be used to calculate the age.

Let N_0 be the initial number of K-40 nuclei in the rock.

At time t, $N_K = N_0 e^{-\lambda t}$, where λ is the decay constant of potassium-40.

$\therefore$ The number of K-40 nuclei decayed $= N_0 - N_K = N_0(1 - e^{-\lambda t})$

$\therefore$ If k is the fraction of decays resulting in Ar-40, $N_{Ar} = kN_0(1 - e^{-\lambda t})$

$$\therefore \qquad \frac{N_{Ar}}{N_K} = k\left(\frac{1 - e^{-\lambda t}}{e^{-\lambda t}}\right) = k(e^{\lambda t} - 1)$$

Rearranging: $e^{\lambda t} = \frac{N_{Ar}}{kN_K} + 1$

Taking (natural) logs: $\lambda t = \ln\left(\frac{N_{Ar}}{kN_K} + 1\right)$. Dividing by λ and putting $\lambda = \frac{\ln 2}{t_{1/2}}$ gives

$$t = \frac{t_{1/2}}{\ln 2}\ln\left(\frac{N_{Ar}}{kN_K} + 1\right).$$

Determining the ratio $\frac{N_{Ar}}{N_K}$ in a mass spectrometer and inserting $t_{1/2} = 1.248 \times 10^9$ years and $k = 0.109$ leads to the age, t, of the rock.

Quickfire answers

Chapter 1

1.1 $[\text{work}] = M\,L^2\,T^{-2}$

1.2 $[\text{power}] = M\,L^2\,T^{-3}$

1.3 $[\text{charge}] = T\,I$

1.4 (a) 4.5 V   (b) 50 m

1.5 (a) 5 kN   (b) 1.5 mA

     (c) 200 GPa   (d) 160 zC [or 0.16 aC]

1.6 (a) 10 mg   (b) 3.5 MN

     (c) 15 kA   (d) 9.6 µC

1.7 (a) 400 kPa   (b) 1.5 MN

     (c) 150 µA   (d) 4 GPa

1.8 (a) $200 \times 10^3\,N$ (b) $76 \times 10^{-3}\,A$

     (c) $75 \times 10^3\,V$ (d) $900 \times 10^{-12}\,kg$

1.9 (a) $0.0027\,m^2\ [2.7 \times 10^{-3}\,m^2]$ (b) $5.7 \times 10^4\,mm^2$

     (c) $9 \times 10^{-9}\,m^3$ (d) $2.5 \times 10^7\,m^2$.

1.10 $8.0 \times 10^{-8}\,m^2$

1.11 (a) $2.5\,m\,s^{-1}$ (b) $105\,N\,s$ (c) $20\,m\,s^{-1}$

     (d) 0.548 kg [548 g]   (e) $12\,m\,s^{-1}$

1.12 $J = kg\,m^2\,s^{-2}$

1.13 $W = kg\,m^2\,s^{-3}$

1.14 $C = A\,s$

1.15 $[u^2] = L^2\,T^{-2}$. $[2as] = [a] \times [s] = L\,T^{-2} \times L = L^2\,T^{-2}$. These two are the same so the right-hand side is homogeneous.

     $[v^2] = L^2\,T^{-2}$ which is the same as the right-hand side so the equation is homogeneous.

1.16 $s = m^a\,(m\,s^{-2})^b\,kg^c$

Chapter 2

2.1 $150 \times 5.3 + 150 \times 2.8 = 795 + 420 = 1215$

     $150 \times 8.1 = 1215$

2.2 $\frac{5}{3} = 1.67$ [3 s.f.]

2.3 $\frac{3}{4} = 0.75$

2.4 16

2.5 (a) 17   (b) 27

2.6 (a) $\frac{7}{5}$ (b) $\frac{3}{9}$ i.e. $\frac{1}{3}$

2.7 $x = 4y + 2$

2.8 $x = 4y - 5$

2.9 $x - 6 = 4y^2$; then $x = 4y^2 + 6$

2.10 $1.68 \times 10^{-27}\,kg$; anti-proton

2.11 $\frac{12}{20}$

2.12 $\frac{19}{20}$

2.13 (a) $101^2 - 99^2 = (101 - 99)(101 + 99) = 2 \times 200 = 400$

     (b) $101^2 = (100 + 1)^2 = 10\,000 + 2 \times 100 + 1 = 10\,201$

     (c) $99^2 = (100 - 1)^2 = 10\,000 - 2 \times 100 + 1 = 9801$

     (d) $950^2 = (1000 - 50)^2 = 1\,000\,000 - 100\,000 + 2500$

         $= 902\,500$

     (e) $42^2 - 39^2 = (42 + 39)(42 - 39) = 81 \times 3 = 243$

2.14 $x = 12$

2.15 $x = 5$

2.16 $x = 7$

Chapter 3

3.1 +8 and −8, i.e. ±8

3.2 ±3.46

3.3 −1.5 or 2.5

3.4 If the stone had been thrown upwards from the bottom of the shaft with the correct speed (the same as the impact speed) at −5.7 s, it would pass the top of the mine shaft, travelling downwards with a speed of $10\,m\,s^{-1}$, at time $t = 0$.

3.5 9.8 is a and 4.9 is half a, so these have unit $m\,s^{-2}$. The 100 is c as has unit m. Together with the unit of the $10\,m\,s^{-1}$ given we have:

$$t = \frac{-(10\ m\ s^{-1}) \pm \sqrt{(10\ m\ s^{-1})^2 - 4 \times (4.9\ m\ s^{-2}) \times (-100\ m)}}{9.8\ m\ s^{-2}}$$

$$= \frac{-(10\ m\ s^{-1}) \pm \sqrt{100\ m^2\ s^{-2} + 1960\ m^2\ s^{-2}}}{9.8\ m\ s^{-2}}$$

So the two terms in the square root sign have the same units and can be added together.

Taking the square root: $t = \dfrac{-10\ m\ s^{-1} \pm 45.4\ m\ s^{-1}}{9.8\ m\ s^{-2}}$

Again the two terms in the numerator have the same unit and can be added, giving

$t = \dfrac{-55.4\ m\ s^{-1}}{9.8\ m\ s^{-2}} = 5.7$ s or $t = \dfrac{35.4\ m\ s^{-1}}{9.8\ m\ s^{-2}} = 3.6$ s, which has the correct unit.

3.6 $6x + 2y = 4$

3.7 $-10a + 6b = -12$

3.8 $8a = 12$

3.9 $a = 1.5$ and $b = 0.167$

3.10 $a = 7.5$, $b = 2.5$

3.11 1st order 1.105; 2nd order 1.099488; 3rd order 1.100066

3.12 $(1 - x)^{-1} = 1 + (-1)(-x) + \dfrac{(-1)(-2)}{2!}(-x)^2 + \dfrac{(-1)(-2)(-3)}{3!}(-x)^3 + \ldots$

     $= 1 + x + \dfrac{2!}{2!}(-x)^2 - \dfrac{3!}{3!}(-x)^3 + \ldots$

     $= 1 + x + x^2 + x^3 + \ldots$

1st order: 1.1000, 2nd 1.1100, 3rd 1.1110

Chapter 4

4.1 800

4.2 (a) 6561   (b) 43046721

4.3 0.0625

4.4 0.5625

4.5 (a) 16   (b) 512

4.6 $\frac{1}{8}$ or 0.125

4.7 (a) $2^3 \times 3^2$ (b) $2^{12} \times 3^8$

4.8 $5^{-\frac{5}{2}}$ or $5^{-2.5}$

4.9 $\frac{1}{81}$ or $\frac{1}{3^4}$ or 3^{-4}

4.10 (a) 2.594   (b) 2.705

4.11 (a) 7.389   (b) 0.1353   (c) 1.649

4.12 (a) exp(2)   (b) exp(−2)   (c) $\exp\left(\frac{1}{2}\right)$

4.13 (a) 4.0   (b) 0.25

4.14 (a) 0.5   (b) 2.5   (c) −1   (d) −0.5

4.15 $\frac{4}{3}$

4.16 6.30 s

4.17 0.177

4.18 0.038

Chapter 5

5.1 130 mm

5.2 192 mm

5.3 208 mm

5.4 17.3 cm

5.5 40 cm^2

5.6 15 cm^3

5.7 50°

5.8 125°

5.9

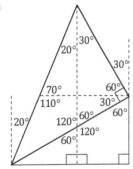

5.10 57.3°

5.11 (a) $\frac{\pi}{180}$ (b) 0.0175 rad

5.12 π i.e. 3.142 rad

5.13 (a) $\sin\theta = \cos\left(\frac{\pi}{2} - \theta\right)$ (b) $\cos\theta = \sin\left(\frac{\pi}{2} - \theta\right)$

      (c) $\tan\theta = \cot\left(\frac{\pi}{2} - \theta\right)$

5.14 $\sin\theta = \frac{\text{opp}}{\text{hyp}}$; $\cos\theta = \frac{\text{adj}}{\text{hyp}}$.

$$\therefore \frac{\sin\theta}{\cos\theta} = \sin\theta \times \frac{1}{\cos\theta} = \frac{\text{opp}}{\text{hyp}} \times \frac{\text{hyp}}{\text{adj}} = \frac{\text{opp}}{\text{adj}} = \tan\theta$$

5.15 $\sin 30° = 0.5$; $\cos 30° = \frac{\sqrt{3}}{2} = 0.866$; $\tan 30° = \frac{1}{\sqrt{3}} = 0.577$;

      $\cos 60° = 0.5$; $\tan 60° = \sqrt{3}$

5.16 (a) 1   (b) 1.62

5.17 (a) $\cos^2\phi = 0.4^2 = 0.16$;

      (b) $\sin\phi = \sqrt{1 - \cos^2\phi} = \sqrt{1 - 0.16} = 0.917$

      (c) $\tan\phi = \frac{\sin\phi}{\cos\phi} = \frac{0.917}{0.4} = 2.29$

5.18 (a) 53.1°   (b) 36.9°   (c) 38.7°

5.19 Between 180° and 270°, x and y are both negative.

      $\therefore \sin\theta = \frac{y}{r} < 0$; $\cos\theta = \frac{x}{r} < 0$; $\tan\theta = \frac{y}{x} > 0$

5.20 Solutions between 0 and 360° are 44.4° and 135.6°

5.21 Applying the cosine rule: $x^2 = (10^2 + 7^2) - (2 \times 10 \times 7 \cos 45°)$;

      $\therefore$ $x = 7.07$

      Applying the sine rule: $\frac{\sin\phi}{7} = \frac{\sin 45°}{7.07}$

      $\therefore$ $\phi = \sin^{-1}\left(\frac{7 \sin 45°}{7.07}\right) = 44.4°$

5.22 $\tan 112.5° = -1 - \sqrt{2} = -2.414$

      We know that $\tan 112.5° < 0$ because it is in the 2nd quadrant.

Chapter 6

6.1 (a) 3   (b) 2

6.2 (a) −1.5   (b) 45

6.3 (a) −1.5 m s^{-2} (b) 45 m s^{-1}

6.4 (a) Gradient = 1, $y = x + 2$

      (b) Gradient = −2, $y = -2x + 14$

6.5 (a) CoM = (3.0, 0.466)

      (b) $y = 0.1x + 0.17$ [least squares fit]

         NB. The 'least squares fit' is the best-fit linear trend line drawn by a spreadsheet program.

6.6 Plot $\sqrt{P}$ against I to obtain roughly equally spaced points.

6.7 T against $\sqrt{m}$ and T^2 against m [ignoring T^4 against m^2 etc.]. Use T^2 v m.

6.8 Use T against $\sqrt{m}$ and the graph should still be a straight line with a non-zero intercept.

6.9 y^2x against x^2. The gradient will be a; the intercept is b on the y^2x axis.

6.10 Straight line through the origin with gradient a^2.

6.11 Divided by 2^3, i.e. becomes one eighth.

6.12 Multiplied by $4^4 = 256$

6.13 10

6.14 30

Chapter 7

7.1 350 m s⁻¹ southwest

7.2 vectors – velocity, momentum; scalars – density, length, pressure

7.3 6 m s⁻¹ due North

7.4 (a) 17 N in the direction of the forces

(b) 7 N in the direction of the 12 N force

(c) 13 N at 22.6° to the direction of the 12 N force.

7.5 8 N horizontal to the right

7.6 13.9 N horizontal to the right.

7.7 $F = 100 \cos 30° = 86.6$ N,

$T = 100 \sin 30° = 50$ N

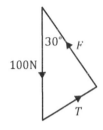

7.8 $R = 56.4$ N; $F = 60.5$ N

7.9 $\theta = \tan^{-1}\frac{10}{30} = 18.4°$; $T = \sqrt{10^2 + 30^2} = 31.6$ N

7.10 14.1 N downwards [or South]

7.11 North component = 104 N; East component = 60 N

7.12 South component = –104 N; East component = 60 N

7.13 $C = 1840$ N

7.14 $v_H = 12.3$ N; $v_v = 8.6$ N

7.15 $v = 12.3i + 8.6j$

7.16 $F = 12i + 16j$

7.17 $F = 20$N; angle = $\tan^{-1}\frac{16}{12} = 53.1°$

7.18. $v = -15i + 10j$ [= 30.4 m s⁻¹ at 9.46° below the horizontal]

7.19 Working in units: Start with the rhs

$[x \tan\theta]$ = m because $\tan\theta$ has no units.

$\left[\frac{1}{2}\frac{g}{u^2 \cos^2\theta}x^2\right] = \frac{m\,s^{-2}}{(m\,s^{-1})^2} \times m^2 = m$ ∴ the rhs is homogeneous.

$[y]$ = m; ∴ the units of the two sides are the same and the equation is homogeneous.

7.20 Working in dimensions: Start with the rhs

$\left[\frac{u^2 \sin 2\theta}{g}\right] = \frac{(L\,T^{-1})^2}{L\,T^{-2}} = L$ [because $\sin 2\theta$ is dimensionless]

$[R]$ = L; ∴ the dimensions of the two sides are the same, so the equation is homogeneous.

7.21 Velocity = $35i + 8j$

7.22 $j \times k = i$

7.23 $(3i - 2j) \times (2i + 3j) = 9i \times j - 4j \times i = 9k - 4(-k) = 13k$

Chapter 8

8.1 (a) $-\frac{\sqrt{3}}{2} = -0.866$, (b) 0.5, (c) $-\frac{1}{\sqrt{2}} = -0.707$

8.2 (a) 0.5, (b) 0.5, (c) 0.5

8.3 (a) –1, (b) 1, (c) $-\sqrt{3} = -1.732$

8.4 1° = 0.0175 rad. Distance $-\frac{50}{0.0175}$ m $- 3000$ m [1 s.f.]

8.5 200 km

8.6 $\omega = 314$ s⁻¹; $f = 50$ Hz; $T = 20$ ms; Amplitude = 339 V

8.7 –185 V

8.8 $\cos\theta = 0$ when $\theta = \frac{\pi}{2}$. ∴ $314t + 1 = \frac{\pi}{2}$ ∴ $t = 1.82$ ms.

8.9 (a) 0 (b) 5 V

8.10 Alternates between –0.25 A and +0.25 A in a square wave with a mark-space ratio of 1.

8.11 1.25 W

8.12 170 V

8.13 (a) 4.0 A, (b) 5.66 A, (c) 480 W, (d) 960 W

8.14 120 Hz

8.15

	R / kΩ	X / kΩ	Z / kΩ
Resistor	1	0	1
Inductor	0	0.63	0.63
Capacitor	0	1.6	1.6

8.16 (a) $X = 63.7$ Ω (b) $I = 0.16$ A

8.17 Power is only dissipated in the resistor so

$\langle P\rangle = I_{rms}^2 R = 2^2 \times 20 = 80$ W.

8.18 (a)

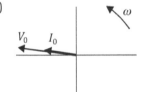

(b)

8.19

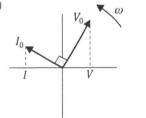

$V > 0$ and decreasing;

$I < 0$ and decreasing, i.e. becoming more negative

8.20 $Z = \sqrt{R^2 + X^2} = \sqrt{1^2 + 1^2} = 1.41$ kΩ

8.21 (a) X is halved to 0.5 kΩ,

(b) the resistance is unchanged,

(c) $Z = 1.12\,\mathrm{k\Omega}$.

8.22 $141\,\Omega$

8.23 (a) R unchanged $= 100\,\Omega$,

(b) X doubled to $200\,\Omega$,

(c) $Z = 224\,\Omega$.

8.24 (a) $X = 1\,\mathrm{k\Omega} - 500\,\Omega = 500\,\Omega$

(b) $Z = \sqrt{R^2 + X^2} = \sqrt{1^2 + 0.5^2} = 1.12\,\mathrm{k\Omega}$

8.25 The reactance of the capacitor is halved to $500\,\Omega$ and the reactance of the inductor is doubled to $1\,\mathrm{k\Omega}$, so the total reactance is still $1\,\mathrm{k\Omega} - 500\,\Omega = 500\,\Omega$. NB the sign of the reactance is unimportant because it occurs as X^2 in the calculation of Z.

8.26 $\varepsilon = \tan^{-1}\left(\dfrac{X_L - X_C}{R}\right) = \tan^{-1}(-0.5) = -0.463\,\mathrm{rad}\,/\,-26.6°$

∴ The phase angle is $0.463\,\mathrm{rad}\,/\,26.6°$ with the current leading the voltage.

Chapter 9

9.1 $N = \mathrm{kg\,m\,s^{-2}}. \therefore N\,\mathrm{kg^{-1}} = \mathrm{kg\,m\,s^{-2}\,kg^{-1}} = \mathrm{m\,s^{-2}}$ QED

9.2 $[G] = \mathrm{kg^{-1}\,m^3\,s^{-2}}$

9.3 $[\varepsilon_0] = \mathrm{kg^{-1}\,m^{-3}\,s^4\,A^2}$

9.4 $8.99 \times 10^9\,\mathrm{F^{-1}\,m}$

9.5 $\mathrm{V\,m^{-1}} = \mathrm{J\,C^{-1}\,m^{-1}} = (\mathrm{N\,m})\,\mathrm{C^{-1}\,m^{-1}} = \mathrm{N\,C^{-1}}$ QED

9.6 (a) $260\,\mathrm{V\,cm^{-1}}$,

(b) $60\,\mathrm{V\,cm^{-1}}$ in the direction of the $160\,\mathrm{V\,cm^{-1}}$ field

(c) $189\,\mathrm{V\,cm^{-1}}$ at $0.559\,\mathrm{rad}\,[32°]$ to $160\,\mathrm{V\,cm^{-1}}$ field

9.7 $\sim 2.5\,\mathrm{N\,kg^{-1}}$

9.8 $\sim 5\,\mathrm{N\,kg^{-1}}$

9.9 $E = 1.5\,\mathrm{kV\,m^{-1}}\,/\,15\,\mathrm{V\,cm^{-1}}$

9.10

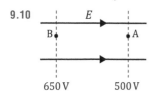

9.11 (a) $1.73\,\mathrm{kV\,m^{-1}}$

(b)

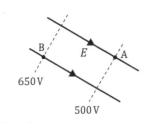

9.12 $T = \mathrm{kg\,s^{-2}\,A^{-1}}$

[NB T is independent of m]

Chapter 10

10.1 $4x^3$

10.2 $-\dfrac{1}{x^2}\,/\,-x^{-2}$

10.3 ± 0.25

10.4 $f' = -50e^{-5x}, f'' = 250e^{-5x}$

10.5 $\dot{y} = 10\dfrac{5}{5t} = \dfrac{10}{t}; \ddot{y} = -\dfrac{10}{t^2}$

10.6 5

10.7 -3.00

10.8 -5

10.9 $\dfrac{d}{dx}\left(\dfrac{1}{n+1}x^{n+1}\right) = \dfrac{1}{n+1}\dfrac{d}{dx}(x^{n+1}) = \dfrac{1}{n+1} \times (n+1)x^n = x^n$

Chapter 11

11.1 $-15e^{-3x}$

11.2 $45\cos(3t + \pi)$

11.3 $x = x_0 e^{-3t}$

11.4 (a) 25 (b) 100

11.5 (a) $x = 1000e^{-0.1t}$ (b) $x(100\,\mathrm{s}) = 0.045$

11.6 $\sin\alpha = 0.4472; \cos\alpha = 0.8944$

11.7 $\sin\alpha = -0.4472; \cos\alpha = -0.8944$

11.8 $\cos\beta = \dfrac{x}{\sqrt{x^2 + y^2}}; \sin\beta = \dfrac{y}{\sqrt{x^2 + y^2}}$

11.9 1×10^{12}

11.10 7.4×10^{12}

11.11 12.5

11.12 21.5

11.13 $0.322\,\mathrm{rad}$